ELECTRICAL CONDUCTIVITY IN ORGANIC SOLIDS

SYMPOSIUM ON
ELECTRICAL CONDUCTIVITY
IN ORGANIC SOLIDS

SPONSORED BY THE OFFICE OF ORDNANCE RESEARCH, U. S. ARMY;
THE OFFICE OF NAVAL RESEARCH, U. S. NAVY; AND THE OFFICE
OF SCIENTIFIC RESEARCH, U. S. AIR FORCE

HELD AT DUKE UNIVERSITY, DURHAM, NORTH CAROLINA,
APRIL 20-22, 1960

Edited by **H. KALLMANN,** *Professor of Physics, New York University and*
M. SILVER, *U. S. Army Research Office (Durham), Durham, North Carolina*

Program Committee

D. Fox   D. S. McClure
H. Kallmann   W. G. Schneider
J. Kommandeur   M. Silver
          H. Sponer

INTERSCIENCE PUBLISHERS
a division of John Wiley & Sons · New York · London

First published 1961

Printed in the Netherlands by
N.V. Dijkstra's Drukkerij,
voorheen Boekdrukkerij Gebr. Hoitsema, Groningen

Contributors

H. Akamatu,
    Department of Chemistry, University of Tokyo, Tokyo, Japan

H. Boroffka,
    Physikalisches Institut der Technischen Hochschule, Stuttgart, Germany

Monisha Bose,
    The Franklin Institute, Laboratories for Research and Development, Philadelphia, Pennsylvania

A. Bree,
    Department of Chemistry, University of British Columbia, Vancouver, Canada

D. P. Craig,
    William Ramsey and Ralph Forster Laboratories, University College, London, England

P. Douzou,
    Section Technique du Service de Santé, Hospital Militaire du Val-de-Grace, Paris, France

D. D. Eley,
    Department of Chemistry, University of Nottingham, Nottingham, England

Arnold Epstein,
    Research and Engineering Division, Monsanto Chemical Company, St. Louis, Missouri

D. Fox,
    State University of New York, Long Island Center, Oyster Bay, New York

J. C. Francq,
    Section Technique du Service de Santé, Hospital Militaire du Val-de-Grace, Paris, France

J. Gergely,
    Departments of Medicine, Massachusetts General Hospital and Harvard Medical School, Boston, Massachusetts

P. E. Gibbons,
    Services Electronics Research Laboratory, Baldock, Hertsfordshire, England

R. Goldstein,
    Section Technique du Service de Santé, Hospital Militaire du Val-de-Grace, Paris, France

C. A. Hutchison, Jr.,
Department of Chemistry and Enrico Fermi Institute for Nuclear Studies, University of Chicago, Chicago, Illinois

Hiroo Inokuchi,
The Institute for Solid State Physics, University of Tokyo, Tokyo, Japan

H. Kallmann,
Department of Physics, New York University, New York, New York

R. G. Kepler,
Central Research Department, E. I. du Pont de Nemours and Company, Wilmington, Delaware

J. Kommandeur,
Union Carbide Corporation, Parma Research Laboratory, Parma, Ohio

Mortimer M. Labes,
The Franklin Institute, Laboratories for Research and Development, Philadelphia, Pennsylvania

L. E. Lyons,
Department of Physical Chemistry, University of Sydney, Sydney, Australia

D. S. McClure,
Radio Corporation of America Laboratories, David Sarnoff Research Center, Princeton, New Jersey

Y. Maruyama,
Department of Chemistry, University of Tokyo, Tokyo, Japan

W. Moore,
University of North Carolina, Chapel Hill, North Carolina

J. N. Murrell,
Department of Chemistry, University of Sheffield, Sheffield, England

R. C. Nelson,
Department of Physics, Ohio State University, Columbus, Ohio

D. C. Northrop,
Services Electronics Research Laboratory, Baldock, Hertfordshire, England

M. Pope,
Department of Physics, New York University, New York, New York

J. A. Pople,
National Physical Laboratory, Teddington, Middlesex, England

P. J. Reucroft,
Pure Chemistry Division, National Research Council, Ottawa, Canada

N. Riehl,
Technical University, Munich, Germany

Barnett Rosenberg,
Department of Physics, New York University, New York, New York

W. G. Schneider,
Pure Chemistry Division, National Research Council, Ottawa, Canada

Robert Sehr,
The Franklin Institute, Laboratories for Research and Development, Philadelphia, Pennsylvania

M. Silver,
U. S. Army Research Office (Durham), Durham, North Carolina

O. Simpson,
Services Electronics Research Laboratory, Baldock, Hertfordshire, England

L. S. Singer,
Research Laboratory, National Carbon Company, Division of Union Carbide Corporation, Parma, Ohio

H. Sponer,
Department of Physics, Duke University, Durham, North Carolina

R. Terenin,
The University, Leningrad, U.S.S.R.

J. M. Thullier,
Ecole Normale Supérieure, Paris, France

Hana Ur,
The Franklin Institute, Laboratories for Research and Development, Philadelphia, Pennsylvania

S. H. Walmsley,
William Ramsey and Ralph Forster Laboratories, University College, London, England

Bernard Wildi,
Research and Engineering Division, Monsanto Chemical Company, St. Louis, Missouri

Franz Wilhelm,
The Franklin Institute, Laboratories for Research and Development, Philadelphia, Pennsylvania

M. R. Willis,
Department of Chemistry, University of Nottingham, Nottingham, England

Contents

Charge-Transport Processes in Organic Materials

H. Kallmann and M. Pope

Introduction

We conjecture that the majority of readers will share the opinion that it is impossible in the space allotted to give a concise review of all the important work that has been published in the field of electronic processes in organic materials.[1] Instead of discussing the various and often quite different approaches that have been undertaken to clarify the situation in this field, we shall be limited to describing and theoretically discussing the more elementary processes of charge motion and displacement that we encounter in organic materials. Certainly the selection we are forced to make will be personally colored, and if someone feels that certain scientific approaches are not thoroughly discussed in this paper, we apologize.

In order to facilitate the survey of this field, it is useful to divide it into three sections. The first comprises the *static phenomena*, in which an equilibrium state is reached where no electric current is flowing. The second comprises *conductivity phenomena*, where the relationship between current and external voltage and other parameters is discussed. We shall add a third one, in which *current multiplication by high fields* is investigated.

1. Static Phenomena

A. Persistent Internal Polarization. Persistent internal polarization [2] is a very striking static phenomenon in the field of electronic processes. If we apply an external field to a photoconductor during illumination, and in some cases even thereafter, a separation of charges takes place in the interior; these separated charges can be frozen in when traps, which are produced either by vacancies or by impurities, are encountered. Thus an internal polarization persists after the illumination and external field are removed. Internal polarization occurs in all materials containing traps, and in which the conductivity drops rapidly to a rather low value upon the removal of the illumination.

We have found that there are two types of internal polarization: one may be described as *barrier polarization* and the other as *bulk polarization*. The first occurs if high resistance layers are close to the sample electrodes. In this situation, barrier polarization will develop regardless of how the sample may be excited, i.e., with uniformly or nonuniformly absorbed radiation. In the latter case, a longer period of field application is required for the polarization to reach the steady state wherein the charges are accumulated near the electrodes.

Bulk polarization occurs under the following conditions: The sample must be nonuniformly excited and the resistance of the layers near the electrodes should not be too high. A further condition is that the charge carriers of one sign have a smaller mobility or that they are more readily trapped than the carriers of the other sign. In organic materials, the negative charge carriers are those that are supposed to have small mobility or to be trapped strongly.

The essential point in all types of polarization is that illumination of the sample produces free charges that are separated by the electric field and that, in barrier polarization, accumulate at high resistance layers. In bulk polarization, the trapped charges are distributed in the whole interior of the sample rather than amassed near the boundaries.

Since many systems show a very slow decrease in the number of free charges after excitation removal, i.e., a slow recombination of free charges, a polarization can also occur by applying an external field in the dark. This is termed "dark polarizing."

Figures 1.1 and 1.2 describe schematically the charge and field distribution for barrier and bulk polarization, respectively. Our knowledge of these distributions stems mainly from two types of investigations: the selective radiation-discharge and internal-field measurements. In the first method, after the polarizing field is removed, the polarized sample is excited through one or the other electrode. This excitation produces free charges that move under the influence of the internal fields in such a way as to cancel the persistent polarization. If there is a strong barrier polarization, the accumulation of charge occurs in such thin layers that any

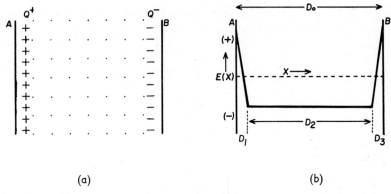

(a)   (b)

Fig. 1.1. Barrier polarization. (a) Charge distribution; (b) field distribution

excitation produces free charges mostly in the interior D_2 region of the sample (Fig. 1.1). By connecting the sample to an electrometer, it can be observed that this excitation produces a current that flows in the reverse direction of the original polarizing current.

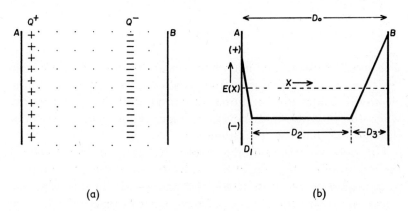

(a)   (b)

Fig. 1.2. Bulk polarization. (a) Charge distribution; (b) field distribution

With the help of this two-layer model, we can determine the field strength in this region; its magnitude was found to be of the same order as the original external field $E_0 = V_0/d_0$ ($V_0 =$ external polarizing voltage) but of opposite polarity. The amount of charge released is almost independent of the electrode that is illuminated, i.e., whether illumination takes place where the positive or negative charges have been accumulated (see Fig. 1.3).

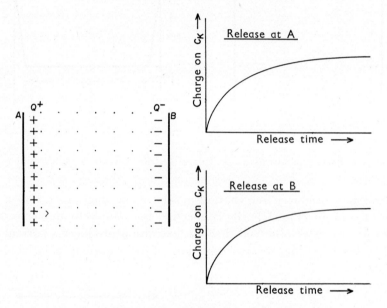

Fig. 1.3. The amount of charge released in barrier polarization.

The speed of discharge [3] may, however, differ in these cases when the releasing excitation is restricted to a narrow layer close to an electrode. Under this condition, the speed of discharge is greatest when the internal field moves the more mobile charge carriers through the bulk of the sample.

For bulk polarization, the results are quite different. Here, the less mobile charges may be distributed over a larger distance, as indicated by $D_3 > D_1$ in Fig. 1.2 and 1.4. If, in this case, the release of polarization takes place through electrode A adjacent to which the more mobile carriers are accumulated, the releasing radiation produces carriers in the D_2 region and again a release current is obtained opposite in direction to the polarizing current, as shown in Fig. 1.4.[4] If, however, the release is produced at the B electrode, the excitation may take place mostly within the D_3 region because of its large value, and the release current will be opposite to that in D_2 and therefore *in the same direction as the polarizing current* (Fig. 1.4). (*Note*: The Q^- layer essentially

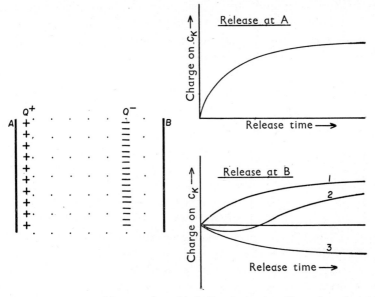

Fig. 1.4. The amount of charge released in bulk polarization. Curve 1, prolonged. polarizing time, D_3 small; curve 2, medium polarizing time, D_3 large; curve 3, very short polarizing time, release at B restricted to D_3 region.

describes the center of the distribution of the less mobile charge carriers). Three cases are considered in Fig. 1.4 when the release is carried out through electrode B. Curve 1 is obtained for very long polarizing periods when even the less mobile charge has accumulated in a thin layer. Curve 2 depicts the situation in which the less mobile charges have not reached a thin layer distribution. Curve 3 is the case in which charges are rather far from the B electrode. In curve 2, initially the excitation is predominantly in D_3, but the polarization charges move towards B, and eventually some charges are released in D_2. Thus the sign of the release current changes. In curve 3, D_3 is so large that this turning point was not reached by release through B. In curve 1 it may be that there is also an initial current in the negative direction, but this can be very soon overshadowed by a current in the positive direction.

These results of barrier and bulk polarization were confirmed by field measurements inside the various regions. These measurements show that indeed the field directions in the D_2 and D_3 regions are opposite to each other. It was further found that the charge of the sample is almost neutral for barrier polarization, whereas for bulk polarization the less mobile charge is always in excess. This means more fast mobile charges have been removed from the sample than the less mobile charges.

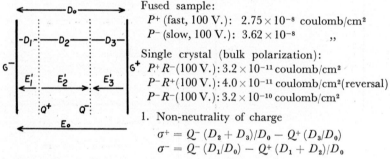

Fused sample:
P^+ (fast, 100 V.): 2.75×10^{-8} coulomb/cm²
P^- (slow, 100 V.): 3.62×10^{-8} ,,

Single crystal (bulk polarization):
$P^+ R^- (100\ \mathrm{V.}): 3.2 \times 10^{-11}$ coulomb/cm²
$P^- R^+ (100\ \mathrm{V.}): 4.0 \times 10^{-11}$ coulomb/cm² (reversal)
$P^- R^- (100\ \mathrm{V.}): 3.2 \times 10^{-10}$ coulomb/cm²

1. Non-neutrality of charge

$$\sigma^+ = Q^- (D_2 + D_3)/D_0 - Q^+ (D_3/D_0)$$
$$\sigma^- = Q^- (D_1/D_0) - Q^+ (D_1 + D_2)/D_0$$

2. Neutrality of charge

$$\sigma_0 = Q_0 (D_2/D_0) = (\gamma K V_0/D_0) [D_2/(D_1 + D_3)]$$
$$\text{From } V_0 = \Sigma V_r, (r = 1,2,3) \text{ and div } \bar{D} = Q_0$$

γ (Attenuation factor): $E_2 = (1-\gamma) E_0$ V_0: External polarizing voltage
K: Static dielectric constant

Fig. 1.5. Formulas charge values and experimental values for polarization densities for anthracene.

The formulas and charge values encountered in this research are listed in Fig. 1.5 for anthracene. Formula (1) describes the general case of a nonneutral polarized sample. σ^+ and σ^- refer to the image charge densities appearing on the positive and negative electrodes, respectively. Since the sample is nonneutral, they need not be of the same magnitude. Formula (2) gives the case of an electrically neutral sample. The case of bulk polarization can be best described with these formulas by making the charge Q^+ smaller than that of Q^- and D_3 considerably larger than D_1. Line Q^- correspond to the center of the more uniformly distributed negative charge.

The experimental values for polarization densities are given in Fig. 1.5, for a sample fused on conductive glass plates [4] and for single crystals.[5] Fused anthracene gives a much larger polarization than single crystals; this is due to relatively high resistance layers at the contact electrode—anthracene. In single crystals with liquid electrodes practically no barrier polarization is observed, but considerable bulk polarization exists. This bulk polarization is spread through the whole crystal, and the crystal is found to be electrically negative. From these polarization values we can calculate the layer thickness D_1 or D_3. It is found that for barrier polarization, the layer thickness is of the order of 10 microns in the fused samples.

The effects of internal polarization have been discussed relatively extensively because they supply us with several important kinds of information which could not be as easily obtained otherwise. In the next sections the concept of hole and electron injection will be employed to interpret many features of conductivity and photoconductivity in organic material. The question will arise as to whether all such conductivity is brought about by charge injection. The observation made with internal polarization strongly indicates that charge formation occurs also inside the material. For instance, consider the experiments that lead to the curves in Figs. 1.3 and curve 1 in 1.4. Independent of the direction of the releasing radiation, we observe a release current which is opposite in sign to the polarizing current, and the total amount of charge released is approximately the same with either direction of illumination. That can only mean that charge transport and thus charge production occurs in the D_2 region. It is difficult to see how charges could reach this region if they all stemmed from injection from the electrode. This idea is confirmed by curve 2 in Fig. 1.4, where the change in sign of the charge release indicates that charges are produced not only at the boundaries. We must keep in mind that the observed polarization charges are only a small fraction of the current that traverses these materials and that is injected into a crystal (see Fig. 1.7, and the quantum yield for charge injection, below).

Especially in single crystals the polarization is extremely small compared to the current which produced the polarization. Further, we must realize that strong polarization only occurs when barrier layers are present, and precisely at these layers can charges be created by radiation inside the material. That charge injection, however, is also necessary for explaining all effects of persistent internal polarization (PIP) is shown by Silver and Moore in their paper (8). We shall find below more evidence from other experiments for injection of negative electrons into the material.

The second type of information that is gleaned from these experiments concerns the negative charges, which in conductivity experiments elude observation to a certain extent. The polarization results quite clearly demonstrate that negative charges are found even inside single crystals (see bulk polarization of single crystals, Fig. 1.5). They also show that these negative charges are strongly trapped inside the crystal. Thus internal polarization also yields information about the trapping of these charges in the sample.

B. Photovoltaic Effects. It is well known that in an organic sandwich cell a photovoltaic voltage appears if the cell is non-uniformly excited. In most cases the illuminated electrode A becomes negative for an open circuit with no current flowing. This means that positive charges tend to diffuse from the illuminated layer into the unilluminated part of the crystal and that this diffusion is stopped by a counter field. This process makes the nonilluminated side positive. The general formula for a photovoltaic effect is given in Eq. (1.1), with $\omega+$ and $\omega-$ and $n+$ and $n-$ representing the mobilities and the densities of the positive and negative carriers, respectively.

$$V_{ph} = -(kT/e)\int_{n_A^+ n_A^-}^{n_B^+ n_B^-} [(\omega^+ dn)^+ - (\omega^- dn)^-]/[(\omega^+ n^+) + (\omega^- n^-)] \quad (1.1)$$

where e is the elementary charge and k is the Boltzmann constant. This formula is interesting, but is sometimes not too helpful if we do not know the distribution of carriers inside the sample or the concentration of both carriers n_A^+, n_A^- and n_B^+, n_B^- at the electrodes A and B. The internal-carrier concentration can be determined from Eqs. (1.2) and (1.3), which represent the particle currents for positive and negative carriers.

$$i^+ = \omega^+[(n^+E) - (kT/e)(\partial n^+/\partial x)] \quad dE/dx = (4\pi/\varepsilon)e(n^+ - n^-) \quad (1.2)$$

$$i^- = -\omega^-[(n^-E) + (kT/e)(\partial n^-/\partial x)] \quad (1.3)$$

$i+$ and $i-$ can be determined easily for the steady state if there is little recombination inside the sample; they are both equal if there is no total electric current. Under such conditions we can get information about n^+ and n^-. The main problem, however, is to determine the concentration at the surface. If only one carrier contributes to the conductive process, both currents are zero in the open circuit case, and the photovoltage is given by Eq. (1.4).

$$V_{ph} = -(kT/e) \log (n_B^+/n_A^+) \quad (1.4)$$

If there is no interaction between electrode and radiation, either directly or indirectly, and if only one type of carrier crosses the electrode boundaries, then $n_A^+ = n_B^+$ and $V_{ph} = 0$. This is the old statement of Landau. A difference between n_A^+ and n_B^+ can only occur if there is some kind of interaction between the radiation and the electrode. For instance, the exciton in the organic material may impinge upon the electrode and interact with it. A negative electron may be absorbed by the electrode and a positive hole released into the organic material. This process was used by the writers to explain many features of the observed photoconductivity in single anthracene crystals (see below).

If such a process occurs, a photovoltage will develop even if the mobility of the negative charges is zero. Because of said injection of positive holes, the density n_A^+ (at the illuminated electrode) increases until it becomes so large that as many holes move back to this electrode as are emitted by the impinging excitons. In this way n_A^+ becomes larger than n_B^+, and a positive photovoltage develops at B. The assumption of such positive hole emission is believed necessary to explain photovoltage if negative carriers do not participate in the conduction process. (For a closer examination of this process, see below.)

From the observed photovoltage [6] we can calculate the concentration ratio of n_A^+/n_B^+, which in anthracene amounts to about three thousand.

The potential gradient inside the electrode has not been considered; it is small, since the field strength or the respective electric displacement D is constant if one goes from the anthracene through the electrode surface into the electrode. Since there is a very high carrier concentration inside the electrodes, the thickness of the potential layer inside the electrode is so small that the total potential drop in the electrodes can be neglected.

We could get a photovoltage also by assuming that charges are created only inside the organic material. In order to obtain a difference between n_A^+ and n_B^+, we must then assume that plus and minus charges flow into the same electrode in equal numbers. Since no appreciable negative currents have been observed, we are inclined to attribute these photovoltages to hole emission from the electrode surface. This idea is supported by the observation that these photovoltages depend considerably on the type of electrodes used.

2. Conductivity Phenomena

The processes that take place at the electrode junction with the organic material are not only important for the understanding of photovoltage, but also for that of dark and photoconductivity.[7] No unambiguous conclusions can be drawn on conductivity without solving the question of how the electrode contacts behave and of what type they are. Again the leading viewpoint will be the fact that for many materials, little or no current of negative carriers has been observed.

A. Dark Conductivity. Dark conductivity is most often treated in the following way: If the top of the band in which the free holes move (valence band) is considered as the zero energy level, then there is a conductivity level for free electrons at an energy E_{cond}. When excitation occurs into this band, a certain density n^+ of positive holes becomes available in the crystal. It is given by Eq. (1.5), assuming that there are no hole donor levels (intrinsic case).

$$n^+ = 2\,(m_p k/2\pi\hbar^2)^{\,3/2} T^{3/2} \exp{-(E_{\text{cond}}/2kT)} \quad E_{\text{cond}} \gg kT \quad (1.5)$$

Electrons are supposed not to contribute to the conductivity process itself, either because of small mobility or strong trapping. There is also the possibility that the positive holes originate at impurity centers or vacancies, then Eq. (1.6) holds, with E_D the energy of these levels above the valence band.

$$n^+ = n_D^{\frac{1}{2}}\,(m_p k/2\pi\hbar^2)^{3/4} T^{3/4} \exp{(-E_D/2kT)} \quad E_D \gg kT \quad (1.6)$$

From the measured conductivity $\kappa = e\omega^+ n^+$, we determine n^+ if the mobility ω^+ is known. The power of the exponential in (1.5) or (1.6) is determined from the temperature dependence of the conductivity. With this knowledge we can test which formula may hold. Boundary effects are not taken care of so far.

There has been some discussion about identifying the energy E_{cond} in Eq. (1.5) with the molecular triplet level. We shall not discuss here the accuracy with which this can be done. We will, however, emphasize two unresolved difficulties that are connected with this interpretation. The first difficulty is that Eq. (1.5) only holds if this excited state is a conductivity band. If this were not so then the factor of 1/2 in the exponential term of this equation would be meaningless. This factor only occurs when the electron and the positive charge are separated from each other. Since the triplet state does not comprise such separation, the correlation of E_{cond} with the triplet-state energy seems to a large extent arbitrary. The other difficulty resides in the factor with which the exponential term is multiplied. This factor can be obtained in a very rough way from conductivity measurements. Such estimation is only approximate, because the effective carrier mass that occurs in this factor as well as the mobilities are not well known for these materials. But if we assume that the effective mass is of the same order of magnitude as the normal mass, we find a value for the density of positive holes that, in some cases, is different by several orders of magnitude from the value derived from Eq. (1.5). Also the huge difference in this factor from material to material seems to indicate that (1.5) does not describe the observed conductivity very well.

These difficulties would be removed with the use of Eq. (1.6). Here the experimentally determined E_D value, which is of the order of 2 ev, could certainly be correlated with suitable hole donor levels. The factor before the exponential is now quite different and contains the number of donor levels that will permit it always to be adjusted to the observed conductivity, and huge differences from material to material in dark conductivity would only mean a different number of donors. This would describe dark conductivity as extrinsic.

There is, however, a quite different approach to the problem of dark conductivity in these materials. It has been shown by Dr. Pope in our laboratory that positive hole emission from the electrode into the semiconductor occurs. Working with a sandwich cell, it was shown that the dark current was considerably larger when one specially prepared (iodine) electrode was at a positive rather than at a negative potential.[8] This clearly shows that positive holes were emitted from this electrode. That such electrodes could emit holes into the anthracene was proved further when these electrodes were irradiated by light. Dr. Pope gives these results in more detail (paper 7).

Because of this demonstrated hole emission into the organic material by thermal action, it seems justified to investigate how dark conductivity can be described in this way. There are two methods of approach:

We can calculate the number of holes that can be emitted into the organic material under thermal action. For this purpose it is necessary to know the energy that is necessary to bring an electron from the valence band of the anthracene into the conductivity band of the adjacent electrode near the Fermi level. This is $E_{ion} - \phi_{el}$, where E_{ion} is the energy necessary to bring an electron from the unexcited organic solid to infinity in a vacuum (in anthracene this is about 5.6 ev), and ϕ_{el} is the work function of the electron in the respective electrode. Both quantities are considered positive. The number of holes N_{th}^{+} emitted in the dark is then given by Eq. (1.7).

$$\mathcal{N}_{th}^+ = AT^2 \exp\left[-(E_{ion}-\phi_{el})/kT\right] \qquad A \simeq m_p k^2/2\pi^2\hbar^3 \quad (1.7)$$

$E_{ion}-\phi_{el}$ is of the order of 1 ev if we assume a work function between 4 and 5 ev for the electrode.

The other way of looking at this problem is that the Fermi level in the organic material may lie at $E_{cond}/2$. Thus in accordance with Eq. (1.5), one has a density n^+ in the interior and an equal number of separated electrons. A contact potential V_{ct} develops between the electrode and the organic material given by Eq. (1.8).

$$V_{ct} = (E_{ion}-\tfrac{1}{2}E_{cond})-\phi_{el} \qquad\qquad (1.8)$$

For $E_{ion}-\phi_{el} \angle E_{cond}/2$, V_{ct} will be negative, which means the electrode will be negatively charged. Consequently, an accumulation layer of positive holes and a depletion layer of negative charges will occur at the electrode. The density of holes n_s^+ at the boundary is then given by Eq. (1.9).

$$n_s^+ = 2(m_p k/2\pi\hbar^2)^{3/2}T^{3/2} \exp\left[-(E_{ion}-\phi_{el})/kT\right] \qquad (1.9)$$

For V_{ct} negative and thus $n_s^+ > n_{int}^+$ the application of an external field would draw positive charges from the positive electrode into the interior, and if n_s^+ is considerably larger than n_{intr}^+, the current of the material may be completely determined by the surface density. The observed temperature dependence of conductivity may then be given by the exponential in Eq. (1.9) and not by that in Eq. (1.5). The energy determined in this way would thus be $\phi_{el}-E_{ion}$ and not $E_{cond}/2$. Fig. 1.6 describes this type of hole concentration in the material if a contact potential occurs only at one face.

We arrive at the same results using Eq. (1.7), the number of emitted holes, instead of Eq. (1.9). The relation between them is given by Eq. (1.10), where $\bar{v}$ describes a velocity.

$$n_s^+\bar{v} = \mathcal{N}_{th}^+ \qquad\qquad (1.10)$$

If the density n_{int} is extrinsic and not intrinsic, then instead of Eq. (1.5) we must use (1.6), and E_{cond} has to be replaced by E_D in all these considerations.

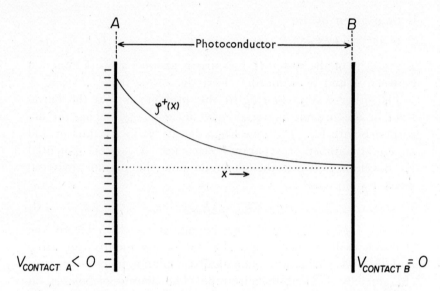

Fig. 1.6. Hole concentration where contact potential occurs on one face only.

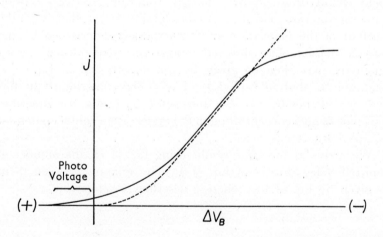

Fig. 1.7. The relationship between current and voltage. Broken line: current without diffusion and no saturation; solid line: current with diffusion and saturation.

More quantitatively, we have for anthracene with $E_{\text{ion}} \sim 5.6$ and, assuming for ϕ_{el} a value between 4 and 5 ev, $E_{\text{ion}} - \phi_{\text{el}} \sim 1$ volt. Thus if the energy level E_{cond} of the conductivity band is larger than 2 volts ($E_F > 1$ ev), we should have the case of hole emission, and the observed activation energy found for anthracene conductivity will be identified with $E_{\text{ion}} - \phi_{\text{el}}$.

Such accumulation layers as described here are often described by the Debye length, which is rather large — about 1 to 10 cm for the densities involved in these dark-conductivity measurements. This would mean that they are larger than the thickness of our crystals. We must, however, consider that the voltage of 1 volt across such layers compresses them very considerably. Their thicknesses are not given by the normal Debye length but essentially by the voltage, as the latter is much larger than kT as long as there is a relationship of the form $n^+ n^- =$ constant between the positive and negative charges.

The current produced by hole injection can be calculated from Eq. (1.2) with i^+ constant. The following approximations are made: n^- is neglected for the current as well as for the space charge. The latter is justified for $E_{\text{ion}} - \phi_{\text{el}} < E_{\text{cond}}/2$, since all negative charge densities are small compared to n_s^+. Also the diffusion term in Eq. (1.2) is in first approximation neglected. Equation (1.11) describes the relationship between current and voltage as a function of the n^+ density at the positive electrode.

$$y = 3/2 \left[(E_s^2 - \tfrac{3}{4}(V/d)^2] \pm \{\tfrac{9}{4}[E_s^2 - \tfrac{3}{4}(V/d)^2]^2 + 3E_s^3[(V/d) - E_s]\}^{\frac{1}{2}} \right.$$
$$E_s = i^+/\omega n^+ \qquad\qquad (1.11)$$
$$y = E_s n_s^+ d 8\pi e/\varepsilon = i^+ d 8\pi e/\varepsilon\omega$$

where i is the particle current, n_s^+ is the surface density, E_s is the field strength at the positive electrode, and ε is the dielectric constant. The relationship is shown in Fig. 1.7 as the dotted curve (where the voltage is described as ΔV). For small voltages the relationship is given by Eq. (1.11a) and for large voltage by (1.11b).

$$i = (9\omega\varepsilon/4 \times 8\pi de)(V/d)^2 \{1 - \tfrac{4}{3}[E_s/(V/d)]^2\} \qquad (1.11a)$$
$$i = \omega^+ n_s[(V/d) - (n_s d 2\pi e/\varepsilon)] \qquad (1.11b)$$

Equation (1.11*a*) describes the well-known V^2 relationship of a space-charge-controlled current that eventually goes over into the linear relationship of Eq. (1.11*b*). Equation (1.11*b*) holds as long as n_s^+ is much smaller than $\varepsilon V/4\pi ed^2$, with ε the dielectric constant of the organic material, e the elementary charge, V the applied voltage, and d the thickness of the sandwich cell.

With the densities calculated from the dark current, the field-strength range in which Eq. (1.11*a*) holds is immeasurably small. Thus at the low field strengths we have measured, the diffusion effect is certainly dominating. It can be determined by integrating Eq. (1.2), with n^- very small. This leads to the following differential equation:

$$dE/dx - eE^2/2kT - \varepsilon i^+/4\pi\omega^+kT + c_0 = 0$$

which can be solved by known functions. The constants of integration can be determined from the hole densities at the two electrode surfaces. The observed deviations from linearity are thus due to the diffusion effect.

A further correction arises from the fact that n_s^+ decreases when a current is flowing. Without current flow n_s^+ and $\mathcal{N}_{th}^+$ are correlated by Eq. (1.10). With current the relationship between n_s^+ and $\mathcal{N}_{th}^+$ is given by Eq. (1.12), which yields for i^+ at large voltages Eq. (1.13), indicating a saturation for large V.

$$n_s^+\bar{v} = \mathcal{N}_{th} - i^+ \qquad\qquad (1.12)$$

The correction for diffusion and saturation is described by the solid line in Fig. (1.7). For low voltages the current is increased by the diffusion effect, and even for a zero applied voltage a current would flow, driven by the contact voltage if this voltage were not compensated for elsewhere in the circuit. This increase of current by the diffusion only occurs when hole emission is produced by illumination. Then this current is the photo-current (see below). We can calculate from Eq. (1.13) the field strength at which saturation should occur.

$$i^+ = \mathcal{N}_{th}\omega^+(V/d)/\{\bar{v}[1+(\omega^+/v)(V/d)]\} \qquad (1.13)$$

Since $\bar{v}$ in the case of dark conductivity is of the order of a thermal velocity, we find that saturation should occur only at fields of several thousand volts per centimeter.

These considerations are valid as long as $n_s^+ > n_{\text{int}}^+$. If this is not the case, the calculations are quite different, since the excess negative charge at the electrode must then be taken into account. This case occurs when a low-lying conductivity band or low-lying donor level E_D exists in the organic material; in anthracene, this would mean E_{cond} or E_D smaller than 2 ev.

The case of $n_s^+ < n_{\text{int}}^+$ is the case of a rectifier with a hole-depletion layer adjacent to the electrode, and the current would be given by Eq. (1.14), with an external voltage drop ΔV across the barrier.

$$i^+ = AT^2 \left[\exp\left(-\Delta V/kT\right)-1\right] \qquad n_s^+ < n_{\text{int}}^+ \qquad (1.14)$$

A is the same as in Eq. (1.9) for the $n_s^+ > n_{\text{intr}}^+$ case. This means that the same saturation current should be obtained in both cases. But in the case $n_s^+ < n_{\text{int}}^+$, we should expect that the saturation is reached for rather low voltages, since $\Delta V/\delta$ ($\delta =$ barrier thickness) will already exceed the contact potential at low external voltage. This has not been observed. This may indicate that the observed dark currents are not described by the assumption of $n_s^+ < n_{\text{int}}^+$.

The situation described here for dark currents in organic materials with hole injection differs from the situation in conventional semiconductors by the following features: no contribution from negative charges to the conductivity is assumed, either because of a high-lying conductivity band, or of small ω^- mobility or of electron traps, and a rather deep-lying valence band (E_{ion} large) is present. This latter condition limits the hole emission from the electrode according to Eq. (1.7).

Experimentally, we can say that in the case of special electrodes (water electrodes with iodine or ceric ions) the case $n_s^+ > n_{\text{int}}^+$ (hole emission) has been proved, as is reported by Pope (paper 7). It is, of course, still an open question whether in the other cases (metal electrodes) the dark current is electrode controlled as described by Eq. (1.11) or n_{int}^+. Finally it may be mentioned that the quantity $E_{\text{ion}}-\phi_{\text{el}}$, which plays such an important role, may actually not be given by the respective values of the basic materials involved but may be affected by surface states; this is well known in inorganic semiconductors.[9]

B. Photoconductivity. If we now turn to photoconductivity, we must discriminate between two cases. The charges that contribute to the photocurrent are injected into the organic material from the electrode, either under the direct influence of irradiation of the electrode or under the influence of impinging excitons through their dissociation at the electrode. This situation has been exemplified with various electrodes by Pope. The other case would be that in which the charges are not injected from the electrode but are created in the organic material.

The first case [10] can occur when Eq. (1.15) holds, where E_{ext} is the energy of the exciton or the light photon impinging on the electrode.

$$E_{ext} + \phi_{el} - E_{ion} > 0 \qquad (1.15)$$

Positive hole emission into the organic material then occurs. If the number of emitted holes is $\mathcal{N}_{ext}$, then Eq. (1.16) gives the hole density at the surface with $\bar{v}'$ representing again a velocity.

$$n_s^+ \bar{v}' = \mathcal{N}_{ext} \qquad (1.16)$$

This formula is quite analogous to Eq. (1.10). It is noteworthy that condition (1.15) for hole emission is independent of the situation of the conductivity band or the donor level, respectively, in the organic material.

Electron emission can also occur; the condition for it is given by Eq. (1.17).

$$E_{ext}^+(E_{ion} - E_{cond}) - \phi_{el} > 0 \qquad (1.17)$$

It may be noted that Eqs. (1.15) and (1.17) can hold simultaneously, depending on the value of E_{cond}, or E_D, which may replace E_{cond} in Eq. (1.17) for the extrinsic case. For anthracene the condition for hole emission is rapidly fulfilled when $E_{ext} > 1$ ev with ϕ_{el} lying between 4 and 5 ev, and that for electron emission is satisfied when E_{cond} is about 2 ev below E_{ion} with $E_{ext} \sim 3$ ev.

The positive current is described by equations similar to (1.11), (1.11a) and (1.11b), replacing Eq. (1.10) by (1.16). Experimentally, curves similar to those described in Figure 1.7 (solid line) have been obtained. In the case of photocurrent, the current at zero voltage is definitely positive because of the diffusion term in Eq. (1.2), which is responsible for the photovoltage. These considerations describe the results in first approximation.

In spite of the fact that for the reported photocurrents the density of positive holes is much larger than in the case of dark current, the voltage range in which Eq. (1.11a) holds lies still at very small voltages.

The following details may be given: The photocurrent displays saturation with water electrodes and some indication of saturation with metal electrodes. It depends upon the intensity of illumination at saturation being $I^{1.2}$ instead of I, which would be expected if we assume that $\mathcal{N}_{ext}$ is exactly proportional to the light intensity. It is not known at this time whether the cause of this deviation is more of an experimental than of a theoretical nature. The so-called "negative" current is essentially given by a small hole emission from the nonilluminated electrode, according to our experiments. Therefore the ratio of the "positive" to the "negative" saturation currents is given by the ratio of n_s^+ at the two electrodes, according to Eqs. (1.16) and (1.11b). This ratio can also be determined from the photovoltage according to Eq. (1.4). The photovoltage gives about three thousand for this ratio, whereas from the plus and minus saturation current, a ratio of about one hundred obtains. This difference may indicate that the $\bar{v}'$ is not constant but may depend on illumination and also upon the field strength at the respective electrodes. The observation that the voltage at which saturation occurs is slightly dependent on the intensity of illumination means indeed that $\bar{v}'$ in Eq. (1.16) depends upon the intensity of illumination to a small extent. In the case of photovoltage the field strength is quite different from that which produces saturation current, even in sign.

We can also compare the photovoltage obtained with different electrodes and correlate them with the respective saturation current. As expected, the photovoltages are smaller for those electrodes that give smaller saturation currents. There is one striking difference between the light-induced current and the normal dark current. The latter does not display saturation in the admissible range of field strengths. We could explain this by a difference between $\bar{v}'$ and $\bar{v}$ in Eqs. (1.16) and (1.10). When thermally injected, holes enter into the organic material with very small energy; when injected by light, they have considerable energy because of Eq. (1.15) with E_{ext} more than 3 ev. Thus in the thermal case holes may be reflected back rather easily and produce a smaller density near the surface than if the same number of holes is injected with higher energy. It may be noted, however, that the dark current obtained with water electrodes containing iodine displayed saturation. This may be due to the fact that in this case holes are injected with an excess of energy.

If, however, the radiation produces charges directly in the organic material, either intrinsically or extrinsically, then a steady photocurrent can only flow when either a supply of positive holes from the positive electrode exists or negative electrons flow from the conduction band inside the organic material into the electrode. If there is no interaction between the radiation or the excitons and the electrode, then the supply of holes is given by Eq. (1.10). This is too small to account for the observed photocurrents. If such interaction occurs then we have the case of hole injection from the electrode, as treated above. Without such interaction a flow of electrons from the conductivity band of the organic into the electrode must occur, and this would require some true negative electron current. Since in our experiments with water electrodes it was shown that the contribution of negative electrons to the negative current is small,[11] it seems unlikely that there is considerable flow of negative electrons from the conductivity band into the electrode. It is possible that under other conditions, particularly when the photocurrents are small, there is a current due to negative electrons. The role of the negative electrons will be discussed in Sec. 3 in more detail.

3. Current Multiplication with Large Field Strengths

Finally, let us discuss briefly a subject that may supply important information on the processes occurring in organic materials. It has been reported several times that at large field strength unusually high currents are observed.[12] We have made very preliminary experiments with single-crystal sandwich cells with evaporated metal electrodes and found a marked increase beginning with field strengths of 200,000 volts/cm. The properties of this current multiplication are summarized here:

(a) With metal electrodes the photocurrent displays some indication of saturation at field strengths of about 10^5 volts cm^{-1}. Beyond this field strength, strong multiplication sets in.

(b) The multiplication is almost exponential.

(c) Ratio of number of incident quanta to number of electrons flowing is approximately 1.

(d) True quantum yield much greater than 1.

(e) The multiplication is roughly proportional to the intensity of illumination.

(f) The multiplication does not alter the intensity of the fluorescent emission.

(g) Similar multiplication is observed for the dark current.

(h) Multiplication is also observed for the negative current (current with the illuminated electrode negative).

(i) The multiplication for the $(-)$ current is about twenty times greater than that for the positive.

Although these experiments are still in a very provisional state, there are some interesting features that may be discussed here. The current multiplication is not due to a cascade effect in the organic materials. It is also not due to an increased number of excitons impinging on the electrode and producing holes. This can be concluded from statement (g). While this multiplied current is flowing through the crystal, the fluorescent light emission is not changed. The multiplication observed up to field strengths of 400,000 volts/cm is of the order of twenty times the saturation current, so that the quantum yield approaches 1. Since, however, more than 90 per cent of all quanta absorbed are reemitted as fluorescent light, the true quantum yield is considerably larger than 1. It is important to stress the fact that the multiplication depends on the intensity of illumination. This means that even in the multiplication range the current intensity is very roughly proportional to the intensity of illumination. Also, the dark current is multiplied, but the maximum dark current obtained is much smaller than the photocurrent obtained with the same field strength.

These results indicate that the process of multiplication occurs at the electrodes. Two possible processes can be envisaged:

The large field strength may deform the barrier at the crystal-electrode interface and thus allow a larger flow of holes into the crystal. But it is then not quite obvious why this increased flow of holes is still dependent upon the light intensity.

Another process which may be suggested by properties (h) and (i) is the following: The so-called "negative" current is also multiplied, but it is multiplied much more than the positive current, so that the ratio between positive and negative currents at high field strength is almost equal to 1. If a positive hole hits the electrode under the influence of a strong field, it may with some probability produce the injection of an electron into the organic sample; this electron would be drawn through the crystal by the large field in spite of its supposed small mobility or its being trapped. In any case the strong multiplication of the negative current seems to indicate that at high field strength negative electrons are also injected.

It is, of course, too early to attempt a more detailed description of the process involved at this stage of the investigation.

Summary

The following experimental and theoretical results should be emphasized. Predominantly positive charges move through most of the organic materials; this is concluded from the difference between the so-called "positive" and "negative" currents. Currents that can be unambiguously attributed to negative electrons are not yet in evidence.

Polarization measurements, however, have shown that negative electrons are present and trapped inside the materials. Positive charges are also trapped but mostly near boundary layers and only weakly in single crystals. The trapping of negative charges spreads through the whole material and is also quite noticeable in single crystals.

Photovoltages occur, and the side of strong illumination is negative; their magnitude strongly depends upon the nature of the electrodes.

Dark conductivity is ordinarily small and shows mostly no saturation up to high field strengths. By using special electrodes the dark current can be made quite large; it then displays saturation, and there is a strong difference between "positive" and "negative" currents when only one special electrode is applied. Photoconductive currents also show that the above-mentioned difference between "positive" and "negative" currents strongly depends upon the nature of the electrodes. The ratio $i+/i-$ can be even reversed when the special electrode itself is illuminated. The current saturates with voltage using electrolyte electrodes; it is almost linearly dependent upon the light intensity, and quantum yields up to 10 per cent have been observed.

High-field-strength experiments have revealed a current multiplication of the $i+$, $i-$, and the dark current. Under such conditions the $i+$ and $i-$ currents become equal.

Theoretical Conclusions

Persistent polarization in crystalline layers between conductive transparent electrodes can be described as being brought about by trapped positive and negative charge layers near the electrodes. The negative layer can display a considerable spread over the interior of the material. In single crystals mostly negative charges are distributed through its whole interior. The light discharge of polarization shows that charges are injected into, as well as produced inside, the material. Silver's experiments indicate negative electron injection and extrinsic internal production.

Photovoltages can be understood by assuming either positive

hole injection or an equal flow of positive and negative charges from the interior into the electrode.

Dark conductivity must not necessarily be due to a relatively high density of positive charge carriers inside the material, which would be a consequence of a relatively low-lying Fermi level. It can be understood by postulating a density of holes near the electrode (as a consequence of thermal hole injection). These holes are moved by the external field through the material. Dark currents due to such hole injection have been observed. In this case the magnitude of the dark current would be determined by the surface charge density, and as a corollary to it the activation energy of the dark current would be given by the difference between the ionization energy of the material and the work function of the electron in the electrode.

Photoconductivity with electrolyte electrodes has been shown to be due very often to hole injection. Similar to the dark-current model, the photoconductivity in this case is determined by the density of holes near the positive electrode. This time, however, this density is produced by the hole emission brought about either by the dissociation of excitons impinging upon the electrode or by light absorbed in the electrode. The current calculated under this assumption displays a V^2 dependence at low voltages and saturation at high voltages. The extent to which internal charge production contributes to photoconductivity and to what extent negative electrons participate in this current has not yet been evaluated. If positive hole injection would not be responsible for the photocurrents, we have again to assume a flow of negative electrons inside the organic material into the electrode.

High field strength multiplication seems to be connected with negative electron injection in addition to positive hole emission as evidenced by the strong increase of the "negative" current. The ratio $i+/i-$ approaches 1.

Acknowledgments. Grateful acknowledgment is made of the assistance in this work of the Office of Naval Research (NONR 285(41)), of the Air Force Cambridge Research Center, Contract AF 19(604)−5495, and of the Air Force Office of Scientific Research, Contract AF 18(600)−1004.

References

1. C. G. B. Garrett *in* N. B. Hannay (ed.), "Semiconductors," Monograph Series No. 140, pp. 634ff., Reinhold Publishing Corporation, New York (1959).
2. H. Kallmann and B. Rosenberg, *Phys. Rev.* **97**, 1596 (1955).
3. H. Kallmann and M. Silver, "Hole Motion in Anthracene Crystals," Garmisch Semiconductor Meeting (1956).
4. M. Silver, "Persistent Internal Polarization Effects in Anthracene," Ph. D. thesis, New York University (February, 1959).
5. M. Pope (unpublished).
6. H. Kallmann and M. Pope, *J. Chem. Phys.* **30**, 585 (1959).
7. For semiconductor liquid interfaces see, for instance, Mino Green *in* J. O. M. Bockris (ed.), "Modern Aspects of Electrochemistry," No. 2, pp. 343ff., Academic Press, Inc., New York (1959), for many of the formulas used here. See further J. T. Law, *in* N. B. Hannay (ed.), "Semiconductors," Monograph Series No. 140, pp. 634ff., Reinhold, New York (1959).
8. H. Kallmann and M. Pope, *J. Chem. Phys.* **32**, 300 (1960).
9. W. H. B. Brattain and C. G. B. Garrett, "Surface Properties of Semiconductors," Amsterdam Conference on Semiconductors (1954), and W. H. B. Brattain and C. G. B. Garrett, *Bell System Tech. J.* **34**, 129 (1955).
10. H. Kallmann and M. Pope, *Nature* **186**, 31 (1960).
11. H. Kallmann and M. Pope, *Nature* **185**, 153 (1960).
12. N. V. Riehl, *Zhur. Fiz. Khim.* **6**, 959 (1959).

2

Photoconductivity in Aromatic Hydrocarbon Crystals

O. SIMPSON

1. Introduction

Photoconductivity has been observed in a great variety of aromatic hydrocarbon crystals when irradiated with light in the fundamental absorption band. In some cases, such as anthracene, absorption in the fundamental band is accompanied by fluorescence, so that the production of carriers must be in competition with the radiative decay of the molecular excited state. This in itself is sufficient to invest the photoconductivity with a special interest, and at least in the case of anthracene there is already a reasonable body of quantitative experimental results available. Some of these results show a square-law dependence of photocurrent on applied voltage, and this is suggestive of a space-charge-limited current. However, the situation is not so simple as this, because a strictly space-charge-limited current is independent of the carrier density in the low field regions of the crystal. Since the carrier density in this case would be highest in the illuminated part of the crystal this implies, contrary to what is found experimentally, that the current in a thick crystal, illuminated on one side, would be independent of intensity.

In an attempt to resolve this dilemma we shall consider a simple model of a photoconductor in which there are both positive carriers of mobility μ_p and negative carriers of mobility μ_n. We shall assume that trapping is negligible, as appears to be the case in anthracene, and that monochromatic light with absorption coefficient of the order 10^5 cm^{-1} is incident on one face of a crystal of thickness much greater than the extinction depth. Since the photoconductivity is not the primary effect accompanying the absorption of light, we shall assume a source function for the creation of pairs of carriers of the form

$$S(x) = S \exp (-x/d)$$

where d is not necessarily equal to the extinction depth of the radiation but is of the same order of magnitude. It follows that Sd is the total rate of production of carriers, so that S is a function of the intensity of illumination but is not necessarily simply proportional to it. We shall neglect the density of carriers in equilibrium in the dark in comparison with the photocarriers, since photocurrents that are several orders of magnitude greater than the dark currents are commonly observed. Under the applied field carriers are swept out of the illuminated region, they may, however, also be removed by recombination, and we assume a bimolecular recombination rate Bnp, where n and p are the concentrations of negative and positive carriers and B is a recombination coefficient.

2. The General Equations and Boundary Conditions

Subject to appropriate boundary conditions the steady-state charge distribution, potential function, and current are determined by simultaneous continuity equations for the negative and positive carriers, together with Poisson's equation

$$\operatorname{div} \mathcal{J}^- + [S \exp (-x/d) - Bnp]e = 0 \qquad (2.1)$$

$$-\operatorname{div} \mathcal{J}^+ + [S \exp (-x/d) - Bnp]e = 0 \qquad (2.2)$$

$$\operatorname{div} E = 4\pi(p-n)e/\kappa \qquad (2.3)$$

where e is the electronic charge, κ the dielectric constant, and the currents $\mathcal{J}^-$ and $\mathcal{J}^+$, neglecting the diffusion current, are given by

$$\mathcal{J}^- = ne\mu_n E \qquad \mathcal{J}^+ = pe\mu_p E \qquad (2.4)$$

Because the source function is confined to a part of the crystal close to the illuminated surface, the total change of field across this region due to the accumulated space charge is small. Thus, for example, an average excess charge density of 10^{12} carriers cm^{-3} gives a change of field across the source region of only 2 volts cm^{-1}. This is small compared with the mean applied fields normally used in experiments with anthracene crystals, which are of the order of 1,000 volts cm^{-1}. It follows that whatever part space charge may play in determining the voltage applied across the whole crystal, the charge distribution within the source region is relatively unimportant. We shall proceed on the assumption that it is legitimate to neglect the field variation within the source region, and consider the problem of two contiguous regions: A, a slice of thickness less than a micron adjacent to the illuminated electrode, in which the field is constant, and B, the remainder of the crystal, which may be of any thickness and in which the current may be space-charge-limited.

If the applied field is positive in Eqs. (2.1) to (2.4) negative carriers will be withdrawn from the crystal at the illuminated surface and positive carriers drawn from region A into region B. A physical assumption concerning the possibility of injecting positive carriers at the illuminated surface is now required to fix the boundary condition at $x = 0$. It seems most reasonable to assume that $p = 0$ at $x = 0$, which is equivalent to the statement that positive carriers cannot be injected. The reason for this assertion is that if cqrriers can be injected when the surface is illuminated, there is no a priori reason to suppose that injection would become impossible if the illumination were reduced. But it is known that the dark current in anthracene is many orders of magnitude smaller than the space-charge-limited current that would be observed if injection were possible.

3. The Solution in Region A

In region A the continuity equations reduce to

$$-\mu_p E_0(dp/\partial x) + S \exp\ (-x/d) - Bnp = 0 \qquad (2.5)$$

$$\mu_n E_0(\partial n/\partial x) + S \exp\ (-x/d) - Bnp = 0 \qquad (2.6)$$

Using the boundary condition $p(0) = 0$, $n(0) = n_0$, and separating the variables, we obtain

$$n\mu_n + p\mu_p = n_0\mu_n \qquad (2.7)$$

$$\mu_n E_0(\partial n/\partial x) + S \exp\ (-x/d) - n_0(\mu_n/\mu_p)Bn + (\mu_n/\mu_p)Bn^2 = 0 \quad (2.8)$$

Equation (2.8) is a form of Riccati's equation and cannot be solved in terms of elementary functions. However, we can obtain approximate solutions in the limiting cases of very small and very large x. The last two terms are together equal to Bnp, and since this tends to zero at $x = 0$, these terms may be omitted for sufficiently small values of x (i.e., close to the illuminated surface the recombination rate is negligible compared with the rate of production of carriers and their rate of removal by conduction). We thus have, for very small x,

$$n = n_0 + (Sd/E_0\mu_n)[\exp(-x/d)-1] \qquad (2.9)$$

where n_0 has entered as the constant of integration and must satisfy also the physical conditions at large values of x. If $n_0 = Sd/E_0\mu_n$, Eq. (2.9) becomes simply

$$n = (Sd/E_0\mu_n)\exp(-x/d) \qquad (2.10)$$

and it may be seen directly that the first term in (2.8) exceeds the third and fourth terms for all values of x if

$$E_0^2 > SBd^2/\mu_n\mu_p \qquad (2.11)$$

In this case, Eq. (2.10) is the required solution of Eq. (2.8), because the recombination terms are everywhere small compared with the rate of removal of the carriers by conduction.

On the other hand if the inequality in Eq. (2.11) is not satisfied, the recombination becomes important for sufficiently large values of x, and we may look for a solution that will be correct at large x by omitting the term $\mu_n E_0\, \partial n/\partial x$. Equation (2.8) now reduces to a quadratic with solution

$$n = 1/2[n_0 - \sqrt{(n_0^2-4c)}] \qquad (2.12)$$

where

$$c = (\mu_p/\mu_n)(S/B)\exp(-x/d)$$

The constant n_0 has not yet been determined, but we can require that (2.9) and (2.12) fit smoothly at some intermediate value $x = x'$, and this will determine n_0 uniquely. In this way we obtain an approximate solution valid for all x, such that $n(x)$ is given by Eq. (2.9) for $x < x'$ and by (2.12) for $x > x'$.

Matching n and $\partial n/\partial x$ from (2.9) and (2.12) we obtain simultaneous equations for n_0 and x'

$$n_0^2 = (E_0^2 \mu_p^2/16B^2d^2)+4c'$$
$$c' = (E_0\mu_p/Bd)[(Sd/E_0\mu_n)-(n_0/2)-(E_0\mu_p/8Bd)]$$

where

$$c' = (\mu_p/\mu_n)(S/B) \exp (-x'/d)$$

and eliminating c'

$$n_0 = (\mu_p/Bd) \{[q/16\ E_0^2+(4SBd^2/\mu_n\mu_p)]^{\frac{1}{2}}-E_0\} \qquad (2.13)$$

For the extreme case $E_0^2 \ll SBd^2/\mu_n\mu_p$ we obtain

$$n_0 = 2(\mu_p/\mu_n)^{\frac{1}{2}}(S/B)^{\frac{1}{2}} \qquad (2.14)$$

We are now in a position to find the current in terms of the field applied across region A.

$$\mathcal{J} = \mathcal{J}^+ + \mathcal{J}^- = n_0 e \mu_n E_0$$

using Eqs. (2.10) and (2.14) we find for $E_0^2 \ll SBd^2/\mu_n\mu_p$,

$$\mathcal{J} = 2(\mu_n\mu_p)^{\frac{1}{2}}(S/B)^{\frac{1}{2}} eE_0 \qquad (2.15)$$

and for $E_0^2 \gg SBd^2/\mu_n\mu_p$,

$$\mathcal{J} = eSd \qquad (2.16)$$

These results show that for low applied fields the photocurrent is proportional to the square root of the source strength and linear with the field. In this regime the photocurrent is symmetrical with respect to the negative and positive carrier mobilities, and the same current should be observed independently of the polarity of the illuminated surface. As the field is increased, the photocurrent increases less rapidly than E_0, and finally at high enough fields $E_0^2 \gg SBd^2/\mu_n\mu_p$, it saturates at a value equal to the total rate of production of carrier pairs.

4. The Solution in Region B

We now consider region B, comprising the majority of the crystal, in which there are only carriers of one sign. Assuming that E_0 in region A is positive, these will be positive carriers, and the boundary conditions at the interface between A and B are

$$p = (\mu_n/\mu_p)n_0 \qquad n = 0$$
$$E = E_0 = J/e\mu_n n_0 \qquad (2.17)$$

Using the ordinary theory of space-charge-limited currents in an insulator where only one carrier is present, we obtain an expression for the field at any point in region B, taking a new origin $x = 0$ at the interface,

$$E^2 = (4\pi Jx/\kappa\mu_p)+E_0^2 \qquad (2.18)$$

from which by integration we derive the potential difference across region B, assumed to be of width a,

$$V = 2/3(\mu_p\kappa/4\pi J)\left\{[(4\pi Ja/\mu_p\kappa)+E_0^2]^{3/2}-E_0^3\right\} \qquad (2.19)$$

For a fixed intensity of illumination in region A we can now consider the photocurrent in B as the applied voltage is increased. The illuminated region acts as a current source that regulates the flow of current into B at a rate determined by E_0 and n_0. We are able to distinguish four separate regimes:

a. $J \propto V^2$. At low applied voltage Eq. (2.19) reduces to the ordinary space-charge formula

$$V = 2/3(4\pi J/\kappa\mu_p)^{1/2} a^{3/2} \qquad (2.20)$$

which is independent of the source function and therefore independent of the intensity of illumination.

b. Intermediate Case. When the current increases until $4\pi Ja/\mu_p\kappa \sim E_0^2$, which from Eq. (2.15) is equivalent to

$$J \sim (16\pi ae^2\mu_n/\kappa)\,(S/B) \qquad (2.21)$$

The current is controlled partly by space charge and partly by the rate of production of carriers. In this condition the current increases more rapidly than the first power of V, but less rapidly than V^2.

c. $J \propto V$. When $E_0^2 \gg 4\pi Ja/\kappa\mu_p$, Eq. (2.19) reduces to

$$V = Ja/en_0\mu_n \qquad (2.22)$$

where the intensity dependence is implicit in n_0. The photo-current will be linear with V so long as n_0 is given by (2.14), but when $E_0^2 \approx BSd^2/\mu_n\mu_p$, Eq. (2.13) must be used.

d. Saturation. Finally, when $E_0^2 \gg BSd^2/\mu_n\mu_p$ the saturation current

$$\mathcal{J}_{\max} = eSd \qquad (2.23)$$

is reached.

One further condition is of interest. If the current defined by Eq. (2.21) exceeds the saturation current (2.23), then the space-charge-limited regime will be maintained until saturation is reached, and there will be no intermediate or linear cases. This condition is

$$16\pi ae\mu_n > B\kappa d \qquad (2.24)$$

which does not contain the source intensity explicitly, but depends on its range.

5. Comparison with Experiment

We can summarize the results of this analysis graphically. Figure 2.1 shows the density of carriers of both signs, and the

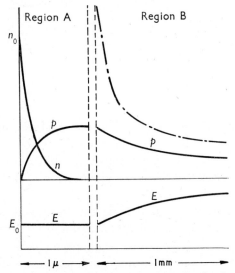

Fig. 2.1. Carrier density and field distribution.

voltage drop, across the crystal for circumstances corresponding
to the intermediate case discussed above. The broken line shows
the density of carriers that would be required to sustain a fully
space-charge-limited current. The regions A and B are not
shown to scale.

Figure 2.2 shows the variation of n_0 with E_0 in region A for
several values of the source strength S. The line marked
$n_0 = (4\mu_p/Bd)E_0$ denotes the onset of saturation.

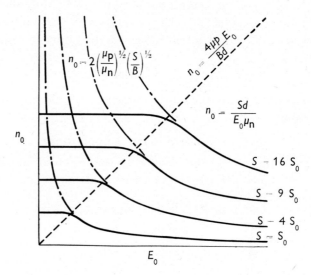

Fig. 2.2 Variation of n_0 with E_0 in region A.

Figure 2.3 shows the current $\mathcal{J}$ in region A as a function of the
field E_0. Ohm's law is obeyed until saturation sets in at
$\mathcal{J} = (4\mu_n\mu_p e/dB)E^2$. This figure shows the ability of the illuminated
region of the crystal to act as a current source, and its limitation
when saturation is reached.

The photocurrent is plotted against the total potential difference
across the crystal in Fig. 2.4 and 2.5. Figure 2.4 shows the case
where the current falls below the space charge limited value
before saturation is reached; there is then a linear range of photocurrent against voltage until saturation of region A occurs. In

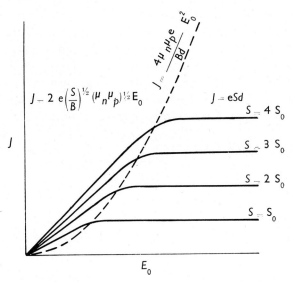

Fig. 2.3. Variation of $\mathcal{J}$ with E_0 in region A.

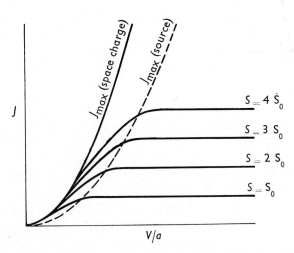

Fig. 2.4. Photocurrent against applied voltage for thin crystals:
$$a < Bd\kappa/16\pi e\mu_n.$$

Fig. 2.5 the saturation occurs while the current is still space-charge-limited, there is no linear range, and only the saturation value is dependent on the intensity of illumination. In both Figs. 2.4 and 2.5 the parabolas $J = (4\mu_n\mu_p/Bd)(V/a)^2$ and $J = (9\kappa\mu_p/16\pi a)(V/a)^2$ are shown. The former defines the saturation current as shown in Fig. 2.3, and the latter is the normal maximum space-charge-limited current.

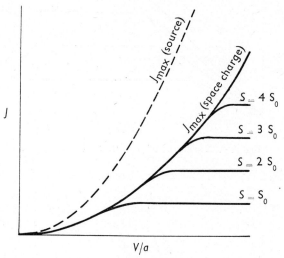

Fig. 2.5. Photocurrent against applied voltage for thick crystals:
$$a > Bd\kappa/16\pi e\mu_n.$$

Although this analysis has been made on the assumption of the boundary condition $p = 0$ at the illuminated surface, the main features would be unaltered even if some injection could occur. Plainly, free injection of carriers cannot occur for otherwise the current would be space-charge-limited at all lightlevels, but if some injection of positive carriers takes place, the only effect will be to increase the conductivity in region A and therefore to alter the values of applied voltage at which the transitions from one regime to another occur.

It is very difficult to compare these results directly with experiment, because we have no direct knowledge of the values of the quantities B, S, μ_p, and μ_n, and even the best estimates may be in error by several orders of magnitude. Figures 2.4 and 2.5 show the cardinal importance of the inequality $16\pi a e \mu_n \gtrless B d \kappa$ in determining whether there exists any range of conditions in which the photocurrent varies with both applied voltage and intensity of illumination. Taking $d = 10^{-5}$ cm and $\kappa = 10$, we find that for a crystal with a thickness of 1 cm the photocurrent will go direcly from the space-charge-limited regime into saturation unless

$$B/\mu_n > 7.5 \times 10^{-2} \text{ volt-cm}$$

Since B is not likely to exceed 10^{-8} cm³ sec⁻¹, this suggests that unless μ_n is less than 10^{-6} cm² volt⁻¹ sec⁻¹ the current will be space-charge-limited up to saturation for crystals of a few millimeters' thickness. On the other hand, crystals with a thickness of 1 micron should show a roughly linear dependence of photocurrent on field so long as

$$B/\mu_n > 7.5 \times 10^{-6} \text{ volt-cm}$$

and this will be the case for most reasonable estimates of B and μ_n.

The results of Northrop and Simpson [1] show an approximately linear field dependence of photocurrent in specimens of 1 micron thickness. These also exhibit $\mathcal{J}$ proportional to the intensity of illumination. On the other hand, the results of Kommandeur and Schneider [2] using anthracene crystals several millimeters thick also show $\mathcal{J}$ varying with light intensity and field, although in some of their experiments $\mathcal{J} \propto V^2$ and $\mathcal{J} \propto (\text{intensity})^{1/2}$. These results seem to be inconsistent with the model we have discussed.

There is, however, one very important factor that has been left out of this discussion so far. Even if the extinction depth of the radiation is as small as 10^{-5} cm, there will be a considerable absorption of fluorescence radiation at greater thicknesses in crystals such as anthracene that have a high fluorescence efficiency. Up to 90 per cent of the incident radiation is reemitted at slightly longer wavelengths, and an appreciable fraction of this is at wavelengths overlapping the tail of the absorption band.

We therefore suggest that although the analysis we have presented is probably a fair approximation for specimens of a few microns' thickness, it will certainly break down for thick crystals, which would be entirely space-charge-limited if the source of carriers were confined to a very thin layer adjoining the illuminated surface. In this case we believe that the current is augmented by carriers produced throughout the bulk of the crystal, in numbers that may well exceed the primary source near the illuminated surface. The analysis does, however, serve the useful purpose of suggesting several critical experiments that could be devised using thick crystals. For example, the use of an anthracene filter to cut off the primary radiation would still permit the bulk production of carriers to occur. It would be interesting to see how much effect this had on the observed photocurrents.

References

1. D. C. Northrop and O. Simpson, *Proc. Roy. Soc. (London)* **A244**, 377 (1958).
2. J. Kommandeur and W. G. Schneider, *J. Chem. Phys.* **28**, 582 (1958).

3

Photoelectric Properties
of Semiconducting Organic Dyes*

A. TERENIN

Introduction

The work in this field is being carried out by us † with the following four main methods: (1) direct-current photo-conduction under constant transverse illumination (d-c ph. cond. tr.); (2) direct-current photo-conduction under intermittent transverse illumination (d-c ph. cond. int.); (3) the alternating photo-electromotive force induced by intermittent light in a condenser (a-c ph. emf); (4) change in the photo-contact potential (ph. cont. pot.).

The results obtained with method 1 have been published in a series of papers by Vartanian and coauthors,[2-9] those with methods 2 and 3 are to be found in the papers by Putzeiko and coauthors,[10-16] the preliminary results with method 4 have been recently described by Akimov and coauthors.[17-18] Some results with the photo emf under constant illumination can be found in the paper by Vartanian and Karpovitch.[8] The photovoltaic effect, observed with pigment films on electrodes immersed into an electrolytic solution, has been studied by Evstigneev and Terenin for the phthalocyanines, pheophytin, and chlorophyll.[19] Quite recently the external photoemission of electrons *in vacuo* from dye films has been measured by Vilessov.[20]

The samples of the dyes were used in the form of thin films**

---

* Although this paper was not presented at the Conference because Dr. Terenin could not attend, we felt that it was appropriate to include it in the proceedings because it represents a survey of work done in Russia.

† A review of the numerous researches on organic semiconductors, outside the limited scope of this paper, has recently been given by Eley.[1]

** 0.1 to 1.0 microns for methods 1 and 2, 10 to 100 microns for method 3, and 1 to 10 microns for method 4.

deposited from organic solvents, or by sublimation *in vacuo*, when admissible. In methods 1 and 2 the dye film covered a gap of about 1 mm between gold or platinum electrodes. These were, deposited on a polished silica plate, which formed a section of the quartz wall of an internal finger in a glass vacuum jacket provided with a window. The temperature of the film was kept constant during the illumination by a suitable temperature bath in the finger.

In method 3 the dye film was deposited on one of the two thin (0.1 to 0.2 mm) mica or quartz laminae inserted into the condenser, or the crystalline dye powder was pressed between them. Different gases could be introduced in the cell to study their action. With many dyes, measurements could be performed in open air without being substantially impaired.

1. Direct-Current Method

The systematic work on the d-c method that was started in 1940 by Vartanian [2] has shown that a large variety of dyes consisting either of uncharged molecules (the phthalocyanines, indigo) or of molecular ions (cationic or anionic) possess a dark specific conductance σ in the range from 10^{-10} to 10^{-14} ohm^{-1} cm^{-1} at 20°C *in vacuo*; e.g., crystal violet (cationic), $\sigma_{20°} = 10^{-10}$; fluorescein-Na (anionic), $\sigma_{20°} = 10^{-13}$; indigo blue (uncharged), $\sigma_{20°} = 10^{-13}$; and the phthalocyanines (uncharged), $\sigma_{20°} = 10^{-12}$ to 10^{-13} ohm^{-1} cm^{-1}.[4-7]

The dark conductivity σ of many dyes obeys, between -50 and $+150$°C, the linear relationship between log σ and $1/T$, known for the intrinsic semiconductors

$$\ln \sigma = \ln \sigma_0 - (E_d/2kT)$$

as can be seen in Fig. 3.1 (Vartanian[2-9]).

Table 3.1 gives some of the values of the activation energy E_d thus obtained. The most reliable values are for those dye films which were deposited by sublimation *in vacuo*, e.g., the phthalocyanines, rhodamin 6G, crystal violet, indigo, etc. The figures for E_d and σ_0 obtained for the sublimated films of the phthalo-

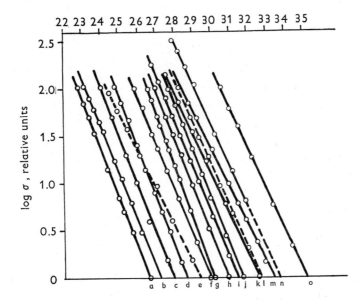

Fig. 3.1. Temperature dependence of the *d–c* conduction for dye films *in vacuo*. The letters in parentheses give the corresponding activation energies E_d, in electron volts. (a) Erythrosin (2.07); (b) rose bengal (2.0); (c) floxin (2.08); (d) eosin (2.10); (e) turquoise blue (1.63); (f) rhodamin 6G (1.93); (g) trypaflavin (2.24); (h) fluorescein-Na (2.03); (i) cyanine (1.90); (j) chlorophyll (2.00); (l) indigo (1,75); pinacyanol (1.80); (m) Cu-phthalocyanine (1.63); (n) fuchsin (1.83); (o) night blue (1.70). [3-9]

cyanines differ only slightly from those known for the mono-crystals of these pigments.[21]

The magnitude of the dark conductance factor σ_0 and of the thermal activation energy E_d so far obtained for numerous dyes varies in rather wide limits, and no simple connection could be found as yet between their magnitude and the dye class or structure.

There seems, however, to exist a qualitative relationship between σ_0 and E_d in the respect that large σ_0 values are often connected with large E_d ones. Such a relationship is well known

Table 3.1. Values for the Activation Energy E_d of the D-C Conduction, for the Quantum Threshold $h\nu^0$ of the Photoconduction and for the Thermal Activation Energy E_{ph} of the Latter. [3-9]

Dye	E_d ev	$h\nu^0$ ev	E_{ph} ev
Trypaflavin	2.24	2.35	0.28
Phenosafranine	2.08	2.07	
Erythrosine	2.07	2.14	0.27
Orthochrome T	2.05	2.02	
Pinacyanole	1.8	1.77	0.22
Zn-phthalocyanine	1.8	1.59	0.25
Cu-phthalocyanine	1.7	1.63	0.25
Phthalocyanine (metal-free)	1.7	1.61	
Indigo	1.75	1.79	0.22
Acridine yellow			0.22
Floxine			0.25
Crystal violet			0.31
Rose bengal			0.37

in the kinetics of many physicochemical processes. For instance, the polynuclear dyes exhibit the values $\sigma_0 = 10^{-6}$ ohm^{-1} cm^{-1}, $E_d = 0.2$ ev (cynananthrone), and $\sigma_0 = 10^{-4}$, $E_d = 0.78$ ev (violanthrone),[22]* whereas for the phthalocyanines we have $\sigma_0 = 10^{-12}$ to 10^{-13}, $E_d = 1.2$–1.7 ev.[7] Anthracene, also a polynuclear uncharged molecule, gives $\sigma_0 = 10^2$, $E_d = 2.7$ ev.[23]

In the case of the intrinsic inorganic semiconductors the factor σ_0 is directly related to the mobility of the charge carriers.[24] We must, however, be cautious in applying the same numerical relationship to the semiconducting molecular crystals, which differ from the former by possessing very narrow conducting bands.

Under a transverse illumination of 100 to 1,000 lux, films of many dyes exhibit a 10^3 to 10^4 increase of the d-c conductance relative to the dark value. The rise and decay of the photocurrent i_{ph} for many of the dyes (crystal violet, fuchsin, etc.) is slow. But there are many dyes (pinacyanol, floxine, indigo, the metal-free-phthalocyanines, etc.) with a very fast relaxation.[4-9] Extreme

* Vartanian gives for violanthrone $E_d = 1.0$ ev.[6]

examples of the current relaxation are shown in Fig. 3.2. Trypaflavine and other dyes have a decay time in the intermediate range (about 1 min).

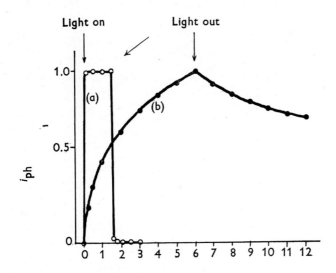

Fig. 3.2. Rise of *d-c* photocurrent under illumination and its decay for dye films *in vacuo*. (a) Pinacyanol; (b) crystal violet. [3–5]

The photoconduction reveals a thermal activation energy E_{ph} that was obtained by method 1, measuring the limiting value of i_{ph} under constant illumination as a function of the temperature. As shown in Fig. 3.3 compiled by Vartanian σ_{ph} obeys the exponential relation

$$\sigma_{ph} = \sigma_{ph}^0 \exp\left(-E_{ph}/kT\right)$$

Some of the values of E_{ph} are given in Table 3.1. It can be seen that they are mostly smaller by one order of magnitude than E_a for the same dye. E_{ph} decreases somewhat on decreasing the wavelength in the same absorption band.

The photocurrent in thin, well-outgassed dye films *in vacuo* varies linearly with the illumination intensity L and obeys approximately Ohm's law.[4–7] In films containing trapping gaseous impurities (see Sec. 4) the photocurrent varies as a power of the illumination L^n, where n can decrease from 1 to about 0.5.[7]

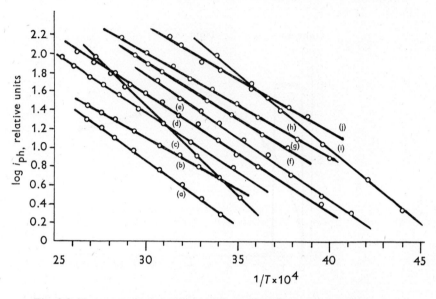

Fig. 3.3. Temperature dependence of the photocurrent for dye films *in vacuo*. The figures in parentheses give the corresponding activation energies E_{ph}, in electron volts. (a) Trypaflavin (0.28); (b) acridine yellow (0.22); (c) rose bengal (0.37); (d) Cu-phthalocyanine (0.25); (e) Zn-phthalocyanine (0.25); (f) erythrosin (0.27); (g) floxin (0.25); (h) pinacyanol (0.22); (i) crystal violet (0.21); (j) indigo (0.22). [3–9]

The shape of the spectral-photosensitivity curve reproduces that of the absorption curve of the dye film when a correction is introduced for the "nonlinearity" of the photocurrent versus light intensity. (See Figs. 3.4 and 3.6a, b.)

For many dyes a close coincidence has been found by Vartanian between E_d, the activation energy of the dark conductivity, and the energy of the light quantum $h\nu^0$ at the onset of the photoelectric sensitivity from the longer wavelengths (Table 3.1). This threshold has been obtained by two different methods: (a) from the value $\lambda^{1/2}$, at which the photosensitivity is half the value at the maximum;[25] (b) from the "photoelectric" straight lines, obtained on measuring the photocurrent under illumination by the integral light from a "black body" incandenscent lamp.[26, 27]

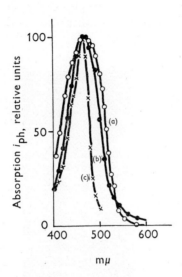

Fig. 3.4. Trypaflavin. (a) Absorption spectrum in ethanol (concentration $1 \times 7 \times 10^{-2}$ mole liter^{-1}); (b) absorption spectrum of the deposited film; (c) spectral curve for the photocurrent, reduced to equal incident energy.[4]

2. Relaxation Curves

In method 2 (dc ph. cond. int.) the light was chopped at a frequency of 50 to 500 cps, the Hg lines being isolated with light filters. The illumination of the dye film in this method varied from 10^{-3} to 10^{-5} watts cm^{-2} sec^{-1}. Putzeiko used the apparatus * devised by Tolstoi and Feofilov,[28] which allows measurements of the photocurrent relaxation times between 5×10^{-6} and 1×10^{-2} sec. The relaxation curves are displayed in this apparatus on the oscilloscope in either a linear or exponential sweep versus the time scale. Thus we can immediately judge whether the rise and decay are strictly exponential or not.

* Widely known here under the name "τ meter."

46   A. TERENIN

As shown by Putzeiko [10, 16] photoconducting dyes, in particular
the metal-free-phthalocyanines, possess a fast initial component of
the rise and decay of the photocurrent with time constants ranging
from 10^{-3} to 10^{-5} sec. There are also slower components present.
The fast component sometimes constitutes 80 per cent of the total
photocurrent.

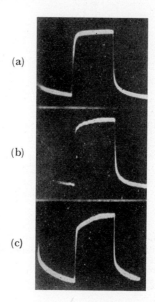

Fig. 3.5. Relaxation curve for the photocurrent. (a) Metal-free phthalocyanine; (b) Cu-phthalocyanine); (c) Cu-phthalocyanine after treatment
at 150°C in air. Initial and final decay time constants: (a) 1.3×10^{-5} and
3×10^{-3} sec; (b) 2×10^{-5} and 4×10^{-3} sec; (c) 5×10^{-5} and 1.2×10^{-2} sec.[10]

In the metal-free-phthalocyanines containing oxygen as trapping impurity, the decay curve is hyperbolic and can be approximated by two exponents with the time constants given in
Fig. 3.5. A hyperbolic law has been previously found by Vartanian
in the slow d-c decay after shutting off the light.[4, 7] In both
methods the relaxation time markedly increases on introducing
oxygen into the metal-free-phthalocyanine films. Metal-free-
phthalocyanine is markedly insensitive to the treatment by

oxygen, which indicates that O_2 molecules are held by the central metal atom.

3. Alternating Photoelectromotive-Force Method

The condenser method mentioned, which we have termed method 3 in the introduction, was originated in the 1930s by Bergmann and coauthors for the study of the photoconduction in inorganic crystalline powders. This method has been applied by Putzeiko for an extensive study of the photoconduction in dye films or powders.[10–16] The intermittent (50 to 500 cps) light coming from a monochromator enters the condenser through a semitransparent conducting coating serving as one of the condenser plates. The intensity of the light absorbed in the semiconducting film or powder, and consequently the concentration

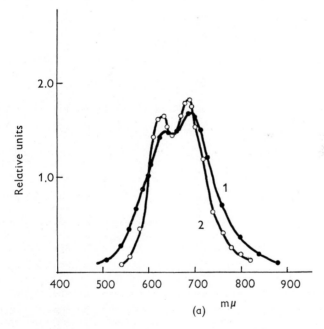

(a)

Fig. 3.6 (a) Spectral curves (reduced to equal-incident monochromatic energies) for a Mg-phthalocyanine film: 1, d-c photoconduction corrected for the nonlinear dependence on light intensity;[7] (2), photoelectromotive force in the condenser.[13]

of the released charges, decreases exponentially along the beam during the light impulse. Thus, a concentration gradient is produced that leads to an alternating diffusion current, inducing

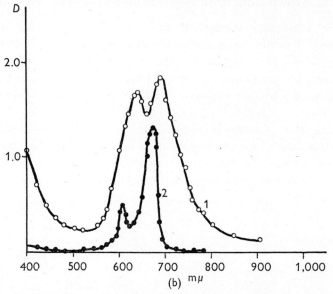

Fig. 3.6. (b) Absorption spectrum (optical densities) for Mg-phthalocyanine. Curve 1, of a sublimed film; curve 2, of a solution in acetone (concentration, 10^{-4} mole liter^{-1}).[13]

a photo-emf on the condenser plates. This emf amounts to 0.01 to 0.1 mv/mw and can easily be measured on amplification.* This setup, fully described by Putzeiko and coauthors, has

---

* The theoretical treatment of the processes going on in the condenser has already been given.[30-32] Later doubts were expressed by some authors [33] as to whether, in the Bergmann condenser, diffusion photocurrents are being recorded or surface effects due to the contact with the dielectric laminae. These authors have found that the magnitude and the sign of the induced photo-emf depend in an undetermined manner on the nature of the dielectric laminae in contact with the inorganic semiconductor studied. These views have been proved (by Akimov) to be groundless by measurements of the contact-potential change on illumination. The magnitude of the dark contact potential depends on the nature of the dielectric laminae, but the sign of the cont. pot. change on illumination is always the same and is related to a diffusion current of definite charges.[17]

a high sensitively, which allowed measurements of the spectral photoelectric sensitivity for a number of carbocyanine dyes, pinacyanol, the metal-free-phthalocyanines, chlorophyll and related pigments, and for numerous dyes of all classes.[10-15]. As can be seen in Fig. 3.6a, the spectral curve of the photo-emf obtained by Putzeiko for a Mg-phthalocyanine sublimed film almost coincides with the photoconduction curve obtained with the d-c method by Vartanian.[7] Both curves closely correspond to the absorption spectrum of the film (Fig. 3.6b).

This condenser method, improved by Putzeiko, has the remarkable advantage of allowing the determination of the sign of the diffusion photocurrent charges. This is achieved by compensating for the photo-emf in the condenser by an additionally applied emf of a regulated magnitude and sign synchronized with the former. This emf was generated by a photocell in a light beam split off from the incident light.[15] Table 3.2 gives a concise

Table 3.2. Sign of the Charge Carriers or the Diffusion Photocurrent in Dyes of Various Classes

Di- and tri-phenyl methanes:		Cyanines:	
Crystal violet	—	Cyanine	+
Malachite green	—	Pinacyanole	—
Pyocyanine	—	3,3'-Diethyl-thia-	
Brilliant green	—	carbocyanine iodide	+
Auramin	+	3,3'-Diethyl-5,5'-dinitro-	
Thiazines:		thiacarbocyanine-n-toluyl	
Methyl green	+	sulfonate	—
Azines:		Neocyanine	+
Phenosafranine	+	Kryptocyanine	+
Acridines:			
Trypaflavin	+	Phthalocyanines:	
Xanthenes:		Metal-free phthalocyanine	+
Methyleosin B	—	Fe^{3+}, Fe^{2+}, Fe^{3+}-sulfur,	
Rhodamin B	—	Co^{2+}, Mn^{2+}, Cu^{2+},	
Floxine	+	Cu^{2+},-sulfur, Zn^{2+}, Mg^{2+}	+
		Ethylchlorophyllide	
		$(a, a+b)$	+
		Chlorophylls $(a, a+b)$	+

summary of the data for the sign of the photocarriers for some dyes.[15, 34, 35] For most of them the sign has been measured in air. In several cases the sign has also been measured *in vacuo* with the same result. It must be remarked, however, that this method is applicable when charges of only one sign are predominant in the investigated semiconductor. When carriers of both signs are released by light of a nearly equal amount, this method does not usually give a measurable photoelectric response.[34, 35]

The sign of the predominant carriers may be different in different ranges of the dye absorption spectrum. Moreover, the presence of adsorbed, or sorbed, gases can cause the appearance of charge carriers of a different sign, which are revealed when the measurement of the photo-emf spectral curve is coupled with the determination of the sign of the charge carriers. In photoelectrically sensitive chlorophyll or chlorophyllide films, there appears besides the dominant p carriers, also n carriers in the range of the longer wavelengths, inside the slope of the main absorption peak.[15] This depends on the state of the surface of the microcrystals that are grown in the treatment by various solvents and their vapors.[13]

4. Action of Gases

It has been found by Petrikaln [36] and Vartanian [3, 5] that for certain cationic dyes, such as crystal violet and rhodamin 6G, oxygen reversibly depresses the d-c photoconductivity and also the decaying dark conductivity after previous illumination, even at a pressure of about 10^{-3} mm Hg. A stronger depressing action is produced by the more electronegative vapors, iodine, and chloroform.

In contrast to these dyes, the anionic dyes — eosin, erythrosin, floxine, and rose bengal — and the cationic dye, trypaflavin, exhibit a rise of d-c photoconduction in the presence of oxygen.

This can certainly be ascribed to a trapping of the conduction electrons by gas molecules possessing a marked electron affinity. The opposite effects can be ascribed to the fact that the first mentioned dyes belong to semiconductors of the n type, whereas the latter group of dyes is of the p type. *

---

*   This opposite action of oxygen was recently confirmed by Meier.[37]

With eosin and tripaflavine films Vartanian has observed after the illumination an increased intake of oxygen by the dye film, as deduced from the increased magnitude of the photocurrent after the oxygen has been pumped off. To restore the initial photoconductivity, a heating to 100°C of the film *in vacuo* was needed. This can mean the formation of dissociable photooxides.[5]

The metal-phthalocyanines are semiconductors of the *p* type [15, 34, 35] and exhibit after a thermal treatment (150 to 200°C) in oxygen at pressure of 100 to 450 mm Hg, a d-c conductivity in the dark enhanced by a factor of 10; the d-c photoconductivity rises by a factor of 100. In the presence of oxygen, transient volume charge effects observed in the pigment film on application of the potential are eliminated. Oxygen is strongly retained in the film, and the initial conductivity *in vacuo* cannot be entirely restored even after prolonged heating *in vacuo* at 200°C.[7] As in the d-c method of Vartanian, the photo-emf for the metal-free phthalocyanine measured by Putzeiko is markedly inert toward oxygen, which points to a special role of the central metal atom in binding the oxygen molecule.[13]

Putzeiko [13, 14] has shown that in order to observe photo-emf in sublimed films of Mg-phthalocyanine, it is necessary to subject them to a thermal treatment (50–80°C) in the vapors of molecules (H_2O, amines, acetone) capable of forming coordinate bonds with this central atom. Under such a treatment, not only is the main spectral-photosensitivity maximum at 680 mμ enhanced, but there appears near 800 mμ a new, equally high maximum, which belongs to a peculiar aggregated form of the pigment. This form can be observed in the absorption spectrum of the colloidal solution of Mg-phthalocyanine in acetone, formed on water addition. In contrast to this behavior of Mg-phthalocyanine, the films of Zn- and Cu-phthalocyanine do not exhibit a similar new maximum at the longer wavelengths.

In the case of the chlorophyllide films it could be shown by Putzeiko's method that the increase in the size of the microcrystals brings about not only a shift of the sharp spectral maximum of the photo-emf, but also an increase of the response by a factor of 3.5.[15]

The method of the alternating photo-emf and likewise those
of the d-c and a-c photoconduction have been used in our extensive study of the optical sensitization of inorganic n and p
semiconductors to light absorbed by dye molecules on their
surface. These results have been reviewed at length several
times [14, 17, 18, 34, 35, 38] and do not need to be treated in this paper.
It may be of interest to mention that not only separate dye
molecules but also the aggregated (colloidal) particles of the dye
can act as sensitizers, transferring the absorbed light energy to
electrons trapped at the surface of the inorganic semiconductor.*

It has been recently shown with the alternating photo-emf
method by Putzeiko [40] that the optical sensitization of ZnO
can be achieved by contacting a thin solid dye film with it.
The light reaches the contact through the solid dye film. Measurements of the voltage-current characteristics have shown that no
transition layer, or photovoltaic emf is formed at the contact.
The observed sharp maximum of the spectral distribution,
contrasting with the shifted broad maximum of the absorption
spectrum and of the photo-emf of the dye film, shows that only
separate dye molecules at the contact are effective in the sensitization. When the dye film is thick, it acts as a light filter, and the
sharp spectral maximum of the molecular sensitization is decreased.

5. Contact-Potential Measurements

Akimov applied the vibrating-condenser method to study the
change in the contact potential of solid dye films and the dyed
inorganic semiconductors under constant illumination by monochromatic light.

The setup he used [15, 17] allows reliable measurements of
changes in the contact potential $(\Delta_{ctp})_L$ amounting to only
0.05 mv. It has been assumed that the sign of the photopotential
$(\Delta_{ctp})_L$ depends on the diffusion of the dominant photocarriers
from the surface into the interior of the dye film. Thus, a change

---

* In our explanation of the dye-sensitized photoconductivity,[18] we differ
from the view advanced by Noddack and Meier [42] and Nelson,[43] who ascribe
it to an electron exchange of the excited dye molecule with the inorganic
semiconductor.

under illumination of the contact potential in the dark to more positive values has been taken as indication of a diffusion of mobile negative charges inward, and the reverse change was ascribed to mobile positive charges released by light. This criterion

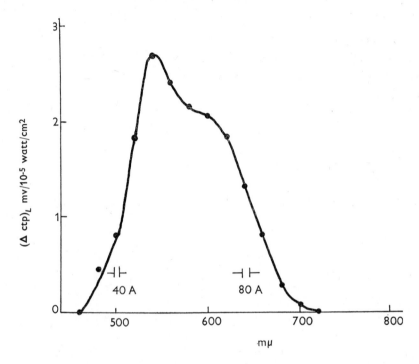

Fig. 3.7. Spectral curve for contact potential change under illumination for a film of crystal violet. [17]

has been checked and confirmed by many photosemiconductors with charge carriers of known sign (ZnO, TlI, CdS). For all the dyes and pigments studied with this method, the sign of the charge carriers coincided with that of the a-c photo-emf method described in Sec. 3.

A typical spectral curve for $(\varDelta_{ctp})_L$ is given in Fig. 3.7 for a vacuum-sublimed film of crystal violet. It coincides with the absorption curve of a film of the same dye.

To obtain direct values of the work function of dyes Vilessov [20] succeeded in measuring the quantum thresholds of the external photoelectronic emission from the surface of these dye films *in vacuo*. Some of these data are given in Table 3.3.

Table 3.3. Work Function Values φ (Photoelectron Emission from Dye Films); Photoionization Potentials I_{ph} of Gaseous Dye Molecules [20]

Dye	φ, ev	I_{ph} ev
Phthalocyanine (metal-free)	6.0	
Zn-phthalocyanine	6.0	
Eosin	6.1–6.2	
Erythrosine	5.8(4.7) [a]	
Rhodamine 6G	5.7	7.26
Methylene blue	6.0(5.0)	
Pinakryptol green	5.2	
Pinacyanole	5.0	7.28
Carotene-β	5.5	
Indigo		7.17
Chinolin blue		7.35
Merocyanine		7.35
Alizarin blue		7.35

[a] The figures in parentheses give a lower threshold, obtained from the feeble continuation of the photoemission toward the longer wavelengths.

The distribution of the kinetic energy for the electrons emerging from the surface has also been determined in a spherical retarding field. It has been found that in addition to the usual normal distribution of electron kinetic energies, known for example, for metals, there are present peculiar high maxima in the distribution, concentrated in a narrow range of low kinetic energies, which do not depend on the energy of the light quantum. Such selective maxima in the distribution of the electron kinetic energies have been found for some inorganic semiconductors and attributed to a secondary process of electron ejection.[48] For some of the dyes (rhodamine 6G, metal-free phthalocyanine) the position of the Fermi level, deduced from these measurements, happens to be in the middle between the upper and ground levels of the solid dye, which corroborates the view that the semiconduction in these dyes is intrinsic.

6. Mechanism of Charge Transport in Semiconducting Dyes

The spectral curves of the photoelectric sensitivity in compact dye films considered here exhibit band maxima with contours closely related to that of the absorption bands of the dye molecules in concentrated solutions.

A strong interaction of the identical molecules in the solid dye is made obvious by the large width of these bands. Nevertheless, when the bands are relatively narrow, which is the case for the metal-free phthalocyanines, the porphyrins, and the chlorophyllides, a striking similarity is observed with the structure of the spectrum of the dye molecules in a concentrated solution (see Fig. 3.6*a* and 3.6*b*).

This fact indicates that a fusion of the outer π-electron shells does not occur in the molecular lattice to such an extent that a common electronic system has been formed by them. In this respect, the molecular semiconductors of the kind of dyes differ from the inorganic ones by the narrowness of their conduction bands, not conspicuously revealed in the spectrum.

As in the case with the molecular crystals of the polycyclic aromatic hydrocarbons, the primary process in solid dyes on light absorption does consist in an excitation of the molecules in the lattice. Similarly, the excitation quantum in the dyes can be assumed to travel as an *exciton* in the array of the closely connected molecules until either a structural defect (eventually, the surface of the microcrystal) or an attachment center is encountered, at which point one or both of the charges of the "exciton" are set free. In the case of dyes of p type semiconductivity, the exciton is deactivated at an impurity center (O_2) with the formation of a trapped electron and a positive hole transported at the ground level of the molecular lattice. Thus we find here an intermolecular electron exchange similar to that known to occur between suitable electron donating and accepting molecules during organic oxidation-reduction processes.

The height of the oxygen traps has been evaluated for the metal-free phthalocyanines by Vartanian and Karpovitch [7] from the decreased value of the activation energy E_d for the dark conductivity after oxygen treatment. For Cu-, Zn-, and Mg-phthalocyanine these E_d are equal to 1.0, 0.73, and 0.53 ev, respectively, whereas in vacuo, E_d is 1.7, 1.8, and 1.2 ev.* As we have said before, these latter values are near to the excitation energy of the singlet level of the dye shown by the absorption spectrum. It must be stressed here that the presence of oxygen traps does not change the spectral-photosensitivity curve.

The presence of trapping levels in the dye, even in the absence of a deliberately introduced impurity, is clearly shown in the following experiment by Vartanian.[5] If a layer of the very photoelectrically sensitive dye, crystal violet, is intensively illuminated at −190°C, no photocurrent is observed. But when such an exposed layer is warming up in the dark, we can notice, starting at −80°C, an enhanced conductivity, which rises as the temperature increases. At 20°C this dark current is now many times larger than that observed before the illumination at low temperature. With time, the conductivity slowly decreases to its normal value at 20°C.

The slowly decaying dark current can be increased by sudden warming; when this is done, however, the decay is accelerated in a manner quite similar to the emptying of the traps observed in inorganic crystal phosphors.

Some time ago the writer [44] considered the possibility that the conduction band in the semiconducting dyes of the n type belongs to a common triplet-level band formed by the separate triplet levels of the dye molecules in the lattice. The close coincidence of the activation energy E_d with the height of the singlet-excited level $h\nu^0$ (see Table 3.1) seems to disprove such a possibility, however.

* This value, 1.2 ev, must be lower than the correct one, owing to the strong binding of oxygen by Mg-phthalocyanine, which precluded its complete removal.

Recently, Vartanian and Rosenstein [45] carried out experiments that would seem to prove that no triplet conduction band exists. They have shown that in simple phosphorescent organic crystals, such as benzophenone, phthalimide, and others, the activation energy E_d of the conductivity is close to the singlet level and definitely higher than the triplet level obtained from the crystal-phosphorescence spectrum.

According to Vartanian and Karpovitch [7] the presence of traps can also be inferred from the linear dependence of the photocurrent on the light intensity in the metal-free phthalo-cyanines even in the absence of oxygen.

The formation of electron-self-trapping levels below the singlet-excited level of the anthracene molecule, which occurs as a result of electron transfer from one dye molecule to the next and the ensuing polarization of the lattice, has been considered in detail by Lyons [46] and later by Murrell.[47]

The values for the work function φ of the dye films obtained by Vilessov [20] are given in Table 3.3.

The photoionization potential I_{ph} of some gaseous dye molecules, also measured by Vilessov,[20] can be seen in the same table. The difference $I_{ph} - \varphi$ can serve as a rough measure of the magnitude of the lattice polarization energy created when an electron is detached from a dye molecule in its interior.[47] An equal polarization energy is evolved in addition on charging the next dye molecule. The sum of these energies amounting to about three to four electron-volts, plus the electron affinity of the accepting dye molecule (probably about one electron-volt), is so large that the existence of an electron accepting level in the dye lattice below the singlet-excitation level of a dye molecule is plausible.

References

1. D. D. Eley, *Research* (*London*) **12**, 293 (1959).
2. A. T. Vartanian and A. Terenin, *J. Physics* (*U.S.S.R.*) **4**, 173 (1941).
3. A. T. Vartanian, *Acta Physicochim. U.R.S.S.* **22**, 201 (1947).
4. A. T. Vartanian, *Zhur. Fiz. Khim.* **20**, 1065 (1946); **22**, 769 (1948); **24**, 1361 (1950); **27**, 272 (1953); **31**, 1792 (1957).
5. A. T. Vartanian, *Izv. Akad. Nauk S.S.S.R.* (*Ser. Fiz.*) **16**, 169 (1952); **20**, 1541 (1956); **21**, 523 (1957).

58   A. TERENIN

6. A. T. Vartanian and I. A. Karpovitch, *Doklady Akad. Nauk S.S.S.R.* **111**, 561 (1956); **113**, 1020 (1957).
7. A. T. Vartanian and I. A. Karpovitch, *Zhur. Fiz. Khim.* **32**, 178, 274, 543 (1958).
8. I. A. Karpovitch and A. T. Vartanian, *Doklady Akad. Nauk S.S.S.R.* **117**, 57 (1957); "Photoelectric and Optical Phenomena in Semiconductors," p. 290, Ed. Akademii Nauk Ukrainskoi S.S.R., Kiev (1959).
9. A. T. Vartanian and L. D. Rosenstein, *Doklady Akad. Nauk S.S.S.R.* **124**, 295 (1959).
10. E. K. Putzeiko, *Doklady Akad. Nauk S.S.S.R.* **59**, 471 (1948); **67**, 1009 (1949).
11. E. K. Putzeiko, *Zhur Fiz. Khim.* **22**, 1172 (1948).
12. E. K. Putzeiko, *Izvest. Akad. Nauk S.S.S.R.* (*Ser. Fiz.*) **13**, 224 (1949).
13. E. K. Putzeiko and A. Terenin, *Zhur. Fiz. Khim.* **30**, 1019 (1956); E. Putzeiko, *Doklady Akad. Nauk S.S.S.R.* **124**, 796 (1959).
14. A. Terenin and E. Putzeiko, *J. Chim. Phys.* **55**, 681 (1948).
15. A. Terenin, E. Putzeiko, and I. Akimov, *Discussions Faraday Soc.* **27**, 83 (1959).
16. E. K. Putzeiko, *Doklady Akad. Nauk S.S.S.R.* **132**, 1299 (1960).
17. I. A. Akimov, *Doklady Akad. Nauk S.S.S.R.* **128**, 691 (1959).
18. A. Terenin and I. Akimov, International Conference on Photographic Science, Liège (1959); *Z. physik. Chem.* (Leipzig) (1961).
19. V. B. Evstigneev and A. Terenin, *Doklady Akad. Nauk S.S.S.R.* **81**, 223 (1951).
20. F. I. Vilessov, *Doklady Akad. Naua S.S.S.R.* **132**, 632 (1960); F. I. Vilessov and A. N. Terenin, *ibid.* **133**, 1060 (1960).
21. P. E. Fielding and F. Gutmann, *J. Chem. Phys.* **26**, 411 (1957).
22. H. Akamatu and H. Inokuchi, *J. Chem. Phys* **18**, 810 (1950).
23. H. Inokuchi, *Bull. Chem. Soc. Japan* **29**, 181 (1956).
24. A. Many, E. Harnik, and D. Gerlich, *J. Chem. Phys.* **23**, 1733 (1955).
25. T. S. Moss, "Photoconductivity in the Elements," Butterworth & Co. (Publishers), Ltd., London (1952).
26. B. Lange, "Die Photoelemente und ihre Anwendung", p. 109, Bd. 1, Leipzig (1940).
27. H. Meier, *Z. wiss. Photo.* **50**, 301 (1955).
28. N. A. Tolstoi and R. P. Feofilov, *Uspekhi Fiz. Nauk* **41**, 44 (1950); N. A. Tolstoi, *Izvest. Akad. Nauk S.S.S.R.* **15**, 712 (1950).
29. L. Bergmann, *Z. Physik* **33**, 290 (1932); *Naturwissenschaften* **20**, 15 (1932); L. Bergmann and J. Hansler, *Z. Physik* **100**, 50 (1936); L. Bergmann and F. Ronge, *Physik. Z.* **41**, 349 (1940)
30. V. P. Juse and S. M. Rivkin, *Doklady Akad. Nauk S.S.S.R.* **62**, 55 (1948); S. M. Rivkin, *J. Tech. Phys.* (*U.S.S.R.*) **18**, 1521 (1948).
31. V. E. Lashkarev, *Doklady Akad. Nauk S.S.S.R.* **80**, 813 (1950).
32. K. B. Tolpigo, *J. exper. theoret. Phys.* (*U.S.S.R.*) **23**, 340 (1952); "Photoelectric and Optical Phenomena in Semiconductors," p. 268, Ed. Akademii Nauk Ukrainskai S.S.R., Kiev (1959).

33. V. E. Kojevin and V. E. Lashkarev, *Radiotek. i Elektro.* **2**, 260 (1957).
34. A. Terenin, E. Putzeiko, and I. Akimov, *J. chim. phys.* **54**, 716 (1957).
35. I. Akimov and E. Putzeiko, "Photoelectric and Optical Phenomena in Semiconductors," p. 301, Ed. Akademeii Nauk Ukrainskai S.S.R., Kiev (1959).
36. A. Petrikaln, *Z. physik. Chem. (B)* **10**, 16 (1930).
37. H. Meier, *Z. wiss. Phot.* **53**, 1 (1958).
38. E. Putzeiko and A. Terenin, *Zhur. Fiz. Khim.* **23**, 676 (1949); *Doklady Nauk S.S.S.R.* **70**, 401 (1950); **90**, 1005 (1953).
39. I. A. Akimov, *Zhur. Fiz. Khim.* **30**, 1007 (1956).
40. E. K. Putzeiko, *Doklady Akad. Nauk S.S.S.R.* **129**, 303 (1959).
41. A. T. Vartanian, *Zhur. Fiz. Khim.* **30**, 1028 (1956).
42. W. Noddack, G. Eckert, and H. Meier, *Z. Elektrochem.* **56**, 1735 (1952); **57**, 69 (1953); W. Noddack, H. Meier, and A. Haus, *Z. physik. Chem. (Leipzig)* **212**, 55 (1959).
43. R. C. Nelson, *J. Opt. Soc. Am.* **45**, 774 (1955); **46**, 10, 13 (1956); *J. Chem. Phys.* **22**, 885, 890, 892 (1954); **23**, 1550 (1955); **29**, 388 (1958).
44. A. Terenin, *Radioteckh. i Elektron.* **1**, 1127 (1957).
45. A. T. Vartanian and L.D. Rosenstein, *Doklady Akad. Nauk S.S.S.R.* **131**, 279 (1960).
46. L. E. Lyons, *J. Chem. Soc.* 1957, 5001.
47. J. N. Murrell, *Discussions Faraday Soc.* (September, 1959).
48. L. Apker and E. Taft, *Phys. Rev.* **82**, 814 (1951); H. R. Philipp, *Phys. Rev.* **107**, 687 (1957); O. M. Sorokin, *J. Tech. Phys. (U.S.S.R.)* **28**, 1413 (1958).

4

Observations on Aromatic Hydrocarbons in Connection with Their Electrical Conductivity

N. Riehl

1. Activation Energy of the Bulk Dark Conductivity in Naphtalene

The value of the activation energy we found before [1] — 0.7 resp. 1.4 ev if calculated from exp $(-\varepsilon/kT)$ resp. exp $(-\varepsilon/2kT)$ — is now confirmed by measurements of Bornmann [2] and Kommandeur.[3] Other results that seemed to indicate a dependance of the activation energy on the presence of oxygen were not confirmed. This influence of oxygen was probably caused by surface effects. (The physical significance of the observed "activation energy" is discussed in Sec. 5).

2. Melting Effects

The dark conductivity of molten hydrocarbons is 10^3 to 10^4 times higher than the conductivity in the solid state at the same temperature. The activation energy of paraffin does not change its value upon melting,[1] but in naphtalene melting causes a diminution of approximately half the solid-state value (also discussed in Sec. 5).

Since for all solid hydrocarbons the dark conductivity rises rapidly at higher strengths of the applied field, we examined whether such an effect occurs also in the molten state. We observed (in molten naphthalene and anthracene) a field effect of the same order as in the solids. This observation rules out some imaginable explanations as to the nature of the field effect, especially the assumption that strong fields release the charge carriers from traps, because in the molten state a trap is not

[61]

immobile (i.e., it is not acting as a "trap"), so that any releasing of the carriers from the trapped state cannot cause effects of the same order as in the solid state.

3. Nature of the Charge Carriers

From observations of Kallmann and Rosenberg [4] and other authors it is known that, in the case of photoconductivity, the carriers should be positive. In the case of dark conductivity that we examined earlier, the question is whether mobile protons can be responsible for the conduction. All our earlier observations indicated that protons are not acting as carriers. Our new observations support this assumption. When we used an acid solution as the positive electrode, the conduction was almost completely blocked. (The conductivity was normal if the acid electrode was negative.) Since the protons cannot be regarded as carriers, the question arises whether positive holes or negative electrons (or both) are acting as carriers in the dark conduction. We tried to decide this question by measurements of the absolute value of the space charges that appear in hydrocarbon crystals after the application of external electrical fields. Kallmann, Rosenberg, and Silver [4,5] have already discovered distinct polarization effects (persistent charge displacements) in irradiated crystals. We measured whether there is a surplus of positive or negative charge in the whole crystal without irradiation. The crystals (naphthalene) were placed for few minutes between silver electrodes, between electrodes covered with a very thin sheet of paraffin, or between electrodes consisting of a gas ionized by α particles.* In all cases the charge of the crystals after removing the voltage was negative. The negative charge on the anode side was greater than on the cathode side. The whole maximal charge that could be accumulated in 1 cm³ of the crystal was of the order of 10^{10} elementar charges. (This order seems to agree with the findings of Kallmann and M. Silver on irradiated crystals.[5])

* The α particles ionized the gas space, but they did not hit the surface of the crystal. The ionization was much greater than the current that could be expected in the crystal.

This indicates that in the case of dark conduction also, the mobility of positive holes is higher than the mobility of electrons, possibly because the latter are trapped in some way.

4. Further Experiments on Dark Conductivity, the Role of Space Charges, and Electrode Effects

Because of electron trapping, negative space charges are built up in the crystal during the conduction process. Therefore the electrical field will not be the same in the whole crystal. The highest field will be concentrated near the anode or at the boundary crystal-anode interface.

The earlier experiments on conductivity of hydrocarbons deal mostly with the constant current that remains after a certain longer voltage application ("reststrom"). Now we have expanded the experiments also on the first period (before the equilibrium

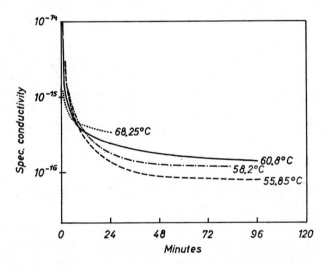

Fig. 4.1. Decay of the current in naphthalene (50,000 volts cm^{-2}).

current is established). Immediately after the application of the voltage, the current is much greater than in the later periods (Fig. 4.1). In naphthalene at 50°C this current is at least one hundred times greater than in the equilibrium state. This first period is shorter, the higher the temperature and the conductivity. During this period the negative space charge is built up in the crystal. In the later states the current can be supported mainly by the (mobile) positive holes delivered by the anode. This remaining current depends strongly on the material of the electrodes, especially of the anode. It depends also upon the state of the crystal surface that is in contact with the electrode. If the surface is very smooth, the current can be blocked almost completely; the blocking effect is not present (or at least it is much weaker) if the surface is rough (scraped or etched).

The influence of the electrode material was emphasized most recently by Kallmann and Pope [6] and by Boroffka.[7] A marked enhancement of dark conductivity was observed if anode materials were used that are particularly effective in injecting positive holes into the crystal.

But on the other hand we can reach a very high conductivity without using p-donor electrodes if we apply a sufficiently strong electrical field. We believe that both effects — the influence of the hole injecting electrodes and the influence of a strong field — can be considered from a single point of view. The strong field is concentrated near the anode (or in the boundary anode-crystal), so that it can extract the holes from the anode even when the anode is a metal and not a special hole-injecting material. If we used very strong fields (up to 400,000 volts/cm), the conductivity of anthracene at room temperature (with ordinary metal electrodes) was raised to 5×10^{-12}. In other words, the ability of electrodes to inject holes and the action of strong fields can replace each other.

In the same way we can explain the observed influence of the roughness of the crystal surface adjacent to the electrode. The strong local fields near the sharp "tops" and edges facilitate the hole injection into the crystal.

It is interesting to note that Kallmann and Pope did not observe any enhancement of the conductivity with increased voltage when they used an effective hole donor as anode. At the same order of field strength a marked field effect can be observed if we use ordinary metal electrodes. This could support the opinion that the electrode effect and the field effect can, at least partially, replace each other.*

The blocking effect of an acid solution as the anode mentioned before does not contradict these conclusions. Because of the high d-c of water the field strength, and therefore the hole extraction, can be very small.

5. Physical Significance of the "Activation Energy"

It seems that the enhancing influence of the field strength on the conductivity is due to effects at the boundary anode-crystal and not to bulk effects in the crystal. Now the question arises as to whether or not the enhancing influence of temperature (expressed by "activation energy") corresponds to any bulk processes in the hydrocarbon crystal itself. The value of the activation energy for different hydrocarbons seems to be a typical constant for every given hydrocarbon. But from this fact it is not quite evident that the processes for which the activation energy is responsible take place in the whole bulk material. Moreover, we must consider the question of whether the observed activation energy is due to the mobility of the charge carriers or to their production.

The first possibility can be ruled out from the observations on the molten hydrocarbons (Fig. 4.1). The value of the observed activation energy is also much too high for mobility processes in liquids.[1] From the same observations it can be ruled out that the activation energy is due to releasing of carriers from traps. The very weak dependance of photoconductivity on temperature compared with the temperature dependance of the dark conductivity shows also that in the latter case the temperature effect cannot be mainly due to the enhancement of the mobility.

If the observed activation energy is involved in the production of charge carriers, a question arises as to why the value of the activation energy is much smaller than the ionization energy of the free hydrocarbon molecules. The following explanation seems

* From Table 1 in the work of Kallmann and Pope [6] a saturation (or even a maximum) of the conductivity with increasing voltage can be calculated.

to support our observations. The first step of separation of positive and negative carriers is a thermal ionization (it might be better termed thermoexcitation). In most cases an immediate recombination occurs. In a very few cases the thermoionization is followed by a total separation of the positive and negative carriers due to tunnel effects. The probability of this total separation is therefore independent of temperature. The observed "activation energy" is, therefore, only a part of the whole ionization energy and may be called better "excitation" or "preionization" energy.

Let us consider whether this model is compatible with the results and conclusions mentioned in Sec. 4. The magnitude of the "equilibrium current" depends not only upon the delivery of positive holes by the anode but also on the lifetime of the free carriers and the equilibrium concentration of ions in the crystal. The current is given by $ec_p\tau$ (c_p = number of pairs produced per second; τ = lifetime). Since $c_p\tau$ is the equilibrium concentration, the current must be proportional to $\exp\left(-\varepsilon/kT\right)$, i.e., the "activation energy" can be interpreted in the same sense as it was before.

From the results of our earlier experiments we concluded [1] that the value of the activation energy must be calculated from $\exp\left(-\varepsilon/kT\right)$ and not $\exp\left(-\varepsilon/2kT\right)$, because the recombination of an ion pair (which is not a pair of completely separated ions) is a reaction of the first and not the second order. Using this conclusion we can propose an explanation for the change of the observed effective activation energy of naphthalene upon melting. Because of the greater separation and diffusion rate and the higher ion concentration in the liquid, we can assume the recombination process to be a reaction of the second order. That means that — in agreement with our observations — the effective value of the activation energy will be one-half the value of the solid state ($\varepsilon/2$ instead of ε) if the true value of ε is not changed. From the observations of Bornmann [2] follows that the value of κ_0 in $\kappa = \kappa_0 \exp\left(-\varepsilon/kT\right)$ is about five hundred times smaller for the molten naphthalene than for the solid. This surprising fact also can be easily explained if we assume that the recombination of charges is a reaction of the first order in the solid state and of the second order in the melted state.

6. Oxygen and Other Gases in Hydrocarbon Crystals

In connection with the often-discussed role of oxygen content for the photo- and dark conductivity of hydrocarbons, experiments on the solubility of different gases in hydrocarbon crystals were made. For the determination of oxygen content two methods were used: a chemical method and a very sensitive radioactivation method.

For chemical determinations the oxygen originally enclosed in the crystals was transferred to a aqueous solution of Cr-2. The amount of oxidation of Cr-2 to Cr-3 quantitatively determined the oxygen content.

Our extremely sensitive radioactivation method [8] consists of the following: the surface is covered with a thin foil of Li^6; on irradiation with thermal neutrons from a reactor, the reaction $Li^6 + n = \alpha + H^3$ produces fast H^3 particles, which enter the crystal and react there with the oxygen — $H^3 + O^{16} = n + F^{18}$.

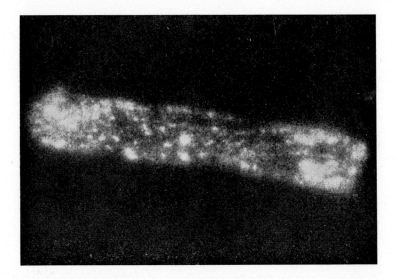

Fig. 4.2. Autoradiograph of an anthracene crystal loaded with krypton-85.

The amount of produced radioactive F^{18} indicated the oxygen-content.

Besides determining the oxygen content we examined also the behavior of other gases in hydrocarbon crystals. We used especially the radioactive krypton 85 because of the possibility of highly sensitive determination. We have found that krypton 85 at room temperature shows no detectable true solubility in the lattice of the hydrocarbons. The self-radiographs of the crystals loaded with krypton 85 show a quite irregular distribution of krypton within the crystal (Fig. 4.2, anthracene). The measured "solubility" is due to the localization of krypton in dislocations or in other imperfections of the crystal.

Analogous experiments on the distribution of oxygen in the crystals have not yet been completed. But we have carried out determinations of the total amount of oxygen absorbed by naphthalene crystals. It is of the order of 10^{-7} (gram of oxygen per gram of naphthalene) if the oxygen pressure is 1 atm. We can now say, therefore, that the Henry law of distribution between gas phase and crystal has not been proved. This indicates that the absorption of oxygen by anthracene crystals is not due to a true solubility.

References

1. N. Riehl, *Zhur. Fiz. Khim.* **29**, 959, 1152 (1955); *Naturwissenschaften* **43** 145 (1956); *Ann. Physik* (6) **20**, 93 (1957).
2. J. A. Bornmann (in private communication).
3. J. Kommandeur, Ph.D. thesis, University of Amsterdam (1958). (The activation energy can be calculated from fig. 14, p. 45).
4. H. Kallmann and B. Rosenberg, *Phys. Rev.* **97**, 1596 (1955).
5. H. Kallmann and M. Silver, "Semiconductors and Phosphors," p. 435, Braunschweig (1958).
6. H. Kallmann and M. Pope, *J. Chem. Phys.* **32**, 300 (1960).
7. W. Boroffka (in private communication).
8. H. J. Born and N. Riehl, *Angew. Chem.* (in press).

The Photovoltaic Behaviors of Aromatic Hydrocarbons

H. Inokuchi, Y. Maruyama, and H. Akamatu

Introduction

When a contact between a semiconductive material and a metal is made, we can expect that a potential barrier is induced at the boundary, and the photovoltaic effect is observable with illumination on this barrier. It has been found that this is the case for semiconductive organic solids, too. However, few experimental works have been done on this effect in comparison with the many surveys that have been made on their photoconductions.[1]

H. Baba, K. Chitoku, and K. Nitta [2] reported that they observed a photoelectromotive force induced at a junction between Cu-phthalocyanine and platinum net under an illumination of light. The electrical potential, however, was not a steady one but decayed to zero in about one minute. It seems to the authors, therefore, that this might be produced by a release of space charge in that junction but not by an intrinsic photovoltaic effect.

In connection with optical sensitization in photography, R. C. Nelson [3] investigated the photovoltaic behavior of a junction between organic dye and cadmium sulfide. He proposed that the produced photovoltage is related to the energy difference between the conduction band of the dye and that of cadmium sulfide or between the valence bands of these two substances.

Recently, M. Calvin and D. Kearns [4] reported an interesting result on organic photovoltaic junctions; Mg-phthalocyanine — tetramethyl-p-phenylene diamine and coronene — chloranil junctions. In these cells, both semiconductive organic solids played as electron donors under illumination.

In this chapter, we present our observations of the photovoltaic effect in a simple cell consisting of a junction between the aromatic compound and the metal or stannic oxide. The produced electromotive force will be discussed in comparison with other semiconductive behaviors of polycyclic aromatic compounds.

Experimental Procedures

For an observation of photoelectromotive force, a photocell of the sandwich type was employed. Such a cell, prepared by vacuum evaporation, is illustrated in Fig. 5.1. A metal film (c),

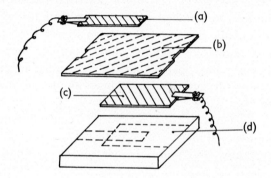

Fig. 5.1. The sandwich-type conductivity cell.

the terminal electrode, was evaporated on a pyrex plate that measured $20 \times 25 \times 2$ mm (d). Aluminium or gold was used for this electrode. Then, the evaporation of polycyclic aromatics was made under a pressure 10^{-5} mm Hg on the substrate. Finally, the junction electrode (a) was made on the organic film (b) with evaporated layer of alkali metals. This junction electrode was made so thin as to be transparent. On the other hand, when platinum, gold, tin, or lead was used as a junction electrode, its thin film (c) was evaporated on a glass plate (d) first. Thereafter, by means of vacuum sublimation, the organic solid (b) and the terminal electrode (a) were accumulated on it in successive layers.

For the preparation of stannic oxide-aromatics junction, the organic compound was sublimed onto a conductive glass plate. The conductive layer (stannic oxide) of the substrate acted as a junction electrode. The terminal electrode, aluminium, was produced on the aromatic compound subsequently by means of vacuum evaporation.

All observations of photoelectromotive force were carried out *in vacuo* or in an atmosphere of inert gas. White light from a tungsten lamp illuminated the side of the junction metal. The measurement of produced photovoltage had to be associated with a vibration-reed electrometer, because its electric power was extremely low.

By means of a quartz-prism monochrometer and also of interference filters, a spectral response of photoelectromotive force ranging from 3,500 to 13,000 A was observed.

The applied polycyclic aromatic compounds, perylene, coronene,* violanthrene, and violanthrone, were purified using a combination of three methods: recrystallization, sublimation, and chromatography.

Results and Discussions

With the illumination of light from a tungsten lamp, the induced photovoltage rose immediately to a saturated value, and this was kept quite steady. In the alkali metal-aromatics junction, however, it was observed that its electromotive force changed to a smaller value than the original one. This was probably produced by the high reactivity of alkali metals to moisture and by the formation of a charge-transfer complex between the metal and the aromatic compound.[6,7]

For the noble metal-aromatics junction, the observed photoelectromotive forces varied from a few to 20 mv, depending on the sorts of metals applied to the junction, as illustrated in Table 5.1. In all these photocells, the junction metal acted as negative electrode to the terminal electrode. Thus, at the junction, electrons transferred from the hydrocarbons to the junction metals, or the hydrocarbons played as donors, under the illumination.

---

* This seven-membered aromatic hydrocarbon was provided from Badisch Anilin und Soda Fabrik, Germany.[5]

Table 5.1. The Photovoltage of Metal-Aromatics Junctions

Photovoltaic junction		Photoelectromotive force	
Aromatics (sign)	Metal (sign)	Voltage, mv	Wattage
Violanthrene (+)	Platinum (−)	2–3	~ 10^{-17}
Violanthrene (+)	Gold (−)	6–9	~ 10^{-16}
Violanthrene (+)	Silver (−)	Detectable	
Violanthrene (+)	Tin (−)	2–8	~ 10^{-16}
Violanthrene (+)	Lead (−)	4–14	~ 10^{-16}

A stable photovoltage was produced at the contact between perylene and stannic oxide, and its value reached 80 mv when a light was incident on it through the transparent stannic oxide electrode. The spectral response of this voltage was a curve that was in good coincidence with the optical-absorbance curve and also with the response curve of photoconduction for solid perylene, as shown in Fig. 5.2. A similar behavior of photovoltaic effect was

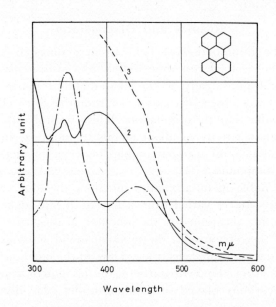

Fig. 5.2. The spectral responses. Curve 1, of photocurrent; curve 2, of optical absorbance; curve 3, of photovoltage for perylene.

observed in the junction between coronene or violanthrene and stannic oxide, whose electromotive forces were 20 and 450 mv, respectively. These hydrocarbons acted as electron acceptors with respect to SnO_2 under the illumination, whereas an opposite result was obtained in a junction between violanthrone and stannic oxide; violanthrone was an electron donor. Further, its spectral response of photovoltage was quite a peculiar one. The different response curves of photovoltage were obtained, depending upon which side was illuminated, on the photocell. Both spectral responses observed in a near infrared region, however, showed similar behaviors, and their threshold values were found to be around 0.9 ev, which was in agreement with that of photoconduction, as summarized in Table 5.2. These

Table 5.2. The Spectral Threshold Value of Photovoltage in the Junctions between Polycyclic Aromatics and Stannic Oxide

Aromatics	Photo-voltage mv	Threshold value ev			Energy gap from thermal activation, ev
		Photo-voltage	Photocon-duction	Optical absorbance	
Perylene	80	2.4	2.3	2.5	2.0
Coronene	20	1.9		1.9	1.7
Violanthrene	450	~ 0.9	0.8_8	0.8	0.8_5
Violanthrone	80	~ 0.9	0.8_4	0.7_5	0.7_8

results imply that the spectral responses are dominated by the electronic structures of polycyclic aromatic compounds but not by those of stannic oxide. In this connection, no optical absorption in stannic oxide film is found in a visible region longer than 3,900 A.

In the alkali metal-aromatics system, the induced value of photovoltage reached almost 1 volt, as illustrated in Table 5.3. Its spectral response was a curve falling monotonously from short wavelength side to long wavelength side. An extrapolation of this decrement found a tentative threshold value that is located in a range between 6,000 and 7,000 A, as shown in Fig. 5.3. In a

Table 5.3. The Photoelectromotive Force of Alkali Metal-Aromatics Junctions

Photovoltaic junction		Photoelectromotive force		
Aromatics (sign)	Alkali metal (sign)	Voltage	Wattage	$\varepsilon/2$, ev
Perylene ($-$)	Lithium ($+$)	0.3–1.0	10^{-10}	1.0
Coronene ($-$)	Lithium ($+$)	0.3	10^{-10}	0.8
Violanthrene ($-$)	Lithium ($+$)	0.3–0.8	10^{-9}	0.4_3
Violanthrone ($-$)	Lithium ($+$)	0.2–0.9	10^{-10}	0.3_9
Perylene ($+$)	Sodium ($-$)	0.3–1.0	10^{-11}	1.0
Violanthrene ($+$)	Sodium ($-$)	0.3–0.8	10^{-10}	0.4_3
Violanthrone ($\pm$)	Sodium ($\mp$)	0.1–0.5	10^{-8}	0.3_9
Perylene ($\pm$)	Potassium ($\mp$)	0.2–0.9	10^{-10}	1.0
Violanthrene ($+$)	Potassium ($-$)	0.2–0.8	10^{-10}	0.4_3
Violanthrone ($-$)	Potassium ($+$)	0.2–0.5	10^{-9}	0.3_9

longer wavelength region, the weak but definite response of an electromotive force was found. A fluctuation in the direction of electromotive force in these cells was frequently observed. In the

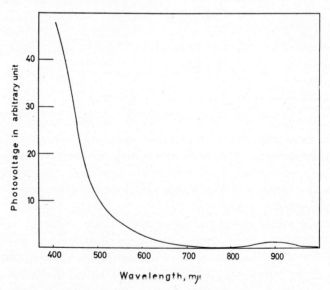

Fig. 5.3. The spectral response of photoelectromotive force for sodium-violanthrene junction.

lithium-aromatics junction, the metal acted as an electron donor. Most of the aromatic compounds in the sodium-aromatics junctions, however, acted as electron donors with respect to sodium. In the potassium-aromatics junction, the direction of the photoelectromotive force changed depending on the sorts of organic solids involved and also on the wavelengths of incident light.

It is believed theoretically that a photovoltage V_{opc} (measured for open-circuit conditions) across the barrier at a contact between metal and semiconductive solid is expressed as

$$V_{opc} = (kT/e) \ln \{1 + I_L/I_0 \exp [(-\varepsilon/2)/kT]\} \qquad (5.1)$$

where ε is the band gap in the semiconductor, and $I_0 \exp [(-\varepsilon/2)/kT]$ is the flow of electrons across the barrier, which is in equilibrium in both directions in the dark, whereas the excess flow of electrons I_L is induced under illumination.

When an induced current I_L with illumination of light is large, Eq. (5.1) is rewritten as

$$V_{opc} \doteqdot \varepsilon/2e + (kT/e) \ln (I_L/I_0) \approx \varepsilon/2e \qquad kT \ll e \qquad (5.2)$$

Further, for small I_L, V_{opc} is given by

$$V_{opc} \doteqdot (kT/e)(I_L/I_0) \exp [(\varepsilon/2)/kT] \ll 1 \qquad (5.3)$$

For the alkali metal-aromatics junction, it is expected that the produced photoelectromotive force V_{opc} follows Eq. (5.2), because its illuminated current I_L is large. Some discrepancies between the observed value and the calculated one $(\varepsilon/2)$, as listed in Table 5.3, may originate from the complex formation between alkali metals and aromatics.

On the other hand, the minute photovoltage for the noble metal-aromatics junction is tentatively explained by Eq. (5.3).

References

1. H. Akamatu and H. Inokuchi, in "Proceedings of the Third Conference on Carbon," p. 51, Pergamon Press, Ltd., London (1959).
2. H. Baba, K. Chitoku, and K. Nitta, *Nature* **177**, 672 (1956).
3. R. C. Nelson, *J. Chem. Phys.* **29**, 388 (1958).

4. M. Calvin and D. Kearns, *J. Chem. Phys.* **29**, 950 (1958).
5. L. Boente, *Brennstoff-Chem.* **36**, 210 (1955).
6. J. P. V. Gracey and A. R. Ubbelohde, *J. Chem. Soc.* **1955**, 4089.
7. R. C. Pastor and J. Turkevich, *J. Chem. Phys.* **23**, 1731 (1955).

Pulsed Photoconductivity in Anthracene

R. G. KEPLER

It has been found that it is possible to measure the drift mobility of both electrons and holes in very pure anthracene crystals by using a method similar to that used to measure ion mobilities in gases. The experimental arrangement used is shown in Fig. 6.1.

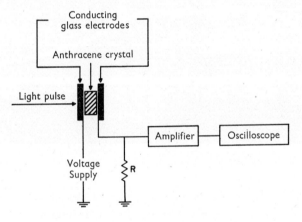

Fig. 6.1. Block diagram of experimental arrangement.

Crystals approximately 1 to 2 mm thick were mounted between a pair of conducting glass electrodes with a voltage supply connected to one electrode and a resistor connected to the other. A short light pulse, approximately 2 μsec long, was applied to the crystal through one of the electrodes. The light pulse, which was all absorbed within 10^{-4} to 10^{-5} cm of the surface of the crystal, produces a group of charge carriers near the illuminated electrode, and under the influence of the applied electric field, charge carriers of one electrical polarity drift through the crystal.

The motion of the charge carriers is observed by measuring the current displaced in the external circuit as a function of time.

An example of the type of pulses obtained is shown in Fig. 6.2. The initial slow rise of the pulse is caused by the RC time constant of the electronic circuit, and the abrupt change in slope near the

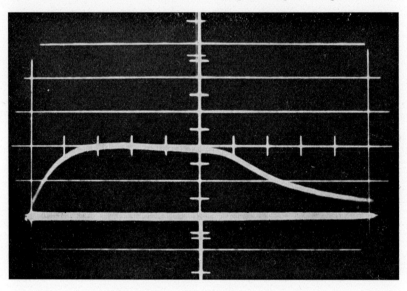

Fig. 6.2. Example of pulses observed.

end of the pulse occurs when the group of charge carriers begins hitting the back surface of the crystal. The length of the pulses is proportional to the thickness of the crystal with constant applied field and inversely proportional to the applied field.

In order to show that surface current was not causing the observed pulses, a band of silver paint was placed around the middle of a crystal 4 mm long, so that it acted as a third electrode halfway between the two end electrodes. Experiments with this arrangement showed that surface currents were not causing the observed effects and also proved that the charge carriers were moving in the directions assumed. The silverpaint electrode, although distorting the electrid field in the crystal, allowed the application of electric fields that varied with position in the crystal. When the electric field was small near the illuminated electrode and large near the back electrode, the current pulses were small initially and became large near the end. The reverse was true when the electric field was large near the illuminated electrode and small near the other.

The mobility of the carriers was calculated from the relation $\mu = d^2/Vt$, where μ is the mobility, d the crystal thickness, V the applied voltage, and t the time from the light flash to the abrupt change in slope near the end of the pulse. The length of the tail of the pulses is considerably longer than would be expected from the Einstein relation between mobility and diffusion coefficient; therefore the time to the abrupt change in slope was used rather than some other value.

The mobilities found for both holes and electrons are in the range 0.3 to 3 cm²/vsec. The mobilities vary with crystal orientation, and which carrier is most mobile depends on crystal orientation. The number of crystals available with sufficiently high purity to be useful with this technique is as yet too small to allow a determination of mobility anisotropy or even the repeatability from crystal to crystal of the mobility in a given crystal direction.

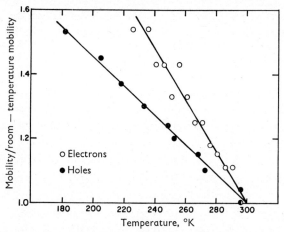

Fig. 6.3. Temperature dependence of the mobility of the charge carriers.

The temperature dependence of the mobility of both holes and electrons is shown in Fig. 6.3. The fact that the mobility increases as the temperature decreases appears to eliminate an activated process for the motion of the charge carriers in anthracene.

Figure 6.4 shows the wavelength dependence of the number of charge carriers produced by a pulse of light. The upper curve shows approximately the wavelength dependence of the optical

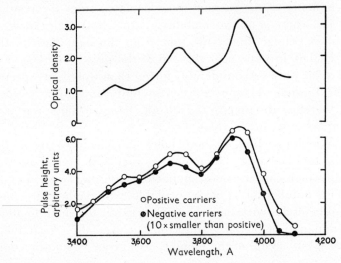

Fig. 6.4. Wavelength dependence of the number of charge carriers produced by a pulse of light. The upper curve shows approximately the wavelength dependence of the optical density observed by Craig and Hobbins.[1]

density of anthracene at room temperature, as observed by Craig and Hobbins.[1] The results are similar to those observed in steady-state surface-photoconductivity experiments.[2] These results indicate that, when the light is absorbed most strongly, the largest number of charge carriers is produced. In order to explain these results, either a two-photon or two-exciton process is required, or a surface effect is involved. The observation of the effect described indicates that recombination is not important, and therefore if two photons or two excitons were required to produce a free charge carrier, the number of charge carriers produced by a pulse of light would increase as the square of the light intensity. The light-intensity dependence observed was linear, as shown in Fig. 6.5.

The results of the present experiment, therefore, indicate that both holes and electrons have mobilities on the order of 1 cm²/vsec in anthracene crystals, that the mobility varies with crystal

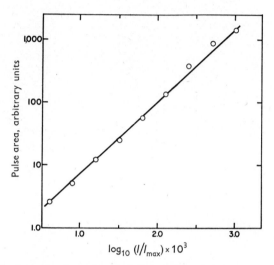

Fig. 6.5. Light-intensity dependence of the number of charge carriers produced by a pulse of light.

orientation and increases as the temperature is lowered, and that the charge carriers are produced only at the surface or in a surface layer of the crystal. The conclusion that the charge carriers are produced at the surface is in agreement with a proposal by Carswell and Lyons.[2]

Acknowledgements. The author is greatly indebted to Dr. G. J. Sloan for working out the anthracene purification procedure and growing the crystals and would like to express his gratitude to Dr. M. S. Sadler and Dr. R. E. Merrifield for many helpful and stimulating discussions.

References

1. D. P. Craig and P. C. Hobbins, *J. Chem. Soc.* **1955**, 2309.
2. D. J. Carswell and L. E. Lyons, *J. Chem. Soc.* **1955**, 1734.

7

A-C and D-C Photoconductivity in Anthracene Single Crystals

M. POPE and H. KALLMANN

Introduction

There have been many studies made in the past on the photo-conductivity of anthracene. A review of this history is given by Garrett.[1] The present study differs in that a transparent electrolyte solution was used for the electrodes touching the crystal faces.[2] Another distinctive feature of the present work is that thin (~ 10 micron) single crystals of anthracene were used.[3] Early work on a semiconductor-electrolyte system was carried out by Brattain and Garrett [16] and recent work has been reported by Green.[17]

The use of electrolyte solutions for electrodes would certainly be expected to yield results different from those of metal or metal oxide electrodes. This has been the case. The absolute magnitude of the photocurrents has been greater (currents as high as 1 ma/cm² have been observed at high light intensity), and a distinct tendency toward saturation of photocurrent with voltage was noted. As a consequence of the relatively large photocurrents, it was possible to study the a-c photoconductivity without the usual inter-ference from circuit parameters. Since we observed saturation photocurrents, it was possible to calculate quantum efficiencies in a straightforward manner.

By using light pulses of short duration, we were able to estimate the mobility of the majority carrier, and by changing the nature of the electrolyte, we were able to alter markedly the spectral response of the photoconductivity. In some cases the dark con-

ductivity was almost as large as the photocurrent. To explain
our results, we have proposed a mechanism of hole injection
from the electrodes, that we feel is of great significance in understanding photoconductivity in organic compounds. In this process,
a hole is injected into the organic crystal in a manner parallel
to the photoelectric ejection of an electron into a vacuum from
the surface of a metal.

Experimental Results

The apparatus used for our studies has been described elsewhere.[2] Basically, an electrolyte was used as an electrode contact
to the crystal. Connection to each electrolyte was made with
either silver-silver chloride electrodes, or platinum electrodes;

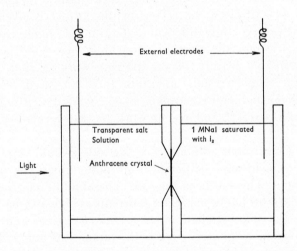

Fig. 7.1. Crystal holding cell.

there was no difference in the behavior of these external electrodes
at the current densities we encountered. The cell is shown in
Fig. 7.1. All experiments were carried out at one temperature,
25°C. All light was 3,650 A, unless otherwise specified.

All measurements were made through the bulk of the anthracene
crystal (perpendicular to the *ab* crystallographic plane). Guard

rings were used in one series of experiments to estimate the extent of surface conductivity participation in bulk-conductivity measurements. The surface currents were less than 1 per cent of the total current, and guard rings were dispensed with in all other measurements.

As was found by all other investigators,[1] we observed that the photocurrent flowing when the illuminated face of the crystal was at a positive potential (i^+) was larger than when the illuminated side was negative (i^-).

The ratio i^+/i^- in our work varied between 25 and 100 in the case where both cell compartments contained NaCl, the average being 60. This asymmetry is generally considered to be a consequence of a positive-hole majority carrier in anthracene. With other electrode systems, the ratio i^+/i^- could change drastically, as may be noted in Tables 7.1 and 7.2.

The convention followed in this paper concerning polarity is that the polarity of the crystal face will be identified with the polarity of the external metal dipping electrode immersed in the same solution that is in contact with that face (Fig. 7.1).

Thus, a crystal face is said to be at a positive potential if the external dipping electrode in its compartment is at a positive potential. It should be understood, however, that during any flow of current through the cell, if an oxidation reaction occurs at the metal electrode, a reduction will occur at the crystal face in the same solution compartment, and vice versa. Thus, if a crystal face is at a positive potential while current is flowing through the cell, a reduction process will take place in the electrolyte solution adjacent to that crystal face producing H_2 at that face. Oxygen will be produced at the opposite face.

In the dark, the electrodes were completely symmetrical. The current-voltage relation was ohmic up to 100,000 volts/cm. Under illumination the contacts were not symmetrical. The photocurrent flowing when one side was illuminated was different from that when the opposite side was illuminated. In the extreme case, the difference was a factor of 2.5. Generally, the variation of i^- between opposite faces was less than the variation in i^+.

Dependence on Concentration of Electrolyte Used As Electrode

Most experiments were carried out with 0.02 M NaCl. There were no concentration effects over a concentration range from 0.005 to 2 M NaCl. There were minor differences at 1 M concentrations among KCl, LiCl, NaCl, NaNO$_3$, and Na$_2$SO$_4$. Experiments with HCl and NaOH were carried out at about 1 M.

Photocurrent with 1 M HCl electrodes was smaller than that with the neutral salts, and about half that obtained with 1 M NaOH electrodes. There was some evidence that the crystal surface was altered after the NaOH experiments. This is still under investigation. The behavior of NaI was similar to that of NaCl at 0.02 M but was quite different at 1 M. This will be discussed later. The introduction of oxidizing agents, such as I$_2$ and Ce^{4+} had extreme effects, and these too will be discussed later.

Conductivity as a Function of Field Strength

D-C Dark Current. In our experiments, the specific resistance of anthracene was found to be at least 10^{15} ohm-cm. Leakage resistance in our cell limited measurements above this value. With this limitation in mind, we can report that our dark currents were ohmic up to 100,000 volts/cm and were symmetrical with respect to current direction.

D-C Photocurrent. Using 3,650-A light, i^+ and i^- were measured as a function of field strength for increasing and decreasing fields. A typical result is shown in Fig. 7.2. While there was no saturation in i^+ up to 10^5 volts cm^{-1} there was a distinct change in slope at about 10^4 volts cm^{-1} for this 12-micron crystal. For i^-, this change appeared at 0.5×10^4 volts cm^{-1}.

At very low field strength, both i^+ and i^- were approximately proportional to V^2, as had been found by Kommandeur.[6] At high field strength the dependence of both i^+ and i^- on V were almost the same, i^- showing a greater tendency to saturation.

The ratio of i^+/i^- varied with field intensity. For example, in Fig. 7.2 the ratio at low fields was about 18, and at high fields it was 38. In general, the ratio i^+/i^- varied from 30 to 100, the mode being about 50.

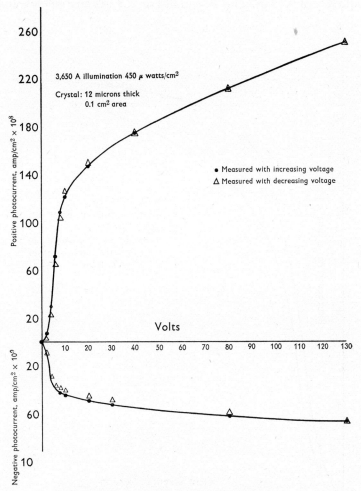

Fig. 7.2. D-c photoconductivity in anthracene.

The tracking of i^+ and i^- for increasing and decreasing fields can be seen in Fig. 7.2; it was excellent at the larger voltages and fairly good at the lower voltages, with some slight evidence of hysteresis, particularly in i^-.

A-C Photocurrent. Using alternating current, both i^+ and i^- showed a more pronounced saturation with voltage, even at a frequency of 0.1 cps. This is seen in Fig. 7.3. At any given voltage,

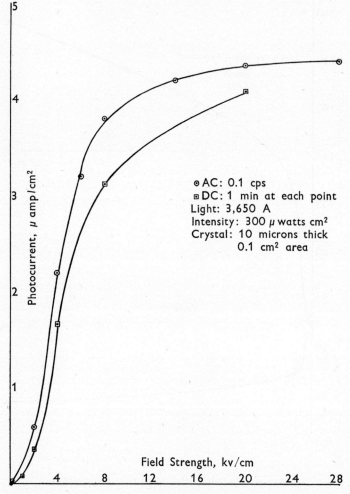

Fig. 7.3. Comparison of a-c and d-c photoconductivity in anthracene.

i^+ was lower with direct than with alternating current. (The d-c values were obtained by waiting 1 min at each voltage.) This result was taken as evidence of the existence of trapped charges in the d-c experiments. The time required to build up the space charge was estimated to be of the order of a minute, since in a different experiment, comparing i^+ at 0.3, 3, 30, and 300 cps, there were no significant differences at these frequencies.

Light intensity: 730 μ watts/cm²

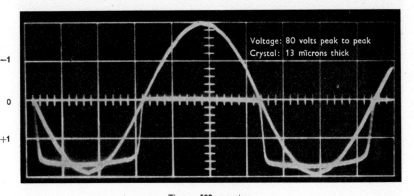

Time → 500 m sec/cm

Fig. 7.4. A-c photoconductivity in anthracene: 0.3 cps; 3,650 A.

Some a-c results may be seen in Figs. 7.4 through 7.7. The crystal in this case was 13 microns thick, and the light intensity was about 800 μwatts cm^{-2}.

Light intensity: 730 μwatts/cm²

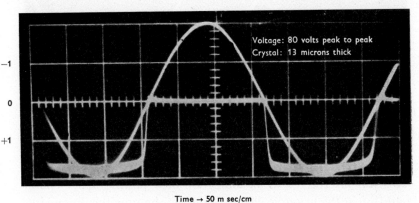

Time → 50 m sec/cm

Fig. 7.5. A-c photoconductivity in anthracene: 3 cps; 3,650 A.

The effect of frequency on i^- was more marked. As the frequency increased, there was a current pulse through the crystal just as the voltage on the illuminated side of the crystal became negative.

Light intensity: 730 μ watts/cm²

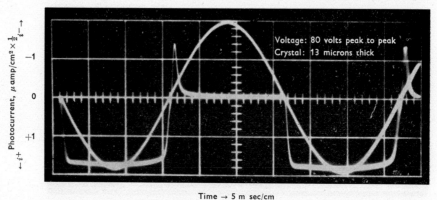

Voltage: 80 volts peak to peak
Crystal: 13 microns thick

Time → 5 m sec/cm

Fig. 7.6. A-c photoconductivity in anthracene: 30 cps; 3,650 A.

Light intensity: 730 μ watts/cm²

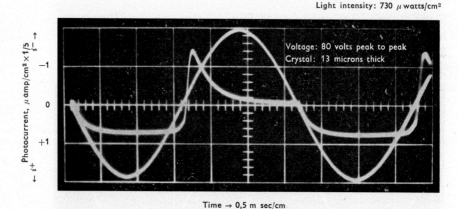

Voltage: 80 volts peak to peak
Crystal: 13 microns thick

Time → 0,5 m sec/cm

Fig. 7.7. A-c photoconductivity in anthracene: 300 cps; 3,650 A.

This was interpreted as an indication of a positive space-charge build-up at the negative electrode during the time the illuminated crystal face was positive. This build-up could be caused by a delay in discharging the holes reaching the negative face of the crystal. Thus, with the reversal of the polarity of the crystal, the positive holes would be quickly swept back to the negative illuminated face.

A-C Photocurrent as a Function of Light Intensity

Using a frequency of 0.1 cps, a series of curves were obtained for i^+ as a function of voltage at different light intensities. This is shown in Fig. 7.8. From these data, it was possible to determine

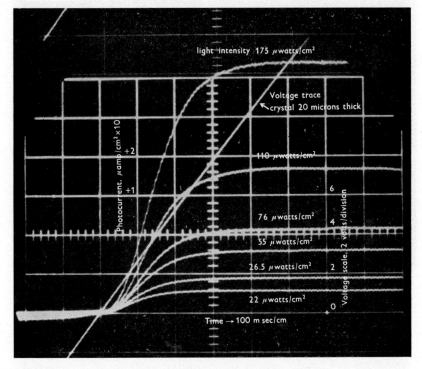

Fig. 7.8. A-c photoconductivity in anthracene: 0.1 cps; i^+, light-intensity dependence; 3,650 A.

i^+ as a function of the light intensity I at different voltages. At 1,000 volts cm^{-1} i^+ varied as $I^{1/2}$; at about 3,700 volts/cm, i^+ varied directly with I; at 7,000 volts cm^{-1} (saturation), i^+ varied

as $I^{1.2}$. It may also be noted that the voltage at which saturation
occurred was slightly dependent on light intensity, diminishing
as the intensity decreased.

The dependence of i^+ on I is thus a strong function of the
field strength, an observation that was also made by Kommandeur.[6] At low field strength, the results agreed with those of
Kommandeur made at similar field strength and light intensity.

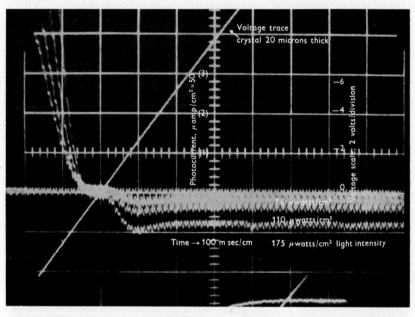

Time → 100 m sec/cm

Fig. 7.9. A-c photoconductivity in anthracene: 0.1 cps; i^-, light-intensity-
dependence; 3,650 A.

At higher fields, our results were similar to those of Lyons and
Morris,[7] who obtained a linear dependence of i^+ on I, except that
their measurements were made at lower field strengths.

The i^+ dependence on $I^{1.2}$ appeared at the onset of current
saturation. At slightly higher voltages the dependence sometimes
dropped to linearity.

Using direct current, it was observed that the dependence of i^+ on I was also a function of the field strength. The d-c experiments were made at only two light intensities: at 1,630 volts cm,$^{-1}$ $i^+ \propto I^{0.9}$ and at higher fields, $i^+ \propto I^{1.2}$. Thus the dependence of i^+ on I was the same for direct and alternating current.

As for i^-, the voltage dependence at different light intensities is shown in Fig. 7.9. Saturation was more pronounced, occurring at lower field strengths. In general $i^- \propto I^{1.1}$, although in many cases $i^- \propto I$, and in a few cases $i \propto I^{1.6}$. Here again, Kommandeur[6] has also noted the effect of field strength on i^-, the dependence at higher fields being $i^- \propto I$. The d-c dependence of i^- on I was very similar to that of the a-c field, the exponent of I varying between 1.1 and 1.2.

Effect of Crystal Thickness on Photoconductivity. The range of crystal thicknesses varied from about 10 to 30 microns. Over this range of thickness, there was no effect that could be unequivocally attributed to a change in crystal thickness. For example, the same crystal, cut into two fragments, gave photocurrents that differed by a factor of 3.

Quantum Efficiencies. The appearance of saturation photocurrents provided an opportunity for determining the quantum efficiency of charge-carrier production. The a-c saturation currents were considered to be closer to the real saturation currents than the d-c currents, because of polarization effects in the latter. Over a variety of crystals ranging in thickness from 6 to 20 microns, with direct and alternating current, the average efficiency was 1 electron flowing in the external circuit for every 60 quanta of 3,650 A light incident upon the crystal. The true efficiency is higher since there were reflection losses at the crystal surface.

Rise Time of Photoconductivity. An attempt was made to estimate the carrier mobility by exciting the photocurrent with 3,650-A light from a high-speed, high-intensity flash lamp. The result of this experiment is shown in Fig. 7.10. At 100,000 volts cm^{-1}, the rise and decay of photocurrent is practically the same as that of the light flash. There may be a 1- or 2-μsec tail on the photocurrent pulse. At 2500 volts cm^{-1}, however, there was a distinct plateau and a 20-μsec tail in the photocurrent response. This may be seen in Fig. 7.11. Assuming that the plateau (and part of the peak) of 4 μsec was a reflection of the transit time of the charges across the crystal, it was estimated that a lower limit for the mobility of the carriers was about 0.2 cm^2 (volts sec)$^{-1}$ in this 20-micron crystal.

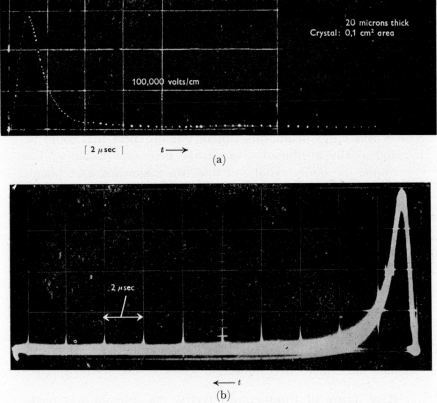

Fig. 7.10. (a) Rise time of photoconductivity in anthracene (maximum current, 1.5 ma cm^{-2}); (b) rise time of light-intensity of flash lamp.

Dependence on Nature of Electrolyte Solution. In one series of experiments, the electrode efficiency of a 1 M NaCl solution was compared with that of a 1 M NaI solution.[9] Side

A and *B* refer to separate compartments in Fig. 7.1. A summary of the results is shown in Table 7.1. (Lines 3 and 5, which should be identical, are a measure of the contact asymmetry.) It may be seen that at equal light intensity and field strength, i^+ with

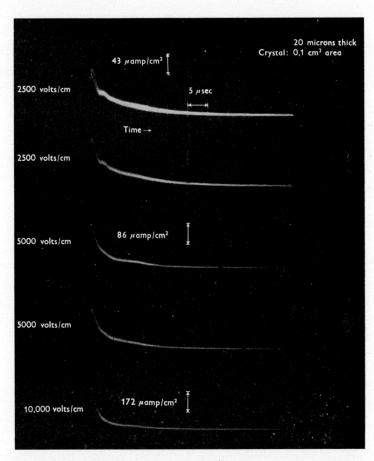

Fig. 7.11. Photoconductivity in anthracene, high-intensity flash lamp.

NaCl is thirteen times that of i^+ with NaI (lines 5 and 6). We attribute this to the ability of the I^- to quench the fluorescence and also the photoconductivity. A relationship between fluorescence

Table 7.1. Surface-controlled Bulk Conductivity in Anthracene Using NaCl and NaI Electrolyte Electrodes [a]

Experiment	Solution composition		Type of current	Current $\times 10^{12}$ amp [c]	
	Side A [b]	Side B		i^+	i^-
1	NaI	NaI	Dark	3.0	3.0
2	NaI	NaCl	Dark	4.4	6.0
3	NaI	NaI	Photo	42,000	620
4	NaI	NaCl	Photo	35,000	5,000
5	NaI	NaI	Photo	25,200	870
6	NaCl	NaI	Photo	328,000	1,150

[a] Voltage: 50 volts. Area of crystal: 0.1 cm². Intensity of 3,650-A light: 320 μwatt cm⁻². All solutions are 1 M in concentration.

[b] Side A is side illuminated.

[c] i^+ and i^- refer to currents measured when the polarity of the side illuminated by light was positive and negative, respectively. These currents are based on a crystal area of 0.1 cm².

Table 7.2. Hole Injection into Anthracene [a,b]

	$i^+ \times 10^{12}$ amp [a]	$i^- \times 10^{12}$ amp [a]
Dark current	3.0	3.0
Sensitized dark current	11	245
3,650-A photocurrent	42,000	620
Sensitized 3,650-A photocurrent	47,000	89,000
4,360-A photocurrent	19	18
Sensitized 4,360-A photocurrent	20	48,000

[a] Voltage: 50 volts, direct current. 3,650-A light intensity: 320 μwatt cm⁻². 4,360-A light intensity: 920 μwatt cm⁻². Area of crystal: 0.1 cm².

[b] i^+ and i^- refer to currents measured when the polarity of the face of the crystal not in contact with the I_2 was made positive and negative, respectively; they are also the currents measured when the polarity of the side through which the light entered was positive and negative, respectively. These currents are based on a crystal area of 0.1 cm².

quenching and photocurrent decrease has already been noted.[8] Moreover, the ratio of i^+/i^- shown in line 6 is 323. This would indicate that at most the true electron current in anthracene cannot be greater than 0.3 per cent of that carried by i^+. Considering the fact that a good deal of i^- is probably due to holes generated by fluorescent light at the back face, the contribution of i^- is probably less than 0.1 per cent.

In another series of experiments, stimulated by the work of Akamatu, Inokuchi, and Matsunaga,[18] a solution of I_2 in 1 M NaI was used as one electrode. Due to the opacity of this solution, the I_2 electrode was always distant from the light. These results are shown in Table 7.2. The addition of I_2 increased i^- by a factor of 143 over that of the iodine-free solution, when 3,650-A light was used. Here i^- refers to current flowing when the I_2 solution is at a positive potential. When 4,360-A light was used, to which the anthracene was practically transparent, i^- increased by a factor of 2,700 over the iodine-free solution. The dark current was also increased by a factor of 80 and saturated with voltage at about 40 kv cm^{-1}. Upon removal of the I_2, the behavior of the crystal was similar to that before the addition of the I_2.

Discussion

In view of the large photocurrents that were observed with electrolyte electrodes and the large effects upon the bulk conductivity that could be produced by changing the nature of the electrolyte, we have proposed that the electrodes inject positive holes into the anthracene.[11] To the extent that this process is efficient, the photocurrent will be increased, and even the dark current.

The energetics of the hole injection process at the electrodes can be described as a first approximation by the equation

$$W_E + E_X - I_A > 0 \qquad (7.1)$$

where W_E is the energy required to remove an electron from the electrode; I_A is the energy required to take an electron out of solid anthracene, creating a positive hole $A^+(s)$; and E_X is the energy externally supplied (optically, thermally, or by the electric field).

Applying Eq. (7.1) to the I_2-electrode experiment without light, E_X is the energy which dissociates $I_2(aq)$ producing a small concentration of $I(aq)$. It remains therefore to investigate the role of the $I(aq)$ in the process of hole injection. I_A is given as about 6 ev,[1] but our estimate is between 5 and 6 ev; W_E is about 6.2 ev, calculated as follows:

$$I(aq) \rightarrow \qquad I(g) \quad + 0 \text{ ev}$$
$$I(g) + e^-(g) \rightarrow I^-(g) \quad + 3.2 \text{ ev}$$
$$I^-(g) \rightarrow \qquad I^-(aq) + 3.0 \text{ ev}$$
$$I(aq) + e^- \rightarrow \quad I^-(aq) + 6.2 \text{ ev}, \qquad W_E = 6.2 \text{ ev} \qquad (7.2)$$

The energy balance is seen to be favorable for the extraction of an electron from the anthracene, even in the dark, and the injection of a positive hole into the anthracene. At the opposite electrode, the process is the discharge of the positive hole similar to the discharge of an ion at a metal electrode.

When external radiation is absorbed by I_2 (and also I_3^-), it increases the dissociation of I_2 into iodine atoms; on the above basis, hole injection should also be increased in accordance with Eq. (7.2), as was indeed the case. Thus, when 4,360 A was used, the light was absorbed by the I_3^- ion, and its enhanced dissociation increased the current by a factor of 16,000 over the dark current.

The case where the external radiation is absorbed by anthracene in contact with salt solutions containing no iodine produces hole injection in a similar way. It is assumed that when exciting radiation is absorbed, excitons are produced. Most excitons are found near the illuminated electrode, frequently colliding with it. During a collision, the injection of positive holes is possible according to the following scheme, where A^* is the excited anthracene molecule at the illuminated surface

$$A^*(s) \rightarrow A(s) + E_X, \qquad E_X = 3.3 \text{ ev}$$
$$H^+(aq) + e^- \rightarrow 1/2 H_2(g) + W_E, \qquad W_E = 4.7 \text{ ev} \qquad (7.3)$$

Placing these values in Eq. (7.1), there is an excess in energy of about 2.5 ev for the injection of a positive hole into the anthracene.

At the dark electrode, the following reaction takes place:

$$OH^-(aq) \rightarrow 1/2H_2O(l) + 1/4O_2(g) + e^- + W_E, \quad W_E = -4.2 \text{ ev} \quad (7.4)$$

$$e^- + A^+(s) \rightarrow A(s) + I_A, \qquad\qquad\qquad I_A = 5.5 \text{ ev}$$

There is thus an excess in energy of about 1.3 ev for the discharge of the positive hole appearing at the negative electrode, taking an electron from OH^- and neutralizing A^+. The use of H^+ and OH^- even in neutral solutions where the concentration of these species is about 10^{-7} M presents no problems, since the water itself enters into the surface reaction to provide the appropriate ions.[12]

From the above, it is evident that from an energy viewpoint, hole injection and discharge at the crystal-solution interface are favorable for the cases of photoconductivity and where an electron acceptor is used as an electrode.

It has been seen that the insertion of the value of W_E of Eq. (7.2) into (7.1) provides an energy excess of about 0.7 ev for hole injection into anthracene. The value of I_A for naphthalene can be reasonably estimated as about 6.5 ev, which would mean that the I_2 solution would not be very effective as an electron acceptor for naphthalene. Unfortunately, only one experiment has been made with naphthalene, but it has been found that there is no enhancement of i^- by iodine in the dark, and none in the light using 3,000 A, although this light does produce a definite photoconductivity.

Again, considering the implication of Eq. (7.1), if we used a very powerful electron acceptor (or oxidizer) the energy balance could be made even greater. Thus, when Ce^{4+} ion was used as an electrode, the dark current increased by a factor of 50,000 at 40,000 volts cm^{-1} over that in the dark. In this case, there was some slight evidence of chemical attack on the anthracene crystal.

As for the normal dark conductivity, the picture here is apparently different, since we have not observed any current saturation with voltage up to 100,000 volts cm^{-1}. If we insert the value for W_E from Eq. (7.3) into (7.1), we note that the energy deficit for hole injection would be 0.8 ev. Since there is no light, this must be supplied either thermally or by the electric field or by both. Using the simple considerations outlined by Moelwyn-Hughes [13] it was calculated that the number of molecules of water that strike the anthracene surface is about 5×10^{26} molecules $sec^{-1} cm^{-2}$. Using Boltzmann statistics, the calculated fraction of any population of molecules that possesses an energy larger than 0.8 ev is about e^{-32}. Therefore, the number of water molecules that strike the anthracene surface with sufficient energy to cause hole injection is $5 \times 10^{12} cm^2 sec$.

For the 10-micron crystal, we observed a dark current of about 10^{-10} amp cm^{-2} at an applied field of 100 volts. This would represent a flow of 6×10^8 holes $cm^{-2} sec^{-1}$. Comparing this with the number of active water molecules striking the anthracene surface, we see that if 1 impact in 10,000 is successful, we can account for the observed current.

The fact that we do not get saturation indicates that the process by which holes are reflected back into the electrode is faster than the rate of removal at 100 volts. In some experiments with evaporated Ag electrodes on anthracene, the dark currents were measured at fields up to 500,000 volts cm^{-1}, the currents did not saturate up to 200,000 volts cm^{-1} but started to increase rapidly thereafter. This was probably the onset of a field-emission process.

The process of hole injection, from the point of view of energy, does not require that any chemical reaction take place between the anthracene and the electrode. It may be argued, however, that in some respects the experiments described here resemble a situation in which oxidation and reduction of organic compounds is carried out electrolytically. It may further be argued that as a result of electrolysis perhaps a surface oxidation product was decreasing the energy required to remove an electron from the anthracene and placing it in the electrolyte. It is doubtful, however, whether there is any simple oxidation product of anthracene that could function in this manner. Add to this the fact that the current is largest when the illuminated side of the crystal is at a positive potential, which means that in accordance with our Eq. (7.3) H_2 would be given off at that face. This would, if anything, remove any oxidation product. On the other hand, if H_2 gas is given off (this has not been experimentally observed), there might be a tendency for some adsorption of H prior to the formation of H_2. The adsorbed H might lower the work function of the surface for hole injection.

At the dark side of the crystal, O_2 would be given off in accordance with Eq. (7.4), and despite the fact that the surface conductivity of anthracene is greatly increased by exposure to oxidizing gases,[15] the "negative" current, which is a hole current from this face, is very small.

In fact the ratio i^+/i^- is about the same for electrolyte electrodes as it is for metal electrodes, which makes it unlikely that the crystal faces have been materially altered by the electrodes.

We have, therefore, no indication nor need to rely on the existence of any coatings. It may be that certain surface states at the anthracene-electrolyte interface are of influence. These states would determine the actual energy difference $W_E - I_A$ used in Eq. (7.1).

A remark may be made regarding the question of the possibility of proton transport from the solution through the anthracene to the opposite side. This is considered quite unlikely from at least two considerations: A *decrease* in H^+ concentration in the electrolyte by a factor of 10^{14} *increases* the photocurrent by about 100 per cent. Then it is doubtful that the proton would travel through the anthracene in its hydrated state, and to divest itself of its water molecule would require 11.2 ev, while conductivity commences at a fraction of a volt.

Summarizing, our picture of the events succeeding the illumination of an anthracene crystal provided with electrolyte electrodes would be as follows: The absorbed photon creates an exciton that in its diffusion path may strike the electrolyte-crystal surface. There, an activated complex may be formed between the excited anthracene molecule and either the hydronium ion or the water molecule. This complex dissociates into an anthracene molecule containing a hole, the electron being taken up by the water or hydronium ion. Under the influence of the field, the hole in the anthracene moves with a mobility of about 0.5 cm² (volts sec)$^{-1}$ to the opposite surface of the crystal, where it strikes an hydroxyl ion (or water molecule). Again, an activated complex may be formed which dissociates into a neutral anthracene molecule and oxygen.

When an electron acceptor like I_2 is used as an electrode, the activated complex may be formed between the iodine atom (or other acceptor) and the anthracene molecule and dissociates into an anthracene molecule containing a hole and the negatively ionized iodide ion. The discharge of the hole proceeds as before.

In some cases, it is possible to decrease the photoconductivity by using a solution containing the I^- ion, which has the ability to interact with the activated complex, depriving it of its energy without permitting dissociation to take place.

Again, on the dark side, the discharge of the holes is not instantaneous, and if the polarity of the applied potential is switched fast enough, it will be possible to catch some positive holes before they have had a chance to be discharged, whereupon they will flow back through the crystal to the negative illuminated face. Since there is no replenishment of charge on the dark side, this appears as a decaying current. Furthermore, since the decay is almost exponential, it means that there are not many trapping sites for the holes. The relatively long delay in discharging all the positive holes would mean that the resultant field strength at the dark electrode is quite low due to space-charge effects.

In the dark, the thermal energy is sufficient to produce the currents observed, using the same mechanism as was used for the photocurrent.

The current is carried by holes at least to better than a ratio of 1,000 : 3 for electrons.

The great importance of the electrode on the behavior of anthracene has been verified beyond doubt. We do not claim that this is the only mechanism for conductivity in anthracene, but it is predominant.

Aside from the interesting results we can obtain by using electrolyte electrodes, the design of the experimental equipment is suggestive of many systems found in biology, consisting of a membrane separating salt solutions. The fact that an oxidation and reduction occur on opposite sides of the crystal (which transports only electricity) without mixing the products is a model that may be useful in that field. The products in the case of dilute-salt-solution electrodes are probably oxygen and hydrogen produced by the electrolysis of water at the interfaces of the crystal and the solutions. This decomposition of water would be accomplished at the relatively long wavelength of 3,650 A. It should be borne in mind that salt water can be decomposed into H_2 and O_2 at very small potentials, and the anthracene crystal can carry out this decomposition even with its photovoltaic potential of 0.2 volt.

It should also not be overlooked that by changing the pH of the electrolyte at the surface of the crystal from acid to base, it was possible to effect a significant increase in the transport of charge through the crystal. Finally, it may be suggested that by using the electrolyte electrodes with the phthalocyanines containing a central metallic atom capable of undergoing redox reactions, even more marked changes in conductivity may be found than reported by Vartanian and Karpovich,[14] who used oxygen gas. Phthalocyanines are structurally similar to the porphyrin nucleus present in chlorophyll and hemin.

Acknowledgments. Grateful acknowledgment is made of the assistance of the Office of Naval Research (NONR 285(41)) in this work and of the Air Force Cambridge Research Center, Contract AF 19(604)—5495.

References

1. C. G. B. Garrett, *in* N. B. Hannay (ed.), "Semiconductors," Monograph Series No. 140, Reinhold Publishing Corporation, New York (1959).
2. H. Kallmann and M. Pope, *Rev. Sci. Instr.* **30**, 44 (1959).
3. H. Kallmann and M. Pope, *Rev. Sci. Instr.* **29**, 933 (1958).
4. H. Mette and H. Pick, *Physik* **134**, 566 (1953).
5. H. Inokuchi, *Bull. Chem. Soc. Japan* **29**, 131 (1956).
6. J. Kommandeur, Ph.D. thesis, University of Amsterdam (1958).
7. L. E. Lyons and G. C. Morris, *J. Chem. Soc.* **1957**, 3648.
8. Lipsett, D. M. S. Compton, and T. C. Waddington, *J. Chem. Phys.* **26**, 1444 (1957).
9. H. Kallmann and M. Pope, *Nature* **185**, 153 (1960).
10. H. Kallmann and M. Pope, *J. Chem. Phys.* **32**, 300 (1960).

11. H. Kallmann and M. Pope, *Nature* **186**, 31 (1960).
12. B. E. Conway, *Chem. in Can.* (April, 1957), p. 41.
13. Moelwyn-Hughes, "Kinetics of Reactions in Solutions," Oxford University Press, London (1947).
14. A. T. Vartanian and I. A. Karpovich, *Zhur. Fiz. Khim.* **32**, 178 (1958).
15. W. G. Schneider and T. C. Waddington, *J. Chem. Phys.* **25**, 358 (1956).
16. W. Brattain and C. G. B. Garrett, *Bell System Tech. J.* **34**, 129 (1955).
17. Mino Green *in* J. O. M. Bockris (ed.), "Modern Aspects of Electrochemistry," No. 2, chap. 5, Butterworth & Co. (Publishers), Ltd., London (1959).
18. H. Akamatu, H. Inokuchi, and Y. Matsunaga, *Bull. Chem. Soc. Japan* **29**, 213 (1956).

8

Spatial Distribution of Trapped Electrons in Anthracene

M. SILVER and W. MOORE

Introduction

Although photoconductivity in anthracene has been investigated since 1906,[1] the mechanism of free-carrier production is still not understood. Information on the source of free carriers may be obtained from a knowledge of the position and quantity of charge carriers trapped in the bulk. Trapping of charge carriers in the bulk has previously been investigated by Kallmann and Rosenberg[2] and Kallmann and Silver[3] and is referred to as the persistent internal polarization effect. Kallmann and Silver have shown that this effect is mainly due to a spatial distribution of trapped electrons. The lifetime of trapped electrons is large (several days) allowing the measurements described below to be made using the trapped charge as a field source.

Theory of Measurements

From Gauss' theorem we can show that the field near either of two grounded, parallel-plane electrodes due to a distribution of charges between them is the same as that due to the same total charge placed in a thin layer located at the center of charge of the original distribution. In anthracene we are concerned only with electrons, since holes, which are the majority carriers, are not easily trapped. This simplified distribution of trapped charge is shown in Fig. 8.1. The electrode that is positive during polarization is labeled electrode A, Q_t is the total charge trapped, D_1 is the distance from electrode A to the center of charge of the trapped electrons, and D_0 is the thickness of the sample.

D_1 is determined from the value of the image charge on each of the electrodes after the sample has been shorted. The image charge Q_{iA}, on electrode A is approximately equal to the charge collected on a capacitor in parallel with the sample when the

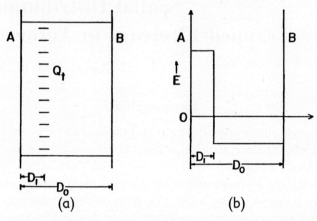

Fig. 8.1. Charge and field distributions for a thin layer of electrons located a distance D_1 from electrode A. (a) Charge distribution; (b) field distribution.

polarization is discharged with highly absorbed radiation transmitted through electrode B. The charge Q_B on the capacitor after the polarization is completely discharged is

$$Q_B \approx Q_t[D_0 - D_1/D_0] = Q_{iA} \qquad (8.1)$$

Similarly the image charge Q_{iB} on electrode B can be found by discharging the polarization with highly absorbed radiation through electrode A. In this case, the charge Q_A on the capacitor is

$$Q_A \approx Q_t(D_1/D_0) = Q_{iB} \qquad (8.2)$$

This measurement of the image charge on electrode B, although convenient, was found to be not too accurate, because the rapid change of the field near electrode A with distance causes some of the displaced charges to move in opposite directions. The net effect is to make the measured value of Q_A smaller than it would be if all charges moved in the same direction.

As an alternative to discharge measurements, we can determine Q_{iB} from the value of the internal field at electrode B. The field at electrode B is measured by opposing it with an external field, irradiating side B with a short pulse of light, and adjusting the applied field until no current pulse accompanies the light pulse. When this null is found, the magnitude of the applied field is equal to the internal polarization field. Here,

$$Q_{iB} = CV' \tag{8.3}$$

where C is the geometric capacitance of the sample, and V' is the externally applied voltage necessary to give no current pulse when the light is pulsed. Using the expressions for Q_{iA} and Q_{iB} we get

$$D_1 = Q_{iB}/(Q_{iA} + Q_{iB}) \approx CV'/(Q_B + CV') \tag{8.4}$$

and

$$Q_t = Q_{iA} + Q_{iB} \approx Q_B + CV' \tag{8.5}$$

The circuits for making charge and field measurements are shown in Fig. 8.2.

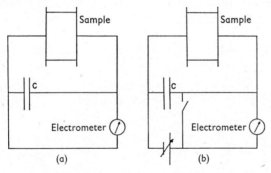

Fig. 8.2. Apparatus for making charge displacement and internal field measurements. (a) Charge measurements; (b) field measurements.

The samples used in this study were 60 microns thick and were grown from the melt between two semitransparent inconel-coated vycor plates. Scintillation grade anthracene was used without further purification.

Results

If carriers are produced only by direct excitation by the incident radiation transmitted through the positive electrode

(electrode A), then

$$n(x) = (n_b/x_0) \exp -x/x_0 \qquad (8.6)$$

where x_0 is the absorption depth of the polarizing radiation. Assuming that trapping is a monomolecular process we find, using an analysis similar to that of Brown and Van Heyningen,[4] that the number of charges produced at x that are subsequently trapped at x' is

$$d[n_t(x')\,dx'] = [n(x)/w] \exp - (x-x'/w)\,dx\,dx' \qquad (8.7)$$

where $n_t(x')$ is the density of trapped charges at x', and x and x' are distances measured from the positive electrode $(x > x')$. Taking into account all the charge produced by the light in the interval x' to D_0, we get

$$n_t(x') = \int_{x=x'}^{D_0} [n(x)/w] \exp -(x-x'/w)\,dx \qquad (8.8)$$

If carriers are produced according to Eq. (8.6) only, the expression for the distance to the center of mass is

$$D_1 \approx x_0 \qquad (8.9)$$

assuming $\exp(-D_0/x_0) \ll 1$.

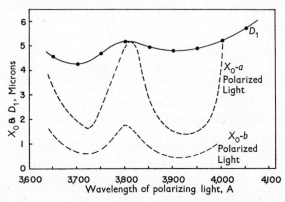

Fig. 8.3. Comparison of D_1 and absorption depths as a function of wavelength of the incident radiation.

The sample was polarized with a beam of monochromatic, unpolarized light. D_1 was measured as a function of the wavelength of the polarizing radiation using measurements of Q_A and Q_B. The value of D_1 as a function of wavelength is given in Fig. 8.3. Also shown are the Craig-Hobbins data on absorption depth in anthracene. The bandwidth of the incident polarizing radiation was approximately 25 A. We see from Fig. 8.3 that D_1 varies with the absorption depth of the polarizing light. There are, therefore, some carriers produced in the bulk at or near the point where the light is absorbed. However, D_1 does not equal x_0, as predicted by Eq. (8.9). Thus, there is a source of carriers other than excitation by incident light.

Information on the other source of free carriers was obtained by studying the dependence of Q_t, the total charge trapped, and D_1 on the potential across the sample during polarization. Since the range of the carriers is proportional to the field strength, we should expect a smaller fraction of the total charge generated to be trapped at high voltage than at low voltage. A determination of the amount of charge trapped as a function of voltage was made from measurements of Q_B and CV'. The fraction of the total

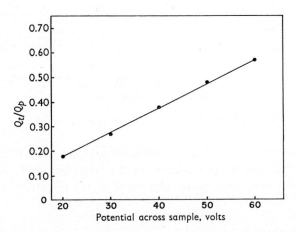

Fig. 8.4. Total charge trapped as a function of applied voltage.

charge passed through the sample that is subsequently trapped is plotted in Fig. 8.4 as a function of polarizing potential. The sample was polarized with 3,650-A light for a time sufficient to pass about 4×10^{-9} coulomb/cm². It is seen that the fraction of charge trapped, Q_t/Q_p, increases with voltage. (Q_p is the charge passed through the sample.) This indicates that there is a field or voltage dependent source of negative charge carriers.

This additional source of electrons may be in the bulk or at the negative electrode. If this field-dependent process operates throughout the bulk, the maximum value D_1 could have is half the total thickness of the sample. D_1 was computed from the same Q_B and CV' data that were used to obtain the Q_t/Q_p values shown in Fig. 8.4. The D_1 results are shown in Fig. 8.5. From

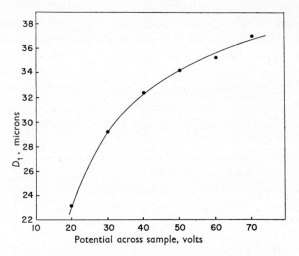

Fig. 8.5. Dependence of D_1 on applied voltage.

Fig. 8.5 we see that at high voltages D_1 is larger than 30 microns, which is half the total thickness of the samples used. Negative carriers are, therefore, being generated at the negative electrode.

Discussion of Results

From the value of D_1 versus wavelength, we see that D_1 does vary according to the absorption depth. This indicates that some charge is created in the bulk at or near the point at which the light is absorbed. Measurements of Q_t/Q_p as a function of polarizing voltage show that the amount of charge trapped increases with an increase in polarizing potential. Therefore, there is a voltage or field-dependent source of electrons. Determinations of D_1 as a function of polarizing voltage show that the field-dependent source of charges is at the negative metal electrode. That a donor electrode can inject electrons is consistent with the results of Kallmann and Pope, who have shown that holes can be injected into the anthracene by an acceptor electrode (iodine-iodide solution).[5]

An attempt has been made to fit the measured value of Q_t/Q_p to values calculated by integrating Eq. (8.8), assuming intrinsic charge production by the light and injection at the negative electrode. The calculated values did not agree with the measured Q_t/Q_p. It is therefore concluded on the basis of these results that anthracene is an extrinsic photoconductor.

References

1. A. Pochettino, *Atti. accad. Nasy. Lincei Rend.* **15**(1), 355 (1906).
2. H. Kallmann and B. Rosenberg, *Phys. Rev.* **97**, 1596 (1958).
3. M. Silver, "Persistent Internal Polarization Effects in Anthracene," Ph.D. thesis, New York University (Feb., 1959).
4. R. S. van Heyningen and F. C. Brown, *Phys. Rev.* **111**, 462 (1958).
5. H. Kallmann and M. Pope, *J. Chem. Phys.* **32** 000 (1960).

9

Trapping Centers and Electronic Conduction Processes in Anthracene and 9,10-Dichloroanthracene

A. BREE, P. J. REUCROFT, and W. G. SCHNEIDER

Introduction

Earlier measurements on anthracene single crystals have indicated that both the semiconductivity and photoconductivity currents are space-charge-limited and that the majority carriers are positive holes.[1-3] The space charge builds up a back electromotive force in the crystal that can be observed experimentally by removing the applied field and measuring the reverse current flow. The latter is found to decay exponentially with a relatively long time constant of the order of 20 min and frequently much longer.[4] These effects, together with the dependence of the photocurrent on the applied field and the light intensity,[3, 5] point to the existence of a relatively high density of trapping levels in anthracene crystals. A more direct experimental confirmation of these levels has been recently reported.[6] The present chapter describes a further study of the nature of these trapping centers and their effect on semiconduction and photoconduction in anthracene.

Trapping Levels in Anthracene and 9,10-Dichloroanthracene

The most convenient method for the direct observation of trapping centers is the glow curve technique. Attemps were made to observe optical glow curves. These were largely unsuccessful, and accordingly only conductivity glow curves were measured. In this method [7, 8] the crystal is cooled to low temperatures and then illuminated. On subsequently heating the crystal at a uniform rate in the dark, the conductivity is found to exhibit characteristic peaks resembling those of a "thermoluminescent glow curve." Illumination of the crystal at low temperatures generates charge carriers, a high proportion of which become trapped. On heating the crystal these carriers are thermally ejected and give rise to an enhanced conductivity. For a single set of discrete trap levels of depth E_T, the rate of carrier release is given by

$$-dn/dt = ns \exp(-E_T/kT)$$

where n is the number of trapped carriers, and s is a frequency factor. Thus on heating at a uniform rate the conductivity will rise exponentially at first, but because of the rapid depletion of the number of trapped carriers, after passing through a maximum the conductivity will again fall to a small value. For a crystal having several discrete trap levels of different depth, several conductivity peaks (glow peaks) may be observed, the one appearing at highest temperature corresponding to the deepest trap. Detailed theoretical analyses of glow curves have been given by several authors.[8-10]

To observe the conductivity glow curve the crystal was mounted on a copper block with an internal heater, the copper block having been incorporated in a dewar vessel with a quartz window. Illumination was with a mercury-discharge lamp, while the crystal was maintained at liquid nitrogen temperatures. The heating rates used could be varied within the range 0.05 to 2.0°/sec. The glow curves appeared to be largely independent of the type of crystal electrodes employed. Three different arrangements were used: (1) evaporated silver electrodes, (2) blocking electrodes, and (3) platinum foil and conducting glass electrodes pressed against opposite faces of the crystal. Of these, methods 2 and 3 cause less strain on the crystal, permitting repeated heating and cooling with little danger of cracking the crystal. Blocking electrodes were obtained by inserting thin sheets (0.003in.) of Mylar between the crystal and the conducting glass electrodes. Crystal temperatures were measured by two thermocouples, the one in contact with the copper block, the other in contact with the upper surface of a second "dummy" crystal mounted on the copper block immediately adjacent to and having the same thickness as the crystal being measured.

a. Anthracene. The crystals employed were 0.2 to 1.0 mm thick and approximately 8 mm in diameter. The starting material was commercial "scintillation"-grade anthracene (Reilly Tar and Chemical Co.) purified by elution through a chromatographic column charged with aluminum oxide. Single crystals were grown either from the melt in a Bridgeman-type furnace of from solution in the mixed solvent benzene-chloroform (1 : 1 by volume). In both cases the system was evacuated and sealed to avoid contamination by atmospheric oxygen. Measurements on a number of crystals showed no significant differences in the glow curves of crystals grown from the melt and from solution, although minor differences were observable in the behavior of individual crystals from the same source.

A typical conductivity glow curve for anthracene in the temperature range −100 to +20°C is reproduced in Fig. 9.1. The most prominent peak appears at a temperature in the range

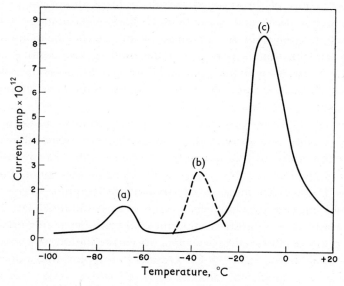

Fig. 9.1. Typical conductivity "glow curve" for anthracene monocrystal.

—20 to 0°, depending on the heating rate. The current increase on the low-temperature side is very nearly exponential, and the peak becomes higher and shifts to higher temperature as the heating rate is increased. This behavior is typical of that for a discrete trap level. The trap depth was evaluated from the temperature of the maximum and the temperature of half height, according to the method of Grossweiner.[9] The mean value found is near 0.8 ev. This must be regarded as approximate, since as the current increases, there is undoubtedly an increased build-up of space charge in the crystal, which will affect somewhat the peak position and the shape of the curve. In many crystals a minor glow peak was also observed in the region near −70°C, corresponding to an approximate trap depth of 0.6 ev. A further peak that tended to be less reproducible and "noisier" was also observed in some crystals near −40°C (Fig. 9.1).

Since positive holes are known to be the majority carriers, the most reasonable assumption is that the carriers being trapped are electrons. To preserve electrical neutrality of the crystal then requires an equivalent number of positive holes to be distributed in the vicinity of the trapped carriers. This is the origin of the space-charge field and the observed back electromotive force referred to above; in the presence of an external field applied to the crystal, some separation of the immobilized positive and negative carriers will take place. However, the possibility that positive holes are trapped to some extent cannot be definitely excluded.

The effect of the wavelength of the exciting light on the glow curve response was examined. Glow peaks were found following low-temperature irradiation only at wavelengths shorter than 4,000 A, within the low-energy singlet-singlet absorption band of the crystal. Attempts to depopulate the trapping levels by infrared radiation (while the crystal was maintained at low temperatures) were unsuccessful, nor could any detectable optical absorption be observed at wavelengths corresponding to energies in the neighborhood of 0.8 ev. Optical detrapping thus appears to be a very inefficient process.

Regarding the nature of the trapping centers two possibilities suggest themselves: (1) lattice defects and (2) acceptor molecules, which may be either anthracene molecules or impurity molecules. To consider possibility (1) we must imagine lattice vacancies or dislocations providing potential wells of the order of 0.8 ev. In a molecular crystal this appears rather improbable. On the other hand, possibility (2) which involves a "bound" state for the trapped electron, might be realized if a neutral anthracene molecule at a "favored" position in the lattice captured an electron to form the negative ion: $A+e \rightarrow A^-$. The electron affinity of anthracene, quoted as 1.19 ev for the isolated molecule [11] and 1.38 ev for anthracene in solution,[12] is sufficiently near the measured trap depth in order of magnitude to consider ion formation in the crystal a plausible mechanism.

A common impurity molecule in anthracene is tetracene. The glow curve response of several anthracene crystals strongly doped with tetracene ($\sim 10^{-3}$ mole/mole) was investigated. The large glow peak in the vicinity of $-10°C$, peak 3 in Fig. 9.1, as well as peak 1, characteristic of pure anthracene were absent. A similar behavior was observed when pure anthracene crystals were irradiated with X rays (1.3×10^5 roentgens from a 100-kv source). After irradiation the crystals were not discolored, and visually their fluorescence appeared unaltered. It appears unlikely that the anthracene trapping centers are destroyed either by tetracene doping or by X-irradiation. Evidently it is not possible to populate the trapping centers on illumination at low temperature, possibly because the crystal excitation, which would otherwise lead to charge-carrier formation, was effectively degraded by other processes taking place in the treated crystals.

Another probable impurity molecule is anthraquinone, trace quantities of which may be expected whenever anthracene is contaminated with air and exposed to light. When anthraquinone replaces an anthracene molecule in the crystal lattice, it may be assumed to form a charge-transfer complex with a neighboring anthracene molecule. Such a complex is readily ionized with a transfer of an electron from the hydrocarbon molecule to the quinone, as illustrated in Fig. 9.2(a). Subsequent hole migration leaves the electron trapped (bound) on the anthraquinone, as in

Fig. 9.2(b). Thus anthraquinone may be expected to provide acceptor levels, and on the basis of this model, charge-carrier formation is an extrinsic process. The trapped electron may ultimately recombine with a hole, regenerating the initial complex, or, given sufficient energy, may become mobile by transfer

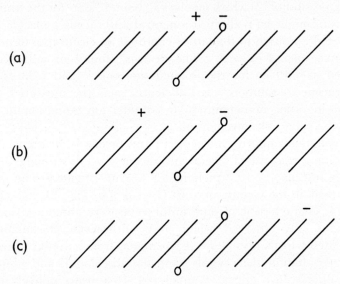

Fig. 9.2. Schematic illustration of an anthraquinone impurity molecule (identified by the two oxygen atoms in the diagram) in an anthracene crystal. The lines give an approximate indication of short molecular axes of a row of parallel molecules. (a) Charge transfer and ionization of the anthracene-anthraquinone complex; (b) hole migration with electron trapped; (c) electron detrapping.

to neighboring anthracene molecules, in Fig. 9.2(c), corresponding to detrapping of the electron. Thus in addition to providing acceptor levels, anthraquinone molecules may also provide trapping centers and recombination centers.

In the light of our present lack of knowledge generally of such organic crystals, the models outlined above must be regarded as highly speculative. All that we can conclude with certainty on the basis of the conductivity glow curve experiments is that when the crystal is illuminated at low temperatures certain metastable states are populated and that these states are depopulated when the crystal is heated. Needless to say, other plausible models consistent with these observations are possible. Present investigations are directed toward a study of anthracene crystals doped with anthraquinone and other impurities. A further experiment, which if successful might be expected to provide additional information about the nature of the trapping centers, suggests itself. When the trapping levels are filled, the trapped electron may be expected to have an unpaired spin. Experiments are being undertaken to explore this possibility by electron-spin-resonance techniques.

b. 9,10-Dichloroanthracene. The crystal structure of 9,10-dichloroanthracene [13] differs very considerably from that of anthracene and other aromatic hydrocarbons. An examination of its electronic properties is therefore of some interest. Some measurements of the luminescence and photoconduction have been reported earlier.[14] Single prismatic crystals (about 3 mm × 0.1 mm × 2 cm, elongated along the a axis) were grown from chloroform solution by controlled evaporation. A few crystals were also

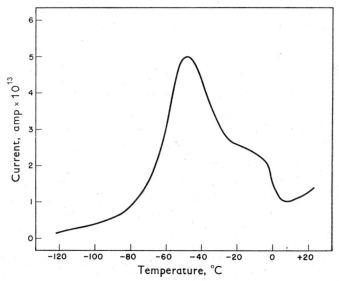

Fig. 9.3. Conductivity glow curve of 9,10-dichloroanthracene.

successfully grown from the melt. The best developed crystal face is 010. For the measurements electrodes were placed on this face on opposite sides of the crystal. The conductivity glow curve typical of 9,10-dichloroanthracene is reproduced in Fig. 9.3. There is a prominent peak near $-50°C$, with smaller peaks near $-10°$ and $30°C$. Analysis of the peak at $-50°$ indicated that the trap depth was not single valued, the mean value being in the region of 0.5 ev.

Glow curves could be observed by illumination of the crystal at low temperature with wavelengths in the main absorption band of the crystal (absorption edge near 4,700 A), as well as with longer wavelengths extending to 10,000 A. This is a rather surprising result, and in this respect the results differ markedly from those observed with anthracene. However, it has been observed [14] that photoconduction in 9,10-dichloroanthracene occurs at wavelengths down to 10,000 A, and at the longer wavelengths the quantum efficiency of carrier formation is at least an order of magnitude greater than that at wavelengths in the main absorption band.

Semiconductivity in Anthracene

The presence of relatively deep carrier traps will have a dominant effect on the measurement of electronic conduction and the interpretation of such measurements. Although a number of measurements of semiconduction in anthracene have been carried out, the basic questions of whether these materials are intrinsic semiconductors and what role, if any, is played by impurities or crystal imperfections have not been settled. The semiconduction activation energy measured by several workers [15-18] using both monocrystals and polycrystalline anthracene was found to have a mean value near 0.8 ev. A further measurement on anthracene monocrystals by Inokuchi [19] resulted in the higher value, 1.35 ev. Such measurements are ordinarily carried out by recording the conduction current in the dark as a function of temperature and taking the slope of the plot of the logarithm of the current versus the reciprocal temperature. If relatively deep traps (of the order of 0.8 ev) are present, the interpretation of the activation energy measured in this way requires closer examination. The measured conduction current will depend strongly on the particular experimental conditions as well as on the previous history of the crystal being measured. This is illustrated by the curves shown in Fig. 9.4, where the measured current is plotted against temperature when an anthracene crystal is heated at a slow and uniform rate of

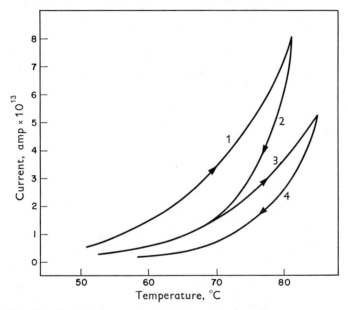

Fig. 9.4. Conductivity versus temperature in an anthracene monocrystal.

1 deg/min, curve 1, and then cooled at the same rate, curve 2. There is clearly an irreversibility, which was observed in all crystals measured. If the crystal is permitted to stand for a period of the order of 24 h in the absence of an applied field, the measured currents with increasing temperature always follow curve 1, and curve 2 is followed on subsequent cooling. If now the crystal is immediately reheated (at the same rate as previously), curve 3 is followed, and curve 4 on cooling. The semiconduction activation energy obtained from curve 1 is found to be about 20 per cent less than that from curve 2. These differences arise from variations in the space-charge field with temperature, which in turn depends

on the population and distribution of trapped carriers. The value of E derived from heating curves such as curves 1 and 3 in Fig. 9.4 is 0.83 ev. It was found that this value is always reproduced with good precision for all heating curves, even though the magnitudes of the currents are not.* (As mentioned earlier the cooling curves give rise to a higher, but still reproducible, value). In measurements of this type a space-charge-limited current is being measured.

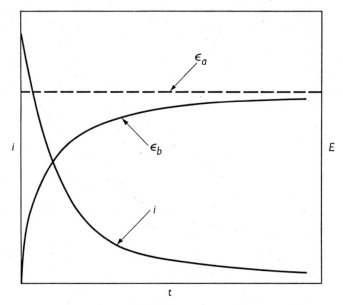

Fig. 9.5. Schematic illustration of the current i and the back electromotive force ε_b as a function of time. ε_a is the applied voltage.

If we start with an anthracene crystal completely free of space charge) e.g., stored in the dark for several days), then on the application of an applied field ε_a, the initial current is high and rapidly falls in time to a small value, as illustrated in Fig. 9.5.

* It is worth noting in this respect that the measurements of Mette and Pick [15] on anthracene were carried out with a heating rate of 10°C min^{-1}, ten times greater than that for the curves shown in Fig. 9.4. In the temperature range 85 to 190°C the cooling curve was reported to coincide with the heating curve.

As the minority carriers become trapped a back electromotive force ε_b is rapidly built up, which in time approaches ε_a. The effective field acting on the carriers is $\varepsilon_a - \varepsilon_b$, which at equilibrium attains a small value, resulting in a small limiting current. The distribution of trapped carriers as a function of x, the distance normal to the two electrodes, will be determined in part by the local field gradients $[d(\varepsilon_a - \varepsilon_b)/dl]_x$. Thus in a region where this gradient is high, there is a greater probability that a carrier will be swept out when it becomes thermally detrapped, whereas when it is low, there is a greater probability of retrapping.

After a sufficiently long time t, a steady-state current is reached. Depending on the particular experimental conditions this time is generally greater than half an hour. Fig. 9.6 shows the measured

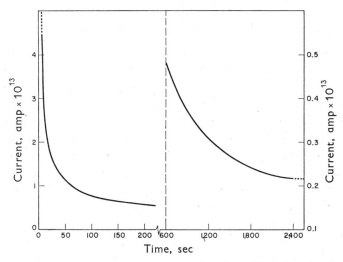

Fig. 9.6. Trace of observed current as a function of time for an anthracene crystal. The expanded right-hand ordinate applies to the right half of the diagram.

current response as a function of time for an anthracene crystal (~ 0.2 mm thick, evaporated silver electrodes 0.4 cm² in area on the *ab* faces on opposite sides of the crystal) immediately following the application of a field of 130 volts. The crystal was maintained at a temperature of 50°C. The current, measured by a vibrating-reed electrometer, was continuously recorded on a paper recorder. The steady state is apparently reached only after times in excess of 40 min. Since the recording system had a time constant of about 1 sec, the initial current could not be measured. Some preliminary measurements using a pulse technique have shown the initial currents to be several orders of magnitude higher than those shown in Fig. 9.6. This is the type of behavior to be expected for an insulator with traps and with ohmic electrodes. A similar type of behavior observed in CdS crystals has been extensively studied by Smith and Rose [20] and by Rose.[21] When a field is applied to an insulator with ohmic electrodes, electrons are injected into the conduction band.[22] But if a high density of trapping centers is present in the insulator, the injected charge rapidly settles into traps, and the current falls to a very small value. At thermal equilibrium the limiting current will depend largely on the ratio of the number of electrons in the conduction band to the number in traps.[21] For a trap depth $E_T \sim 0.8$ ev, this ratio will be very small and will vary with temperature according to a Boltzmann factor, $\exp -(E_T/kT)$. Thermally produced carriers in the bulk of the crystal will not significantly alter the number of carriers in the conduction band unless their ionization energy is low compared to the trap depth E_T. Hence the temperature dependence of the limiting current will in general be determined primarily by the depth and distribution of trapping levels and would give no direct information about the activation energy of carrier production. In the present experiments evaporated silver electrodes were employed, and it is being assumed here these are largely "ohmic" in character. This point requires further experimental investigation, but if the above model can be substantiated, it would be necessary to conclude that the energy gap, as well as the question whether carrier formation is intrinsic or extrinsic, cannot be determined from the measured semiconduction activation energy.

References

1. A. Chynoweth and W. G. Schneider, *J. Chem. Phys.* **22**, 1021 (1954).
2. G. J. Goldsmith, Ph.D. thesis, Purdue University (1955).

3. J. Kommandeur and W. G. Schneider, *J. Chem. Phys.* **28**, 590 (1958).
4. H. Kallmann and B. Rosenberg, *Phys. Rev.* **97**, 1596 (1955).
5. D. M. J. Compton, W. G. Schneider, and T. C. Waddington, *J. Chem. Phys.* **27**, 160 (1957).
6. F. J. Bryant, A. Bree, P. E. Fielding, and W. G. Schneider, *Discussions Faraday Soc.* **28**, 48 (1959).
7. R. C. Herman and R. Hofstadter, *Phys. Rev.* **57**, 936 (1940).
8. J. T. Randall and M. H. F. Wilkins, *Proc. Roy. Soc. (London)* **184**, 366 (1945).
9. L. I. Grossweiner, *J. Appl. Phys.* **24**, 1306 (1953).
10. Böer, Oberländer, and Voigt, *Ann. Physik* **2**, 130 (1958).
11. N. S. Hush and J. A. Pople, *Trans. Faraday Soc.* **51**, 600 (1955).
12. L. E. Lyons, *Nature* **166**, 193 (1950).
13. J. Trotter, *Acta Cryst.* **12**, 54 (1959).
14. A. Bree and W. G. Schneider (to be published).
15. H. Mette and H. Pick, *Z. Physik* **134**, 566 (1953).
16. N. V. Riehl, *Zhur. Fiz. Khim.* **9**, 1537 (1955).
17. D. D. Eley, G. D. Parfitt, M. J. Perry, and D. H. Taysum, *Trans. Faraday Soc.* **49**, 79 (1953).
18. D. C. Northrop and O. Simpson, *Proc. Roy. Soc. (London)* **A234**, 124 (1956).
19. H. Inokuchi, *Bull. Chem. Soc. Japan* **29**, 131 (1956).
20. R. W. Smith and A. Rose, *Phys. Rev.* **97**, 1531 (1955).
21. A. Rose, *Phys. Rev.* **97**, 1538 (1955).
22. N. F. Mott and R. W. Gurney, "Electronic Processes in Ionic Crystals," p. 172, Oxford University Press, London (1940).

The Diffusion of Excitons and Charges in Molecular Crystals

J. N. MURRELL

1. Introduction

There are two aspects of the phenomenon of photoconduction that are of interest to the theoretician. The first is the elucidation of the nature of the charge carriers, their formation and destruction processes and their mobilities, from the electronic structure of the molecular crystal. The second is that, once these properties are known, he should be able to predict the behavior of the photocurrent as a function of such variables as the light intensity, the applied voltage, the extinction coefficient of the crystal, and the temperature. More probably, he may hope to obtain values for the mobilities and rate constants associated with the conduction process by comparing the observed experimental results with his theoretical prediction. It is with this second aspect that we are concerned here.

To begin with we shall summarize a few of the relevant experimental facts that determine the model used in this paper.

a. The dark semiconductivity is small compared with the photoconductivity, at the light intensities that are used experimentally. From this we infer that the injection of charge carriers from the electrodes is negligible in a dark crystal and probably also in an illuminated crystal.

b. Mobile charges are not formed as a primary process of light absorption, but occur via the formation of excitons. To support this view there is the evidence that if the lifetime of the excitons is reduced, for example, by irradiating or adding tetracene impurities to anthracene, the reduction in fluorescence is accompanied by a reduced photocurrent.[1-3] This is to be compared with an increased dark current on irradiation.[2] In the same vein, azulene gives no photocurrent when illuminated by light whose wavelength lies in the first absorption band,[4] and this compound is unusual in that there is no fluorescence from the first excited state but only from the second.[5]

c. The formation of charge carriers from the excitons is an inefficient process. Lyons and Morris [6] estimate that only 1 photon in every 10^7 that are absorbed gives rise to charge carriers. It follows that the formation of charge carriers will not affect the exciton distribution in the crystal.

d. The photocurrent varies with the light intensity anywhere between $j \propto I$ and $j \propto I^{0.5}$, but it is not found to vary as some higher power. This indicates that the formation of charge carriers is of first order in the light intensity and eliminates the possibility that they arise from the collision of two excitons, as has been suggested.[7]

e. The applied fields used in the experiments range up to about 10^5 volts cm^{-1}. This is negligible compared with molecular fields that are of the order of 10^9 volts cm^{-1}. It is unlikely therefore that the formation of charge carriers is a field-dependent process. This is supported by the experiments that showed that a field applied perpendicular to the direction of motion of the charge carriers in a surface cell gave no change in the photocurrent that was of even power in this secondary field. (There was a small first-order effect due to a change in the rate of migration of carriers to the surface.[1])

f. There is evidence for the existence of traps for the mobile charges. Glow-curve experiments have shown traps in anthracene of 0.6, 0.7, and 0.8 ev.[7]

In the light of these facts we shall examine the problem of the photoconduction of a molecular crystal. A model will be used in which it is assumed that the excitons and charge carriers behave as classical particles possessing characteristic diffussion constants and mobilities. There are several earlier papers in this field that use a similar approach but that have an emphasis on inorganic photoconductors.[9–12] We shall consider first the equations governing the distribution of excitons in the crystal, as this exciton distribution can then be used to give the rate of production of charge carriers at different points in the crystal.

2. The Distribution of Excitons in the Crystal

We shall consider a crystal of thickness r (along the x-coordinate) and of infinite extension in the yz plane. The face Oyz is uniformly illuminated by monochromatic light normal to the surface. If G represents a molecule in its ground state, X one in an excited electronic state (an exciton), and ν a photon, then the process of formation and decay of excitons can be represented as follows:

$$\nu + G \underset{\beta}{\overset{\alpha c}{\rightleftharpoons}} X \overset{\gamma}{\rightarrow} G + kT$$

αc will be the rate constant for absorption of a photon where α is the absorption coefficient and c the velocity of the photons in the crystal. β is the rate constant for emission of a photon and γ the rate constant for the decay of an exciton in which the energy is liberated to the vibrational modes of the crystal.

There are two possible mechanisms whereby an exciton can move through the crystal:

a. A resonance exchange mechanism, which we can represent by

$$G_r + X_s \rightarrow X_r + G_s$$

where r and s label the lattice site. The rate at which this process occurs will depend on the matrix element of the Hamiltonian between the states $|rs^*\rangle$ and $|r^*s\rangle$, the asterisk representing an exciton. If the transition from the ground to the excited state is an allowed one, this matrix element falls off as the reciprocal third power of the distances between r and s. If the transition is not allowed, the matrix element will fall off more rapidly than this.

b. Emission followed by reabsorption of a photon is

$$G_r + X_s \rightarrow G_r + G_s + \nu \rightarrow X_r + G_s$$

The probability for this process will be proportional to $\alpha \exp\left(-\alpha\,|r-s|\right)$, where α is the absorption coefficient. If α

is small it can therefore have a much larger range than mechanism a, but if α is large, it will have a much shorter range.

If we assume that under the influence of mechanism a the motion of the excitons is governed by a diffusion equation and that none of the emitted photons are reabsorbed, then we have in a steady state

$$dX/dt = \delta(d^2X/dx^2) - (\beta+\gamma)X + \alpha cI \exp(-\alpha x) = 0 \quad (10.1)$$

where δ is the diffusion constant of the excitons, and X now represents the exciton concentration. The solution of this equation under the boundary conditions $X = 0$, when $x = 0$, or $x = r$ (which assumes that the electrodes are exciton quenchers), is as follows

$$X = \alpha cI/[\delta(\lambda^2-\alpha^2)\sinh \lambda r]\{[\exp(-\alpha x)\sinh \lambda r]$$
$$-[\exp(-\alpha r)\sinh \lambda x] - [\sinh \lambda(r-x)]\} \quad (10.2)$$

where λ^2 equals $(\beta+\gamma)/\delta$, $(\beta+\gamma)^{-1}$ is the lifetime of the excitons, and $1/\lambda$ is the diffusion length. When the extinction depth $1/\alpha$ is equal to the diffusion length, we have a special case

$$X = (Ic/2\delta \sinh \alpha r)[(x \sinh \alpha r \exp(-\alpha x))$$
$$-(r \sinh \alpha x \exp(-\alpha r))] \quad (10.3)$$

The penetration of the light into the crystal follows the relationship

$$\nu = I \exp(-\alpha x)$$

and we can compare the penetration of the photons and excitons by examining the ratio of the rate at which excitons are given up at the dark electrode $(\delta X'_r)$ to the rate at which photons are transmitted $(\nu_r c)$. From Eq. (10.2),

$$\delta X'_r/c\nu_r = [\alpha^2/(\alpha^2-\lambda^2)]\{1 + (\lambda/\alpha \sinh \lambda r)[\cosh \lambda r - \exp(\alpha r)]\} \quad (10.4)$$

If λr and αr are both much greater than unity, we see that this ratio is independent of r if $\lambda \gg \alpha$ (the extinction depth greater than the diffusion length). However if $\alpha \gg \lambda$ the excitons can penetrate the crystal appreciably more than the light, the ratio shown in Eq. (10.4) increasing as r increases. Simpson [13] found that the condition $\lambda \gg \alpha$ satisfied the experimental results for anthracene illuminated in the first absorption band. He has discussed expressions similar to those derived above in more detail.

If the electrodes do not quench excitons, then we have as boundary conditions $(dX/dx)_0 = (dX/dx)_r = 0$, and it follows that

$$X = \alpha c I/[\delta\lambda(\lambda^2-\alpha^2) \sinh \lambda r] \{[\lambda \sinh \lambda r \exp(-\alpha x)]$$
$$+ [\alpha \cosh \lambda x \exp(-\alpha r)] - [\alpha \cosh \lambda(r-x)]\} \quad (10.5)$$

To allow for the reabsorption of the emitted light we must consider the equations governing the motion of the photons. Suppose that the light emitted is of just one wavelength and that there is an equal probability of the photons being emitted with positive or negative velocities (we shall designate these photons as v_1^+ and v_1^-). If α_1 is the absorption coefficient for light of the emitting wavelength, then the equations governing the steady state are as follows:

$$dX/dt = \delta(d^2X/dx^2) - (\beta+\gamma)X + \alpha_1 c (v_1^+ + v_1^-)$$
$$+ \alpha c I \exp(-\alpha x) = 0 \quad (10.6)$$

$$dv_1^+/dt = (\beta X/2) - \alpha_1 c v_1^+ - c(dv_1^+/dx) = 0 \quad (10.7)$$

$$dv_1^-/dt = (\beta X/2) - \alpha_1 c v_1^- + c(dv_1^-/dx) = 0 \quad (10.8)$$

It has been assumed that the photons all have the same velocity c and are not scattered. These equations can be readily solved by the method of Laplace transforms. The solutions for the exciton and photon concentrations have the form

$$X = [\alpha c I(\alpha_1^2-\alpha^2)/\delta(\rho^2-\alpha^2)(\sigma^2-\alpha^2)] [\exp(-\alpha x) + A \cosh \rho x$$
$$+ B \sinh \rho x + C \cosh \sigma x + D \sinh \sigma x] \quad (10.9)$$

$$v_1^+ = (\beta/2c)[\alpha c I(\alpha_1+\alpha)/\delta(\rho^2-\alpha^2)(\sigma^2-\alpha^2)] \{\exp(-\alpha x)$$
$$+ [(A\alpha_1-B\rho)/(\alpha_1^2-\rho^2)] \cosh \rho x$$
$$+ [(B\alpha_1-A\rho)/(\alpha_1^2-\rho^2)] \sinh \rho x + [(C\alpha_1-D\sigma)/(\alpha_1^2-\sigma^2)] \cosh \sigma x$$
$$+ [(D\alpha_1-C\sigma)/(\alpha_1^2-\sigma^2)] \sinh \sigma x\} \quad (10.10)$$

$$v_1^- = (\beta/2c)[\alpha cI(\alpha_1-\alpha)/\delta(\rho^2-\alpha^2)(\sigma^2-\alpha^2)]\{\exp(-\alpha x)$$
$$+ [(A\alpha_1+B\rho)/(\alpha_1{}^2-\rho^2)]\cosh \rho x$$
$$+ [(B\alpha_1+A\rho)/(\alpha_1{}^2-\rho^2)]\sinh \rho x+[(C\alpha_1+D\sigma)/(\alpha_1{}^2-\sigma^2)]\cosh \sigma x$$
$$+ [(D\alpha_1+C\sigma)/(\alpha_1{}^2-\sigma^2)]\sinh \sigma x \tag{10.11}$$

where

$$\begin{matrix}\rho^2\\\sigma^2\end{matrix} = (1/2)\{(\lambda^2+\alpha_1^2) \pm [(\lambda^2+\alpha_1^2)^2-4\alpha_1^2\gamma/\delta]^{1/2}\} \tag{10.12}$$

and the constants $ABCD$ are determined by the boundary conditions, e.g., $X = v_1^+ = 0$, $x = 0$; $X = v_1^- = 0$, $x = r$.

If $(\lambda^2+\alpha_1^2)^2 \gg (4\alpha_1^2\gamma)/\delta$, then σ^2 tends to zero, and the terms in $\cosh \sigma x$ and $\sinh \sigma x$ provide for the penetration of the excitons into the crystal to a much greater depth than that reached by the incident photons.

If the emitted light is of the same wavelength as the incident light, then we have a special case for which the following limits are of interest:

$r\rho \ll 1 \qquad r\sigma \ll 1$
$$X = [I\alpha c/\rho^2-\sigma^2][(\cosh \sigma x-\cosh \rho x) + (\alpha/\rho)\sin \rho x-\alpha/\sigma)\sin \sigma x] \tag{10.13}$$

$r\rho \gg 1 \qquad r\sigma \gg 1$
$$X = \frac{2I\alpha^2 c}{\alpha(\sigma^2-\rho^2) + \sigma(\alpha^2-\rho^2)-\rho(\alpha^2-\sigma^2)}[\exp(-\rho x)-\exp(-\sigma x)]. \tag{10.14}$$

$r\rho \gg 1 \qquad r\sigma \ll 1,$
$$X = \frac{2I\alpha^2 c\{[\rho(1+\alpha r)+r\alpha^2][\cosh \sigma x-\exp(-\rho x)]-[r\rho\sigma^2+\alpha\rho+\alpha^2]\sinh \sigma x/\sigma\}}{\delta\rho(r\rho^2\sigma^2+2\alpha\rho^2+\alpha^2 r\rho^2+2\alpha^3 r\rho+\alpha^4 r)} \tag{10.15}$$

We see that only if both $r\rho$ and $r\sigma$ are greater than unity do we have a rapid exponential fall off of the exciton concentration from the illuminated electrode. The ratio of the rate of exciton transfer to the dark electrode, to the transmitted light, is now

$$\delta X r^1/cv_r{}^+ = \frac{\alpha[\rho\sigma(\cosh \rho r-\cosh \sigma r) + \alpha(\sigma \sinh \rho r-\rho \sinh \sigma r)]}{[\sigma(\rho^2-\alpha^2)\sinh \rho r]-[\rho(\sigma^2-\alpha^2)\sinh \sigma r]} \tag{10.16}$$

If ρr and σr are both much greater than unity, this ratio is independent of r except when $(\lambda^2 - \alpha^2)^2 \gg 4\beta\alpha^2/\delta$. Under these conditions we have, from Eq. (10.11), $\rho^2 = \lambda^2$ and $\sigma^2 = \alpha^2$, and if $\alpha \gg \lambda$, the ratio is a function of r as it is in expression (10.4).

3. The Distribution of Charge Carriers in the Crystal and the Resulting Photoconductivity

As mentioned in Sec. 1, experiments indicate that charge carriers are formed by the dissociation of excitons and that there exist traps for these mobile charges in the crystal. It is possible that the carriers are, in fact, only formed in the first place as a result of the collision of an exciton with one of these trapping centers.

We shall take p and n to be the concentrations of positive and negative carriers in the crystal, with s and t the concentration of traps for positive and negative carriers, respectively. s^+ and t^- will be the concentration of trapped charges. We can now consider the following mechanism of formation, trapping, and destruction of charge carriers:

$$
\left.
\begin{aligned}
X + s &\xrightarrow{K_1} s^+ + n \\
X + t &\xrightarrow{K_2} t^- + p \\
X &\xrightarrow{K_3} p + n
\end{aligned}
\right\} \text{Formation}
$$

$$
\left.
\begin{aligned}
p + s &\underset{h_1}{\overset{g_1}{\rightleftharpoons}} s^+ \\
n + t &\underset{h_2}{\overset{g_2}{\rightleftharpoons}} t^-
\end{aligned}
\right\} \text{Trapping}
$$

$$
\left.
\begin{aligned}
n + s^+ &\xrightarrow{l_1} s \\
p + t^- &\xrightarrow{l_2} t \\
p + n &\xrightarrow{l_3} G
\end{aligned}
\right\} \text{Destruction}
$$

The K's, g's, h's, and l's are rate constants. We have assumed that G, t, and s cannot alone give rise to mobile charges, since the dark current is negligible compared with the photocurrent.

In a steady state the concentration of free and trapped charges and the concentration of traps are given by the equations

$$(K_3 + K_2t)X + h_1s^+ - g_1ps - l_3pn - l_2pt^- - dj^+/dx = o \qquad (10.17)$$

$$(K_3 + K_1s)X + h_2t^- - g_2nt - l_3pn - l_3ns^+ + dj^-/dx = o \qquad (10.18)$$

$$K_1sX + g_1ps - h_1s^+ - l_1ns^+ = o \qquad (10.19)$$

$$K_2tX + g_2nt - h_2t^- - l_2pt^- = o \qquad (10.20)$$

$$s + s^+ = v \qquad (10.21)$$

$$t + t^- = w \qquad (10.22)$$

v and w are constants. j^+ and j^- are the currents of mobile positive and negative charges given by

$$j^+ = \mu^+[\mathscr{E}p - (adp/dx)] \qquad (10.23)$$

$$j^- = \mu^-[\mathscr{E}n + (adn/dx)]$$

ε is the electric field obtained from Poisson's equation

$$d\mathscr{E}/dx = 4\pi q(p - n + s^+ - t^-) \qquad (10.24)$$

and the boundary condition for the observed potential difference across the crystal

$$V = \int_0^r \mathscr{E}\, dx \qquad (10.25)$$

μ^+ and μ^- are the mobilities of the charge carriers, and use has been made of the Einstein relationship between the mobility and diffusion constant of a charge carrier [14]

$$\delta = a\mu \qquad a = kT/q \qquad (10.26)$$

where q is the electronic charge, k Boltzmann's constant, and T the absolute temperature.)

From Eqs. (10.17) to (10.22) we can eliminate the variables s, t, s^+, and t^- and obtain equations in terms of the concentration of mobile charges only.

$$(K_3 X - l_3 pn) - v[(l_1 g_1 pn - h_1 K_1 X)/(K_1 X + g_1 p + l_1 n + h_1)]$$
$$- w[(l_2 g_2 pn - h_2 K_2 X)/(K_2 X + g_2 n + l_2 p + h_2)] - (dj^+/dx) = 0$$

$$(10.27)$$

and $dj^+/dx = -dj^-/dx$. The conservation law div $j = 0$ is therefore satisfied where j, the measured current, is given by $j = q(j^+ + j^-)$. Poisson's equation (10.24) likewise becomes

$$d\mathcal{E}/dx = 4\pi q \{p - n + [v(K_1 X + g_1 p)/K_1 X + g_1 p + l_1 n + h_1]$$
$$- [w(K_2 X + g_2 n)/K_2 X + g_2 n + l_2 p + h_2]$$

$$(10.28)$$

Equation (10.27), together with (10.25) and (10.28), determine the photocurrent as a function of the exciton concentration, the potential difference across the crystal, the mobilities of the charge carriers, and the rate constants of the formation trapping and destruction processes. Unfortunately, Eq. (10.27) is nonlinear, and one cannot therefore obtain an exact algebraic solution. The problem is usually tacked by making approximations to this equation, which converts it into a linear form. For example, it has been often assumed that the distribution of the mobile charges is governed by the equation

$$dj^+/dx = -dj^-/dx = I_x - (p/\tau^+) \qquad (10.29)$$

where Ix is some formation process and τ^+ is the lifetime of the positive carriers. Although this equation possesses the advantages of simplicity, together with the satisfaction of the conservation equation (div $j = 0$), it suggests that the rate of formation of the two carriers is the same, and the rate of trapping of negative carriers depends not on the concentration of negative carriers but on the concentration of positive carriers. The lack of symmetry in this equation is rather unsatisfactory. We can see from Eq. (10.27) that for Eq. (10.29) to represent the state of the system it is necessary to put $l_3 = 0$, $l_1 g_1 pn \gg h_1 K_1 X$, $l_2 g_2 pn \gg h_2 K_2 X$, $l_1 n \gg K_1 X + g_1 p + h_1$, and $g_2 n \gg K_2 X + l_2 p + h_2$. These conditions are rather restrictive. We shall look at the equations in more general terms.

From Eq. (10.27) and (10.28), we see that as the light intensity tends to zero, we have

$$dj^+\,dx = KX \qquad \text{and} \qquad dj^-/dx = -KX \qquad (10.30)$$

where $K = vK_1 + wK_2 + K_3$. Also $\mathscr{E} = V/r$, hence

$$j^+ = \mu^+[(V/r)p - a(dp/dx)]$$
$$j^- = \mu^-[(V/r)n + a(dn/dx)] \qquad (10.31)$$

From these equations, knowing X and the boundary conditions for the charge carriers, we can deduce p and n and hence j. For boundary conditions we shall assume that $p = n = 0$ when $x = o$ or $x = r$. This amounts to assuming that the electrodes are infinitely conducting, so that the charge carriers are immediately discharged on touching the electrodes. The solution for the case when the exciton concentration is given simply by

$$X = \alpha I \exp(-\alpha x)$$

is as follows:

$$p = \{KI/a\mu^+[(V/ar)+\alpha]\}\{[\exp(V/a)-1]\exp(-\alpha x)+[1-\exp-(\alpha x)]$$
$$\exp(Vx/ar+[\exp(-\alpha r)-\exp(V/a)]\}[1-\exp(V/a)]^{-1} \qquad (10.32)$$

$$n = \{KI/a\mu^-[(V/ar)-\alpha]\}\{[1-\exp(-V/a)]\exp(-\alpha x)$$
$$+ [\exp(-\alpha r)-1]\exp(-Vx/ar)+[\exp(-V/a)-\exp(-\alpha r)]\}$$
$$[1-\exp(-V/a)]^{-1} \qquad (10.33)$$

$$j = \{qV^2KI[1-\exp(-ar)]\}/(V^2-a^2\alpha^2 r^2)$$
$$[\coth V/2a-(a\alpha r/V)\coth(\alpha r/2)] \qquad (10.34)$$

It is seen that j is an odd function of V, that is, there is no rectifying effect. The trapping of carriers has no real effect on the current, the carrier concentration being limited solely by the rate of migration to the electrodes. The concentration of carriers is seen to be inversely proportional to their mobilities, hence it follows that the current is independent of the carrier mobilities.

If we use expression (10.2) for the exciton concentration, the current has the form

$$j = [qcKI/\delta(\lambda^2-\alpha^2)][1-\exp(-\alpha r)]\{(V^2/V^2-a^2\alpha^2 r^2)$$
$$[\coth(V/2a)-(a\alpha r/V)\coth(\alpha r/2)]$$
$$- (\alpha/\lambda)\tanh(\lambda r/2)\coth(\alpha r/2)(V^2/V^2-a^2\lambda^2 r^2)$$
$$[\coth(V/2a)-(a\lambda r/V)\coth(\lambda r/2)]\}. \qquad (10.35)$$

To see how this expression behaves as a function of the applied potential, we consider the expression

$$(x^2/x^2 - y^2)(\coth x - (y/x)\coth y) \tag{10.36}$$

When $x \ll y$, it behaves as $x/y \coth y$. When $x = y$, it becomes

$$1/2[\coth y - y \operatorname{cosech}^2 y]$$

and when $x \gg y$, it tends to $\coth x - 1/x$ if $y \ll 1$, and $\coth x$ if $y \gg 1$. We see that the function is linear in x only if $x \ll y$; or if $y \ll 1$, only if $x \ll \pi$, since

$$\coth x - 1/x = 1/x \sum_n \{[-1^{n-1} 2^{2n} B_{2n-1} x^{2n}]/[2n]!\} \qquad x^2 < \pi$$

where the B's are Bernoulli numbers.

If $\lambda r > \alpha r > 1$, as usually appears to be the case, expression (10.35) behaves in the following way: where $V/a \ll \alpha r$,

$$j = (qcKI/\delta r\alpha\lambda^2)[1 - \exp(-\alpha r)] \coth(\alpha r/2)(V/a) \tag{10.37}$$

$\alpha r \ll V/a \ll \lambda r$

$$j = \{qcKI[1 - \exp(-\alpha r)]/\delta(\lambda^2 - \alpha^2)\}$$
$$[\coth(V/2a) - (\alpha V/ar\lambda^2)\coth(ar/2)] \tag{10.38}$$

$V/a \gg \lambda r$

$$j = \{qckI[1 - \exp(-\alpha r)]/\delta(\lambda^2 - \alpha^2)\}$$
$$[1 - (\alpha/\lambda)\tanh(\lambda r/2)\coth(\alpha r/2)]\coth(V/2a) \tag{10.39}$$

It is seen that we only observe an ohmic current when V/a is smaller than both αr and λr. The current reaches a saturation value as V tends to infinity.

At this point we must look at the experimental results. Kommandeur and Schneider [15] have studied the bulk photocurrent of anthracene (using a guard ring to remove surface currents) induced by monochromatic light, as a function of the intensity and wavelength of the light and the strength of the applied field. If anthracene is illuminated with light of wavelength greater than 4,350 A (the first absorption band has a maximum at 3,940 A), the photocurrent is found to be proportional to the light intensity, and the applied voltage (at least up to the measured limit of about 4,000 volts). At these wavelengths the extinction coefficient is too small to be measured experimentally, there being a relatively large amount of scattered and reflected light. However, for crystals 1 mm thick it is probably safe to say that $\alpha r < 1$. At 300°C the Einstein constant a has the value of 0.026 volt; hence in the experiments considered the current is found to be ohmic up to a value $V/a \sim 1.6 \times 10^5$. Our expression (10.36) for the current does not behave according to these results, so we must examine Eq. (10.27) again.

If h_1 and h_2 are zero in Eq. (10.27), we can still obtain a current that is of the first order in the light intensity, providing that the recombination term $l_3 pn$ can be neglected and that the electrostatic field $\mathscr{E}$ is relatively unaffected by the presence of free and trapped charges in the crystal. We note from (10.28) that there can be a contribution to the field gradient that is independent of the light intensity if h_1 or h_2 are zero, but this will probably make only a small contribution to the field, compared with its dark value $\mathscr{E} = V/r$. With these conditions, however, we still do not have a linear differential equation, unless some of the formation, trapping, or destruction processes are unimportant. The most general equation for which there is an explicit algebraic solution can be written as

$$K_3 X - (a\eta^2/2)(\mu^+ p + \mu^- n) - (a\zeta^2/2)(\mu^+ p - \mu^- n) - dj^+/dx = 0 \quad (10.40)$$

where η and ζ are constants. For example, if $K_1 = K_2 = 0$, $g_1 p > l_1 n$, and $g_2 n > l_2 p$ we have

$$\eta^2 = (w l_2 \mu^- + v l_1 \mu^+)/a \mu^+ \mu^-$$
$$\zeta^2 = (w l_2 \mu^- + v l_1 \mu^+)/a \mu^+ \mu^-$$

Combining this equation with div $j = 0$ gives

$$2K_3 X - a\eta^2(\mu^+ p + \mu^- n) - a\zeta^2(\mu^+ p - \mu^- n) - (\mu^+ p - \mu^- n)(d\mathscr{E}/dx)^0$$
$$- (V/r)(d/dx)(\mu^+ p - \mu^- n) + a(d^2/dx^2)(\mu^+ p + \mu^- n) = 0 \quad (10.41)$$

and

$$(V/r)(d/dx)(\mu^+ p + \mu^- n) = a\ (d^2/dx^2)(\mu^+ p - \mu^- n) \quad (10.42)$$

$(d\mathscr{E}/dx)^0$ is the contribution to $d\mathscr{E}/dx$ that is independent of the light intensity.

Thus in our example

$$(d\mathscr{E}/dx)^0 = 4\pi q(v-w) \qquad (10.43)$$

In order to obtain an ohmic current, it is necessary that $\mu^+p+\mu^-n$ be independent of the voltage and that $\mu^+p-\mu^-n$ be proportional to the voltage. It follows from (10.40) that $\mu^+p+\mu^-n$ must be a solution of

$$(D^2-\eta^2)(\mu^+p+\mu^-n) = -2K_3X/a \qquad (10.44)$$

for this condition to be satisfied. With $X = \alpha I \exp(-\alpha x)$ this has the solution

$$(\mu^+p+\mu^-n) = [2K_3\alpha I/a(\eta^2-\alpha^2)\,\sinh\,\eta r]\{[\sinh\,\eta r\,\exp(-\alpha x)]$$
$$- [\exp(-\alpha r)\,\sinh\,\eta x]-[\sinh\,\eta(r-x)]\} \qquad (10.45)$$

for the boundary conditions $n_o = p_o = n_r = p_r = o$. By integrating the expression for the current with these boundary conditions, we have

$$j = (qV/r)\int_o^r (\mu^+p+\mu^-n)\,dx \qquad (10.46)$$

from which

$$j = \{2K_3qIV[1-\exp(-\alpha r)]/ar^2(\eta^2-\alpha^2)\}$$
$$[1-(\alpha/\eta)\,\coth\,(\alpha r/2)\,\tanh\,(\eta r/2)] \qquad (10.47)$$

A similar type of expression is obtained if we use Eq. (10.2) to describe the exciton concentration. If αr and ηr are both greater than unity, expression (10.47) becomes

$$j = 2K_3q[1-\exp(-\alpha r)]IV/ar^2(\eta+\alpha) \qquad (10.48)$$

It can be shown that the conditions for expression (10.46) to be valid are that $V/a \ll \eta r$, and that $(\mu^+p+\mu^-n) \gg (\mu^+p-\mu^-n)$. The latter condition suggests that the current of positive and negative carriers must be approximately equal in order to observe an IV current. It can also be shown that this condition is necessary for the observation of an IV current even when the differential equations are nonlinear.

From the two expressions (10.34) and (10.47) it would appear that for low light intensities an ohmic current is the exception rather than the rule. Before proceeding further it may be wise to reconsider our boundary conditions. To do this we consider a simpler example. Suppose we make K_1, K_3, and h_2 zero in our basic equations. This has the result that no free negative carriers are formed. It follows that the current is given by

$$j = qj^+ = q\mu^+[\mathscr{E}p - a(dp/dx)] \tag{10.49}$$

with $dj^+/dx = 0$. At low light intensities and high voltages we can assume that the charge distribution makes no appreciable effect on the electric field, so that $\mathscr{E} = V/r$. Integrating Eq. (10.30) now gives

$$p = \{[p_r - p_o \exp (V/a)] + (p_o - p_r) \exp (Vx/ar)\}$$
$$[1 - \exp (V/a)] - 1 \tag{10.50}$$

with

$$j = (q\mu^+V/r)\{[p_r - p_o \exp (V/a)]/[1 - \exp (V/a)]\} \tag{10.51}$$

Since in practice we always have $V/a \gg 1$, this means that for positive V

$$j = (q\mu^+V/r)p_o \tag{10.52}$$

We see that no current flows unless there is a concentration of positive carriers at the positive electrode boundary. In addition, if positive carriers are being discharged at a given rate at the negative electrode, then positive carriers must be entering at the same rate at the positive electrode. Thus our assumptions that the carriers are immediately discharged on touching an electrode and that there is no injection of carriers from the electrodes are inconsistent with the observation of a current when only the positive carriers are mobile.

It can be shown that if we allow either for injection of carriers at the electrodes from which the carriers are moving or for inefficient quenching at the electrodes, then for positive V we add a term for the current to the expression (10.34) of the form

$$j' = qV/r\{\mu^+ p_0 \exp (V/a)[\exp (V/a)-1]^{-1}$$
$$+ \mu^- n_r[1-\exp(-V/a)]^{-1}\} \quad (10.53)$$

or for large V

$$j' = qV/r(\mu^+ p_0 + \mu^- n_r) \quad (10.54)$$

This expression is obtained while retaining the boundary conditions $p_r = n_o = o$. It may be that (10.54) will give an ohmic contribution to the current. Unfortunately we do not know how the rate of injection of carriers at the electrodes or the efficiency of quenching at the electrodes varies with the applied field so the exact behavior of Eq. (10.54) is difficult to predict.

We can only make a few general remarks about the form of the current when there is a high light intensity. On increasing the light intensity there will come a point, at any rate in the bulk of the crystal, where the concentration of charge carriers is limited by the destruction processes. Thus in an intrinsic conductor with low field strength (no traps) the concentrations of positive and negative carriers would both be approximately equal to $(K_3 X/l_3)^{1/2}$ and hence proportional to the square root of the light intensity. We can see from Eq. (10.27) that at high light intensities the trapping terms do, in fact, become unimportant compared with the mutual destruction of free carriers. For intermediate light intensities we can expect that the concentration of carriers can vary anywhere between a linear and a square-root dependence on the light intensity. Since there is always a contribution to the field that is independent of the light intensity, we expect the current to behave in the same way, and this has been, in fact, observed.[15]

As we increase the potential difference across the crystal, the proportion of charge carriers that are destroyed at the electrodes is increased, and we expect the current to move closer to the linear dependence on the light intensity. Mathematically this is obtained by increasing the terms that are linear in the carrier concentration in Eq. (10.27). This behavior has also been observed experimentally.[15]

For a given incident light intensity, as the absorption coefficient of the crystal increases, the concentration of excitons first increases generally in the crystal and then builds up close to the illuminated electrode. Thus for anthracene, light of 3,900 A, which falls into the first absorption band, has an extinction depth of only 50 microns. It follows that as we increase the absorption coefficient, the current tends more toward the $j \propto I^{0.5}$ behavior. When α tends to infinity, nearly all the carriers are immediately discharged at the illuminated electrode, so that the photocurrent will tend to zero. The anthracene photocurrent appears to reach a maximum for $ar \sim 10^3$, falling off for larger and smaller values.

In the limit when α and V are very large, the photocurrent can be considered to arise essentially from an injection of charges from the illuminated electrode, which travel through the crystal and are perhaps trapped or discharged on the way. Thus if the illuminated electrode is positive, we essentially have no free negative carriers in the crystal, and the current is given by j^+ only. We have obtained an expression (10.52) for j^+ in the case where $\mathscr{E} = V/r$. If the illuminated electrode is negative, the current is due to the negative carriers only, and we should have

$$j = q\mu^- V n_0/r \qquad (10.55)$$

as the expression corresponding to Eq. (10.52). Both currents are ohmic, and if $n_0 = p_0$, they are in the ratio of the carrier mobilities. At high light intensities the approximation $\mathscr{E} = V/r$ is probably not good enough. The diffusion of the charges through the crystal will build up a back electromative force that will reduce the value of the current. However, for a given light intensity (or rate of injection of carriers at the illuminated electrode), as V is increased there will come a time when the field due to the charge distribution becomes negligible compared with V/r, and at this stage a current varying linearly with V should be obtained. This is again observed experimentally; for low V the current varies as V^2, but this tails off until an essentially linear behavior is observed.[15]

When α is large, a rectifying effect is observed, the current with the illuminated electrode positive being greater than that with the illuminated electrode negative. This suggests that

$\mu^+ > \mu^-$, the conclusion reached from experiments using blocked electrodes.[1] It must be emphasized however, that a rectifying effect may be observed through reasons other than that of different carrier mobilities. For example, if only free positive carriers are formed, there is a rectifying effect if the illuminated electrode injects positive carriers at a different rate to that of the non-illuminated electrode. Furthermore, for there to be no rectifying effect it is necessary that $\mathscr{E}(\mu^+p+\mu^-n)$ and $\mu^+p-\mu^-n$ be odd functions of the potential. If $\mathscr{E} = V/r$ and $\mu^+ = \mu^-$, then $p+n$ must be an odd function of V and $p-n$ an even function of V. It can be seen from Eq. (10.40) that this is not generally so if the rates of production, trapping, and destruction of the two carriers are not equal.

4. Discussion and Summary

Organic photoconductors differ from their inorganic counterparts in their low quantum efficiency. Any influences that reduce the lifetime of the excitons reduce the photocurrent. The effect on the exciton lifetime swamps any effect on the rate of formation or trapping of the charge carriers. It is thus difficult to obtain information about the properties of the charge carriers by, for example, adding known impurities to the crystal, since all we see is the change in the exciton lifetime. It is particularly interesting that neutron irradiation lowers the photocurrent but increases the dark current, and it would be valuable to know if tetracene or acridine added to anthracene produced the same result.

In Sec. 2 we discussed the motion of the excitons in the crystal, considering the effect of a resonance exchange mechanism and that of the emission and reabsorption of a photon. The latter may have an important effect on the photocurrent by giving rise to a small concentration of excitons right through the crystal, even though the incident light may be absorbed in the first few molecular layers.

In Sec. 3 we discussed the equations governing the motion of the charge carriers in the crystal when they are subjected to trapping and destruction. The equations are nonlinear and cannot generally be solved. It was shown, however, that for very low light intensities the trapping and destruction processes become unimportant. The nature of the solution of the equations in this case depends on the boundary conditions adopted. If it is assumed that the carriers are immediately discharged on touching an electrode, then we only observe an ohmic current in general if $V/a \ll \alpha r$. The current reaches a limiting value, which depends on the rate of production of charge carriers, at higher voltages. If the regeneration of trapped charges is an unlikely process, then we can also obtain a current that is of the first order in the light intensity, providing that the recombination of free charges can be ignored and that the electric field is not appreciably changed by the presence of the charges in the crystal. A solution was considered for this case, using the most general linear equation governing the motion of the charges. Conditions necessary for the observation of an ohmic current were obtained, one of which was that the currents of positive and negative carriers must be approximately equal. The form for this ohmic current was given.

The situation in which only free positive carriers are formed was considered, and it was shown that no steady-state current can in fact be obtained in this case unless there is injection of carriers at the positive electrode. The effect of relaxing our boundary conditions in the earlier equations was shown to have the effect of adding a term, which may be ohmic, to the expressions for the current that have been derived.

The general behavior of the current in the limit of high light intensities when the carrier concentration is limited by the recombination process was considered. This same limit is reached by having a large absorption coefficient for the crystal when the light is initially absorbed in the first few molecular layers. Under these conditions the carriers may probably be considered as having been injected from the illuminated electrode. A rectifying effect is usually associated with a difference in mobility of the two carriers, and for anthracene it appears that $\mu^+ > \mu^-$. However, it was shown that we can have a rectifying effect, even if $\mu^+ = \mu^-$, when the rates of formation and trapping of the two carriers are different.

In this chapter we have not presented an exhaustive examination of the equations governing the motion of the charge carriers. A much fuller treatment, but differing in some aspects concerning the problem, has been given by Rittner,[10] who emphasizes inorganic photoconductors.

Acknowledgement. The author would like to thank Dr. J. A. Pople for stimulating discussions an this topic.

References

1. D. M. J. Compton, W. G. Schneider, and T. C. Waddington, *J. Chem. Phys.* **28**, 741 (1958).
2. D. M. J. Compton, W. G. Schneider, and T. C. Waddington, *J. Chem. Phys.* **27**, 160 (1957).
3. Zinzer, *Z. Naturforsch.* **11a**, 306 (1956).
4. J. Kommandeur, Ph.D. thesis, University of Amsterdam (1958).
5. Beer and H. C. Longuet-Higgins, *J. Chem. Phys.* **23**, 1390 (1955).
6. L. E. Lyons and G. C. Morris, *J. Chem. Soc.* **1957**, 3648, 3661.
7. D. C. Northrop and O. Simpson, *Proc. Roy. Soc. (London)* **A244**, 377 (1958).
8. F. J. Bryant, A. Bree, P. E. Fielding, and W. G. Schneider, *Discussions Faraday Soc.* **28**, 48 (1959).
9. T. S. Moss, Pincherle, and Woodward, *Proc. Phys. Soc. (London)* **66B**, 743 (1953).
10. Rittner, "Photoconductivity Conference," John Wiley & Sons, Inc., New York (1956).
11. T. S. Moss, "Optical Properties of Semiconductors," Butterworth & Co. (Publishers), Ltd., London (1959).
12. Grosvalet, *Ann. Radioelec.* **9**, 360 (1954).
13. O. Simpson, *Proc. Roy. Soc. (London)* **A238**, 402 (1957).
14. A. Einstein, *Ann. Physik* **17**, 549 (1905).
15. C. J. Kommandeur and W. G. Schneider, *J. Chem. Phys.* **28**, 582 (1958).

Molecular-Orbital Theory and Crystals

J. A. Pople

1. Introduction

Molecular-orbital theory provides a description of electronic structure in terms of delocalized orbital functions spread throughout a molecule, the electrons in different orbitals moving independently except for the restrictions imposed on those of similar spin by the antisymmetry condition (Pauli principle). Although a description of this sort may not be always suitable for discussing localized parts of a molecule (such as particular bonds), it is particularly appropriate for describing processes such as ionization (where an electron is removed leaving a hole distributed over the molecule) and electronic excitation (where one delocalized orbital is replaced by another). In discussing excited states of molecular crystals, we are faced with similar processes on a larger scale, where electrons may move in extended paths covering macroscopic regions. Under certain circumstances, it is appropriate to extend the concept of molecular orbitals to crystal orbitals covering the whole crystal. However, such a method may become unsuitable for processes that retain some localized character on a molecular scale, and there are advantages in treating the system as a set of weakly interacting molecular units.

2. General Features of Molecular-Orbital Theory

In its simplest form, molecular-orbital theory is based on the solution of the Schrödinger equation

$$H\psi = -1/2\nabla^2\psi + V\psi = E\psi \qquad (11.1)$$

for a single electron in a fixed potential field V. This equation has a series of solutions $\psi_1, \psi_2, \ldots$ with energies $E_1, E_2, \ldots$, and the ground-state configuration of the molecule is described by allocating two electrons to each of the orbitals of lowest energy. Ionization then corresponds to the removal of an electron from an occupied molecular orbital ψ_i (requiring energy E_i), and excitation corresponds to taking an electron from an occupied orbital ψ_i and placing it in an unoccupied orbital ψ_j (requiring energy E_j-E_i).

In practice, explicit solution of the Schrödinger equation is not feasible, and the theory is modified by choosing approximate molecular orbitals that are linear combinations of atomic orbitals (LCAO),

$$\psi_i = \sum_\mu C_{i\mu}\phi_\mu \qquad (11.2)$$

The optimum values of the coefficients (in the sense of giving the best approximation to the energy) are then solutions of the linear equations.

$$\sum_\nu H_{\mu\nu}C_{i\nu} = E_i \sum_\nu S_{\mu\nu}C_{i\nu} \qquad (11.3)$$

where the matrix elements $H_{\mu\nu}$ and $S_{\mu\nu}$ are given by

$$H_{\mu\nu} = \int \phi_\mu^* H\phi_\nu d\tau$$
$$S_{\mu\nu} = \int \phi_\mu^* \phi_\nu d\tau \qquad (11.4)$$

These equations are only soluble if the energy E_i satisfies the determinantal equation

$$|H_{\mu\nu}-ES_{\mu\nu}| = 0 \qquad (11.5)$$

Since the quantities $H_{\mu\nu}$ and $S_{\mu\nu}$ are properties of a localized part of the molecule and can be taken from one molecule to another in homologous series, this form of theory is particularly suitable for semiempirical development and the correlation of properties of related molecules.

Although the one-electron LCAO theory has the merit of great simplicity, it has a number of inherent drawbacks that prevent it from giving an adequate description of a number of physical properties involving the interaction of electrons. In particular, it oversimplifies the description of many excited states of molecules.

The basic limitation lies in the assumption that the motion of all electrons can be regarded as determined by a single potential energy function V. In fact, the coulomb repulsion between electrons must mean that the energy of an electron in a particular orbital must depend on the number of electrons in other orbitals. Without taking this properly into account, it is clearly impossible to obtain an adequate description of the relation between ionization potentials and electron affinities, for example. Also, the difficulty in giving a precise meaning to the potential V rules out a priori calculations, which could be used to check empirical parameters in simple cases.

To overcome these difficulties, a more refined form of molecular orbital theory has been developed,[1] using the complete many-electron Hamiltonian

$$\mathcal{H} = -1/2 \sum_i \nabla_i^2 + \sum_i V_i + \sum_{i<j} \frac{1}{r_{ij}} \qquad (11.6)$$

where V_i is now the potential energy of electron i in the field of the bare nuclei. If the molecule is adequately described as a closed-shell ground state (i.e., two electrons in each of the lowest molecular orbitals) a *many-electron molecular-orbital wave function* is written

$$\Psi_0 = \mathcal{A}\{[\psi_1(1)\alpha(1)][\psi_1(2)\beta(2)][\psi_2(3)\alpha(3)][\psi_2(4)\beta(4)] \ldots\} \quad (11.7)$$

where α and β are spin functions and $\mathcal{A}$ is the antisymmetrizing operator. A correct set of molecular orbitals is then a set of one-electron functions $\psi_1, \psi_2, \ldots$, which minimize the total energy integral $\int \psi_0^* \mathcal{H} \psi_0 \, d\tau$. This condition leads to a set of coupled differential equations for the functions $\psi_1, \psi_2, \ldots$, usually known as the "self-consistent" molecular-orbital equations.

The self-consistent theory can also be developed in LCAO form[2] if the molecular orbitals are expressed in the form of Eq. (11.2) and the coefficients $C_{i\mu}$ varied to minimize the total energy. This gives rise to a set of equations.

$$\sum_\nu (F_{\mu\nu} - E S_{\mu\nu}) C_{i\nu} = 0 \qquad (11.8)$$

where the $F_{\mu\nu}$ themselves are quadratic functions of the $C_{i\nu}$.

This means that the equations are cubic rather than linear and must be solved by iteration. This method has been used to determine LCAO molecular orbitals for a number of simple molecules.

The improved molecular-orbital theory in LCAO form can also be applied to excited states if the number of molecular orbitals given by Eq. (11.8) is greater than the number occupied. If an electron is taken from an occupied molecular orbital ψ_i and placed in an unoccupied one ψ_j, appropriate excited-state functions are

$$\Psi_{i \to j} = \{\mathscr{A}[(\psi_1\alpha)(\psi_1\beta) \cdots (\psi_j\alpha)(\psi_i\beta) \cdots] \\ \pm \mathscr{A}[(\psi_1\alpha)(\psi_1\beta) \cdots (\psi_i\alpha)(\psi_j\beta) \cdots]\}/k \qquad (11.9)$$

The positive sign gives the wave function for the excited singlet state corresponding to this configuration, while the negative sign gives one component of the triplet. Estimates of the energies of these excited states are then given by the matrix elements

$$({}^1\Psi_{i \to j} | \mathscr{H} | {}^1\Psi_{i \to j}) \qquad \text{and} \qquad ({}^3\Psi_{i \to j} | \mathscr{H} | {}^3\Psi_{i \to j})$$

The two energies will generally be different giving a singlet triplet separation. This is not properly described by the simple theory according to which both transitions from the ground state require energy $E_j - E_i$.

It may happen that the energies of two excited configurational functions such as ${}^1\Psi_{i \to j}$ and ${}^1\Psi_{k \to l}$ are close together. Under these circumstances the two configurations may interact, so that the best wave functions are linear combinations of the form

$$\Psi = a^1\Psi_{i \to j} + b^1\Psi_{k \to l} \qquad (11.10)$$

The coefficients a and b can be determined by the variation principle again. This effect, which is of considerable importance in many excited states of molecules, is known as "configuration interaction". In Sec. 4 we shall see that it is important in the description of excited states of molecular crystals.

3. Molecular-Orbital Theories of Conjugated Hydrocarbons

Since the study of conjugated hydrocarbons has proved one of the most successful applications of molecular-orbital theory and since the corresponding molecular crystals are of interest to this meeting, we shall give a brief description of some of the work in this field.

The molecular-orbital theory of planar molecules can be split into two parts, dealing with orbitals that are symmetric or anti-symmetric in the molecular plane. Since many of the most important electronic properties of conjugated hydrocarbons depend on the π-electrons, the theory is usually developed for these alone, treating the σ electrons as a core providing an average field. The theory then becomes particularly simple, as there is only one relevant atomic orbital per carbon atom $(2p\pi)$ and the number of independent matrix elements to be chosen as empirical parameters is small.

The one-electron molecular-orbital theory was first applied to conjugated hydrocarbons by Hückel,[3] and it has since been considered in great detail by many other authors. In the simplest form, the diagonal matrix elements $H_{\mu\mu}$ are all put equal to α, the off-diagonal elements $H_{\mu\nu}$ to a second constant β if ϕ_μ and ϕ_ν are neighbours and $S_{\mu\nu}$ is neglected unless $\mu = \nu$. The determinantal equation for benzene, for example, takes the simple form

$$
\begin{vmatrix}
\alpha-E & \beta & 0 & 0 & 0 & \beta \\
\beta & \alpha-E & \beta & 0 & 0 & 0 \\
0 & \beta & \alpha-E & \beta & 0 & 0 \\
0 & 0 & \beta & \alpha-E & \beta & 0 \\
0 & 0 & 0 & \beta & \alpha-E & \beta \\
\beta & 0 & 0 & 0 & \beta & \alpha-E
\end{vmatrix} = 0 \tag{11.11}
$$

which is easily shown to have solutions $E = \alpha \pm 2\beta, \, \alpha \pm \beta, \, \alpha \pm \beta$. Similar determinantal equations are easily constructed for other conjugated hydrocarbons, such as naphthalene, anthracene, etc.

A number of general theorems can be proved for alternant hydrocarbons (those containing no odd-numbered rings).[4,5] The carbon atoms in such a molecule can be divided into two classes (starred and unstarred), such that every number of one class is bonded only to members of the other. Thus for naphthalene

we have

The molecular orbitals of such hydrocarbons can be associated in pairs[4] with energies equally above and below the value α. In the ground state of the molecule, the lower of these will be occupied by two electrons, and the upper will be empty. The coefficients $C_{i\mu}$ of the upper orbital can be obtained by taking those for the lower orbital and changing the sign on the starred atoms.

From these theorems about paired orbitals in alternant molecules it can be shown quite easily that the π-electron charge density defined as

$$q_\mu = 2 \sum_i^{occ} C_{i\mu}^2 \qquad (11.12)$$

(the sum being over occupied orbitals) is equal to unity for all μ. This implies a uniform charge density, which is born out by the absence of dipole moments in molecules such as phenanthrene. In nonalternant molecules such as azulene, however, the theorem no longer holds and considerable dipole moments are found.

Although the one-electron theory is successful in describing some of the ground-state properties, it is less satisfactory when applied to the processes of ionization and electron excitation, which are of particular interest in molecular crystals. The proper description of these needs an adequate treatment of the coulomb interaction between the π electrons, even if it is possible to treat σ electrons as an effective core. A number of completely nonempirical calculations on the πelectron structure have been carried out,[6,7] but they lead to many difficult integrals and can only be applied to the simplest systems. A compromise level of approximation retaining the principal effects of electron interaction was proposed by Pariser and Parr[8] and applied to the self-consistent molecular orbital Eq. (11.8) by the author [9] The approximations used are:

a. Neglect of all electron-repulsion integrals except those of the form

$$\gamma_{\mu\nu} = \int\int \phi_\mu^2(1)(1/r_{12})\,\phi_\nu^2(2)\,d\tau_1\,d\tau_2 \qquad (11.13)$$

which allows for the repulsion between electrons in atomic orbitals ϕ_μ and ϕ_ν. γ_{11} is chosen to be equal to the difference between the ionization potential and electron affinity of the carbon atom in the appropriate valence state.

b. Suppose that the interaction of an electron in ϕ_μ with the σ core of another atom ν can also be represented by $\gamma_{\mu\nu}$, penetration effects being neglected.

With these approximations it can be shown that the theorems about paired orbitals and charge densities in alternant molecules still hold at this higher level of approximation. The application to ionization potentials and electron affinities is modified, however, and the detailed treatment of electron interaction enables good predictions of these quantities to be made from parameters, which also give good fit for spectroscopic data.[10]

The allowance for the effects of electron repulsion and configuration interaction is the key to understanding the excited electronic states of conjugated hydrocarbons,[11,12] which had proved difficult in terms of the simpler theory. For alternant molecules, the excited states may be understood in terms of the highest two occupied orbitals and the lowest unoccupied pair

In the ground state, there are two electrons in both ψ_1 and ψ_2. According to the simple theory, the lowest electronic excited state would correspond to the excitation of a single electron from ψ_2 to ψ_3. The next state would correspond either to the excitation $\psi_1 \rightarrow \psi_3$ or $\psi_2 \rightarrow \psi_4$. Now because of the pairing properties of the orbitals, these two energies are equal, so that two degenerate states are predicted. If we use the self-consistent theory,[13] we get a similar distribution of orbitals and can set up excited-configuration wave functions $\Psi_{2\to3}$, $\Psi_{2\to4}$, $\Psi_{1\to3}$ either as singlets or triplets. The degeneracy between the energies or the latter two persists, however. But if we now allow for the interaction between the two configurations $1 \to 3$ and $2 \to 4$, we find that the energies are split, and the best wave functions are

$$\Psi_{1\to3} \pm \Psi_{2\to4} \qquad (11.14)$$

The splitting may be large enough to bring the lower of the two states below that corresponding to the transition $2 \to 3$. Another fact that follows from the pairing property of the orbitals is that the transition moments from the ground state to $^1\Psi_{1\to3}$ and $^1\Psi_{2\to4}$ are equal, so that if excited states have wave functions shown in Eq. (11.14), we only have a weakly allowed transition from the ground state. It turns out that this is the lower of the two. The excited state $2 \to 3$ is often referred to as the p state and the other pair as α (lower-energy) and β states. The general arrangement of singlet and triplet states is then roughly as illustrated in Fig. 11.1 Detailed calculations on this basis [13,14] using the Pariser-Parr approximations for integrals have given very satisfactory agreement with experimental data.

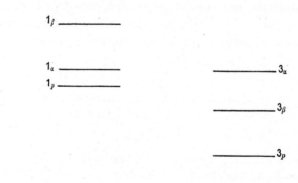

Fig. 11.1. Energies of excited states of conjugated hydrocarbons.

4. Molecular-Orbital Theory and Crystals

If we wish to extend the methods of molecular-orbital theory to molecular crystals, there are two ways of proceeding. We may either allow the individual orbitals to extend over many molecules, so that they become crystal orbitals or Bloch orbitals, or we may restrict the concept of molecular orbitals to individual molecules and try to build up wave functions for the crystal from the wave functions of molecular states corresponding to the neutral molecule and its ionic forms. If sufficient account is taken of configuration interaction, such descriptions become equivalent, but at a lower level of approximation, they may be quite different.

The concept of electrons occupying crystal orbitals extending over a wide region is clearly an appropriate one for describing conduction states where an electron is given sufficient energy to detach itself from its parent molecule completely. We can set up LCAO forms for crystals using the translational symmetry of the lattice. If $\phi_\mu(\mathbf{R})$ is the μth atomic orbital in the unit cell with origin at $\mathbf{R}$, the crystal orbital may be written

$$\psi_i(\mathbf{k}) = \sum_{\mu, \mathbf{R}} [\exp(i\mathbf{k}\mathbf{R})] C_{i\mu}(\mathbf{k}) \phi_\mu(\mathbf{R}) \qquad (11.15)$$

where $\mathbf{k}$ is the appropriate wave vector. If a suitable smoothed potential V is assumed in the independent-electron theory, the variational method can be applied to determine the coefficients $C_{i\mu}(\mathbf{k})$ and the corresponding energies $E_i(\mathbf{k})$. The effect of interaction between the atomic orbitals of different molecules will be to broaden out each energy level i into a band (for simplicity we shall assume one molecule per unit cell). Since the interaction between electrons on different molecules is generally less than that within molecules, the broadening will not cause much overlapping, and there will still be a considerable gap between the occupied and unoccupied orbitals.

The principal drawback to this approach when applied to excited states is that, being based on an independent-electron model, it necessarily neglects any interaction between an excited electron and the positive hole it leaves behind. This means that the exciton states in which electron and hole are associated and remain close to each other must be added to the theory in some ill-defined way at the end, rather than coming naturally from the initial assumptions. Further, the crystal-orbital approach cannot describe the local excitation of molecules that gives many

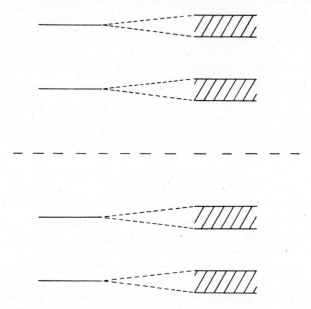

Fig. 11.2. Broadening of orbital energies into bands in crystals.

molecular crystals spectra showing similar features to corresponding vapor-phase spectra. The difficulties are not now overcome by placing the orbitals in a determinental wave function such as Eq. (11.7) and using the full self-consistent LCAO approach. This is because the self-consistent function still does not take account of the effect of coulomb attraction on the relative distribution of electrons (although it does make some allowance for the effect of antisymmetry). In particular, it cannot take account of the correlation between an electron and associated positive hole. This is a deficiency of molecular-orbital theory that becomes more serious the larger the molecule is.

It seems likely, therefore, that a better description of excited states in molecular crystals may be obtained by restricting

molecular orbitals to individual molecules and treating intermolecular effects by the interaction of different molecular states
(including charge transfer). This approach has been used with
some success to explain details of the spectra of molecular crystals.
However, it is important to consider how the conduction-type
states can also be described in the same formalism.

To illustrate this, it is useful to consider the simple example
of a long polyene molecule with alternating single and double
bonds. This is a useful model for a molecular crystal, with the
double bonds representing the molecules and the single bonds the
weaker intermolecular interactions. In the simpler form of theory,

Fig. 11.3. Alternating resonance integrals in model systems.

we should represent this by a chain with two different $H_{\mu\nu}$
elements, β (large) and β' (small). If there are $2N$ atoms in
such a system and if we choose cyclic boundary conditions (so
that we really have a large ring system), then the simplest
secular equation

$$\left| H_{\mu\nu} - ES_{\mu\nu} \right| = 0 \qquad (11.16)$$

is easily solved, and we find $2N$ solutions

$$E = \alpha \pm \sqrt{\{\beta^2 + \beta'^2 + 2\beta\beta' \cos (2\pi k/N)\}} \quad k = 1, 2, \ldots, N \quad (11.17)$$

If β' is less than β, these separate into two bands with a gap
equal to $2(\beta - \beta')$. In the ground state, the lower band will be
completely occupied and the upper one completely empty.

In the simple theory, therefore, the only excited states are those
in which an electron is transferred from an occupied crystal
orbital specified by one value of k to an unoccupied crystal
orbital specified by a different value. This corresponds to a conduction state, but no allowance is made for exciton states in
which the excited electron and the positive hole it leaves are
correlated. The simplest such state corresponds closely to excitation
of individual double bonds, if β' is small. To include this in a

completely delocalized crystal = orbital approach, therefore, involves allowing for configuration interaction.

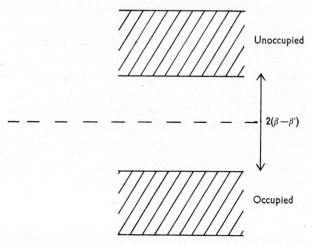

Fig. 11.4. Occupied and unoccupied bands of crystal orbitals predicted by
simple theory.

The alternative method is to base the description of the composite system on wave functions for excited states, which are valid
in the limit $\beta' = 0$, with no interaction between neighboring
double bonds. This corresponds to the "oriented-gas model" of
a molecular crystal in which the molecules are placed in their
correct orientations, but intermolecular interactions are neglected.
There are then two molecular orbitals ϕ_i and ϕ_i' $(i = 1, 2, \ldots, N)$
for each "molecule" or double bond i, the lower ϕ_i being occupied
and the upper ϕ_i' being unoccupied. The excited configurations
of this system (before the introduction of molecular interaction)
may be described as excitation from the occupied orbital ϕ_j of
molecule j to the unoccupied orbital ϕ_l' of molecule l. The two
odd electrons may be coupled to a singlet or triplet giving total
wave functions, which can be written $^1\Phi_{j\to l}$ and $^3\Phi_{j\to l}$. If $j = l$,
we have the configurations in which molecule j is excited, and the
others are left in their ground states.

Single configurational total wave functions, such as $^1\Psi_{j\to l}$,
cannot be stationary state wave functions of the whole system

since they do not possess the necessary translational symmetry. To get stationary state functions, we must combine equivalent functions $^1\Phi_{j\to l}$, in the form

$$^1\Psi(k, p) = \sum_j \exp\,(2\pi ijk/N)\ ^1\Phi_{j\to j+p} \qquad (11.18)$$

Such a wave function now corresponds to the excitation of an electron from the occupied molecular orbital of one molecule into the unoccupied molecular orbital of a second molecule p places to the right, all such excitations being combined in a symmetry represented by the wave number k. This is now a good approximation to a correct excited-state wave function as long as molecular interaction is neglected.

If molecular interaction is now introduced by allowing for the intermolecular resonance-type integral β' and the coulomb interaction between electrons in neighboring molecules, there will be a quantum-mechanical mixing between the all configurational functions corresponding to a given wave number k. To find the energy levels, we must evaluate matirx elements such as

$$\left(^1\Psi(k, p)\left|\mathscr{H}\right|^1\Psi(k, q)\right) \qquad (11.19)$$

and find the eigenvalues of the resulting matrix.

For simplicity, let us consider only the symmetry $k = 0$. Then clearly the configurational function $^1\Psi(0, p)$ corresponding to the transfer of an electron p places to the right will be symmetrically related to the function $^1\Psi(0, -p)$ corresponding to transfer p places to the left. They can therefore be combined into symmetrical and antisymmetrical combinations

$$^1\Psi^+(0,0) = {'}\Psi(0,0) \qquad (11.20)$$

$$^1\Psi^+(0,p) = \{^1\Psi(0,p)+^1\Psi(0,-p)\}/\sqrt{2} \qquad p > 0 \qquad (11.21)$$

$$^1\Psi^-(0,p) = \{^1\Psi(0,p)-^1\Psi(0,-p)\}/\sqrt{2} \qquad p > 0 \qquad (11.22)$$

with separate matrices to be diagonalised.

In the absence of molecular interaction, the matrices would be diagonal, the element corresponding to $^1\Psi^+(o,o)$ being the excitation energy E_1 of a single molecule or double bond, and the others being equal to $(I-A)$, where I and A are the ionization potential and electron affinity of the molecules. The effect of introducing molecular interaction is now threefold.

a. The diagonal element $\left(^1\Psi^+(0,0)\middle|\mathscr{H}\middle|^1\Psi^+(0,0)\right)$ is replaced by $E_1+\varDelta E_1$ where $\varDelta E_1$ is the shift in the energy of the excital state by the interaction of electric transition moments in neighboring molecules. This gives rise to the shift in the molecular absorption in the crystal compared with the gas phase.

b. The other diagonal elements are replaced by $I_c-A_c-\mathcal{J}_p$, where I_c and A_c are now the ionization potential and electron affinity in the crystal, allowing for stabilization of the ionic charge by polarization of neighbors, and $\mathcal{J}_p$ is a correction to allow for the coulomb interaction between an electron in the unoccupied orbital of one molecule and the positive hole it leaves behind in another molecule p places away. This is clearly proportional to $1/p$.

c. Off-diagonal elements proportional to β' are introduced between neighboring values of p because of the resonance-type integrals between the unoccupied molecular orbitals on neighboring molecules.

The complete secular equation for the symmetrical functions (11.20) and (11.21) then takes the form

$$
\begin{vmatrix}
E_1+\varDelta E_1-E & \sqrt{2}\beta' & 0 & 0 & : \\
\sqrt{2}\beta' & I_c-A_c-\mathcal{J}_1-E & \beta' & 0 & : \\
0 & \beta' & I_c-A_c-\mathcal{J}_2-E & \beta' & : \\
\cdots & \cdots & \cdots & \cdots & :
\end{vmatrix} = 0
\qquad (11.23)
$$

and the roots of this equation give approximations to excited-state functions with $k=0$. Without substituting any numerical values for the parameters, certain general features can be noted.

a. If β' is not too large, the lowest root approximates closely to $E=E_1+\varDelta E_1$, giving the excited state to which transitions are normally observed in the ultraviolet spectrum. However, the effect of β' will be to mix the localized excitation configuration slightly with one in which electrons are transferred to neighboring molecules.

b. Far enough down the matrix, that is for large p, the coulomb interaction term $\mathcal{J}_p$ tends to zero, the matrix approximates to one in which the diagonal terms are all equal to I_e-A_e, and the immediate off-diagonal terms are all β'. The roots of such a system form a band from $I_e-A_e+2\beta'$ to $I_e-A_e-2\beta'$ (noting that β' is negative). These are the continuum of conduction states.

c. In between the lowest root and $I_e-A_e+2\beta'$ there will be other roots corresponding to excitons in which electron and hole are not on the same molecule but are nevertheless bound to one another.

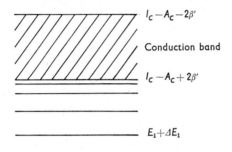

$$I_c-A_c-2\beta'$$

Conduction band

$$I_c-A_c+2\beta'$$

$$E_1+\varDelta E_1$$

Ground state

Fig. 11.5. Energy-level diagram for states with $k = 0$.

The energy-level diagram coming from the matrix of Eq. (11.23) then has the form shown in Fig. 11.5. and allows within the same general treatment for both neutral excitons and conduction states. A similar treatment is clearly possible for other values of the wave number k.

References

1. J. E. Lennard-Jones, *Proc. Roy. Soc.* (*London*) **A198**, 1, 14 (1949).
2. C. C. J. Roothaan, *Rev. Mod. Phys.* **23**, 61 (1951).
3. W. Hückel, *Z. Physik* **70**, 204, 279 (1931).
4. C. A. Coulson and G. S. Rusbrooke, *Proc. Cambridge Phil. Soc.* **36**, 193 (1940).
5. C. A. Coulson and H. C. Longuet-Higgins, *Proc. Roy. Soc.* (*London*) **A191**, 39 (1947).

6. M. Goeppert-Mayer and A. L. Sklar, *J. Chem. Phys.* **6**, 645 (1938).

7. R. E. Parr, D. P. Craig, and I. G. Ross, *J. Chem. Phys.* **18**, 1561, (1950).

8. R. Pariser and R. G. Parr, *J. Chem. Phys.* **21**, 767 (1953).

9. J. A. Pople, *Trans. Faraday Soc.* **49**, 1385 (1953).

10. J. A. Pople, *J. Phys. Chem.* **61**, 6 (1957).

11. J. R. Platt, *J. Chem. Phys.* **17**, 484 (1949).

12. H. C. Longuet-Higgins and M. J. S. Dewar, *Proc. Phys. Soc. (London)* **67**, 795 (1954).

13. J. A. Pople, *Proc. Phys. Soc. (London)* **68**, 81 (1955).

14. R. Pariser, *J. Chem. Phys.* **24**, 250 (1956).

Weak Transitions in Molecular Crystals

D. P. Craig and S. H. Walmsley

Introduction

Following Davydov's [1] application of the exciton theory of Frenkel[2] and Peierls[3] to weakly coupled molecules in a molecular crystal, a number of investigations of the spectra of aromatic crystals have been made, and experimental results compared with calculations of factor group splittings, spectral shifts, and intensity transfers. In absorption systems of strong or medium intensity, defined roughly by the range $f = 0.1$ to 2.0 in oscillator strength, it seems possible to predict [4, 5] reasonably well how a free-molecule transition will be affected by crystal forces in the molecular crystal, once the crystal structure is known and given the frequency, intensity, and polarization of the molecular transition. In weaker transitions, say $f < 0.1$, some new problems arise that will be treated in this paper. Our theoretical discussion is particularly concerned with the class of very weak transitions that occur quite frequently in aromatic molecules with oscillator strength in the order $f = 0.001$, caused by vibrational perturbation of electronic states that are either forbidden or only very weakly allowed in combination with the ground state. Typical examples of these are the 2,600 A system of benzene and the 3,200 A system of naphthalene. Before describing the features of the crystal spectra of these weak systems we shall mention the phenomena in stronger systems that have already been dealt with by application of the exciton theory. This will emphasize the differences in behavior that are of special importance.

1. In very intense molecular transitions with oscillator strengths in the order $f = 1.0$, two or more absorption maxima appear in the crystal for each vapor maximum, according to the number

of molecules in the unit cell, separated by *Davydov splitting intervals*. The several maxima record absorption of light with particular directions of polarization in relation to the crystal axes, and their intensities are approximately in the relation of the squares of projections of the lengths of the active molecular-absorption directions on the crystal axes. First-order perturbation theory applied to free-molecule wave functions, the intermolecular energy being used as the perturbation, is satisfactory in this case, and allows the splittings to be calculated.

2. In somewhat weaker transitions with oscillator strengths of about $f = 0.1$ first-order effects of this type are smaller in proportion to the intensity. Relative to these reduced first-order effects, second-order terms due to the mixing of different electronic transitions begin to be important. As a result a transition of this kind in the crystal has a mixed character, which shows itself in intensity relationships altered from simple expectation. An example of this occurs in the 3,800 A absorption system of anthracene, in which the ratio of polarized intensities along the *a* and *b* monoclinic axes is changed from the oriented-gas value of 7 : 1 to about 3 : 1 by the admixture of some of the intense absorption system at 2,500 A with the weaker one.

Both of these crystal phenomena have been explained as intermolecular-excitation resonance effects ("exciton" effects) due to dipole-dipole coupling between molecules, the dipoles concerned being the transition dipoles for the spectral transitions. Since these transition-dipole moments determine how intense the transitions are, we can see that these effects are determined by (and are in fact proportional to) the intensities of the systems concerned. Thus as we go to weaker and weaker systems, the effects should die out, and the spectra revert to oriented gas behavior in the limit of the extremely weak spectra, of the order $f = 0.001$. We can show that even in a spectrum ten times stronger than this limit, the changes calculated in dipole approximation will be very small.

Some Observed Crystal Effects in Very Weak Transitions

Anticipating later discussion, we can divide the crystal-induced changes in very weak systems into the following categories:

1. The pure-electronic upper state of the transition may be split by as much as 100 to 200 cm^{-1}, even if the transition is forbidden in the free molecule. The magnitude of this splitting is unrelated to the spectral intensity, if any.

2. The vibration-induced transitions of the free molecule show at most a very small splitting in the crystal, of the order of 1 cm^{-1}. This is unrelated in magnitude, and even in sign to the splitting in the pure-electronic transitions of paragraph 1 on p. 163.

3. Gross relative-intensity perturbations occur. The pure-electronic transition, even if forbidden in the free molecule, may appear in the crystal spectrum with an intensity comparable to

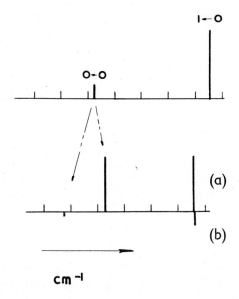

Fig. 12.1. The effect of crystal forces on the 0—0 and 1—0 bands of the naphthalene spectrum at 3,200 A.[6, 7] The electronically "forbidden" 0—0 transition is split by 151 cm^{-1} in the crystal, and its higher b component is intensified. The 1—0 band is split by less than 1 cm^{-1}, with the b component lower. Frequency intervals are 100 cm^{-1}.

that of the vibration-induced bands. Its intensity is divided between the polarization directions in a way that is not simply related to the projections of the molecular axis concerned.

Figure 12.1 illustrates these effects as they occur in the naphthalene 3,200 A system.[6,7]

We shall next give a brief statement of the conventional theory and then go on to apply it to the weaker absorption systems. The presentation follows that of Craig and Walsh,[4] in which earlier references will be found. Each of the molecules in the crystal has a ground-state wave function φ and a set of excited-state wave functions φ^r. Transitions in the free molecule to these excited states are characterized by transition energies Δw^r, measured in the equivalent wave-number units and by transition-dipole moments $\mathbf{M}^r$, measured in units of electronic charge times length. If the oscillator strength f for the transition has been determined experimentally from the absorption curve, the transition-dipole length D can be found from the simple formula (12.1)

$$f = 1/3D^2\nu \qquad (12.1)$$

In Eq. (12.1) the dipole length is in atomic units, and the energy ν in rydbergs. In this chapter values of dipole lengths will, however, be quoted in Angstroms.

It is assumed throughout that electron exchange between molecules can be neglected, and therefore that the crystal ground state can be written as the simple product shown in Eq. (12.2) of the ground-states of the N molecules making up the crystal.

$$\Phi_G = \varphi_1 \varphi_2 \varphi_3 \dots \varphi_N \qquad (12.2)$$

The energy of the ground-state is equal to N times the molecular ground-state energy w_G plus the perturbation energy due to the intermolecular potential $\mathbf{V}_{kl}$ between all pairs of molecules l and k.

$$E_G = N w_G + 1/2 \sum_{l \neq k} \sum \int \varphi_l \varphi_k \mathbf{V}_{lk} \varphi_l \varphi_k \, d\tau \qquad (12.3)$$

The excited states of the crystal are those in which one of the N molecules is in its excited state, and all others in their ground-states. We have a set of localized excitation functions, shown in Eq. (12.4), in which excitation to the rth excited state resides in a

$$\phi_{ip}^r = \varphi_{11} \varphi_{12} \varphi_{13} \dots \varphi_{ip}^r \dots \varphi_{h\,N/h} \qquad (12.4)$$

particular molecule, namely, that occupying the ith site in the pth unit cell in a crystal in which the unit cell has h sites.

Since all the molecules are equivalent, there are N distinct functions (12.4) of the same energy, corresponding to each of the N molecules being excited in turn. The N-fold degeneracy is resolved by selecting linear combinations of the functions (12.4) to transform like representations of the characteristic translation group of the crystal. The most important of the spectrally active combinations is the sum function (12.5). taken over all the mole-

$$\Phi_i^r = (h/N)^{\frac{1}{2}} \sum_p \phi_{ip}^r \qquad (12.5)$$

cules occupying a particular unit cell site. Finally, the functions (12.5) for the several unit-cell sites must be combined to get excited-state wave functions of the crystal. In the common situation of two crystallographically equivalent molecules in the unit cell, as in naphthalene and anthracene, the crystal wave functions are the two for the upper and lower signs in Eq. (12.6)

$$2^{-\frac{1}{2}} (\Phi_1^r \pm \Phi_2^r) \qquad (12.6)$$

It is easily shown that a transition to the state with the upper sign choice is polarized in the ac crystal plane and to the other polarized along the b monoclinic axis.* Beginning with a set of molecular excited-state wave functions φ^r, the nature of which does not need to be specified in detail, we construct the crystal wave functions belonging to each, like those in Eq. (12.6). We then find the crystal-energy eigenvalues from the solutions of secular equations, one for each symmetry species of the factor group, constructed in the basis of the crystal wave functions. The secular equation for the ac polarizedtransition upper states is given in expression (12.7), in which $\mathscr{H}_k$ is the hamiltonian for the kth molecule:

$$\det \{ [(\Phi_1^r + \Phi_2^r) | \sum \mathscr{H}_k + \sum\sum \mathbf{V}_{kl} - E_G | (\Phi_1^s + \Phi_2^s)] \\ - [(\Phi_1^r + \Phi_2^r) |1| (\Phi_1^s + \Phi_2^s) E] \} = 0 \qquad (12.7)$$

* The molecular axes are signed according to the following convention. A right-handed set is located in the molecule at the origin. The axes in the other molecules in the crystal are generated from this one by translation or by reflection in the ac plane followed by translation.

168   D. P. CRAIG AND S. H. WALMSLEY

The secular equation is the same if the functions φ^r are vibronic-product wave functions instead of pure electronic ones, a fact that is important for our discussion of very weak transitions. The diagonal elements of Eq. (12.7) give the first-order transition energies, which in many cases are acceptable approximations to observed values. This is true especially of intense systems. In weaker systems it is more necessary to solve the secular equation, including wave functions as in Eq. (12.6) for several free-molecule states. Reduction of the elements of the secular equation gives, for the diagonal elements, the expression (12.8).

$$\Delta w^r + D^r + \sum_p' I_{lp}^r \pm \sum_m I_{lm}^r \qquad (12.8)$$

Here the upper sign is for the a component referred to in the secular equation (12.7) and the lower sign for the b-polarized component. We have, for the quantities in (12.8), the definitions

$$I_{lp}^r = (\varphi_l\,\varphi_l^r\,|\,\mathbf{V}_{lp}\,|\,\varphi_p\varphi_p^r)$$
$$D^r = \sum_q'\{(\varphi_p^r\varphi_q\,|\,\mathbf{V}_{pq}\,|\,\varphi_p^r\varphi_q) - (\varphi_p\varphi_q\,|\,\mathbf{V}_{pq}\,|\,\varphi_p\varphi_q)\}$$

The summations in (12.8) are over equivalent molecules (subscript p) and inequivalent (subscript m), respectively. The nondiagonal elements reduce to expression (12.9)

$$\sum_p' K_{lp}^{rs} + \sum_m K_{lm}^{rs} + \sum_p' \mathcal{J}_{lp}^{rs} \pm \sum_m \mathcal{J}_{lm}^{rs} \qquad (12.9)$$

with

$$K_{lp}^{rs} = (\varphi_l^r\varphi_l^s\,|\,\mathbf{V}_{lp}\,|\,\varphi_p\varphi_p)$$
$$\mathcal{J}_{lp}^{rs} = 1/2\{(\varphi_l\varphi_l^r\,|\,\mathbf{V}_{lp}\,|\,\varphi_p\varphi_p^s) + (\varphi_l\varphi_l^s\,|\,\mathbf{V}_{lp}\,|\,\varphi_p\varphi_p^r)\}$$

The expressions (12.8) and (12.9) refer to examples such as the monoclinic $P2_1/a$ crystal of naphthalene and anthracene with two molecules in the unit cell, but they may be generalized without difficulty.

Vibration-Induced Transitions

In very weak absorption systems it is common to find that one or more of the nontotally symmetrical vibrations is responsible for the appearance of absorption, in so far as it perturbs a spectrally inactive electronic upper state φ^r by mixing with it a small component of a spectrally active upper state φ^s. Transitions then occur weakly to φ^r, on account of its small mixed-in component of φ^s. We shall suppose that an active vibration is σ and that $\sigma^{r(0)}$ and $\sigma^{r(1)}$ stand for the zero- and one-quantum wave functions for this vibration in the rth electronic state. In a first approximation the upper state for vibrationally induced transitions is $\varphi^r \sigma^{r(1)}$, supposing, as is true in the known examples, that the one-quantum excitation of the vibration is active. In the second approximation the mixing of electronic states is allowed for, giving for the perturbed upper state

$$c_1 \varphi^r \sigma^{r(1)} + c_2 \varphi^s \sigma^{s(0)} \tag{12.10}$$

This formulation presupposes that the electronic functions φ^r and φ^s are calculated for the equilibrium nuclear configuration, according to the Born-Oppenheimer approximation. Also, because the perturbing effect is small, we have $c_1 \gg c_2$. We now consider the linear combination (12.10) replacing either or both of φ_p^r and φ_q^s in the general intermolecular-resonance integral $(\varphi_p \varphi_p^r | \mathbf{V} |_{pq} \varphi_q \varphi_q^s)$. The potential $\mathbf{V}_{pq}$ is given by expression (12.11)

$$\mathbf{V}_{pq} = -\sum_{f,j} (Z_f e^2 / r_{fj}) - \sum_{g,i} (Z_g e^2 / r_{gi})$$
$$+ \sum_{i,j} (e^2 / r_{ij}) + \sum_{f,g} (Z_f Z_g e^2 / r_{fg}) \tag{12.11}$$

where f and g are the nuclei, Z_f and Z_g the nuclear charges, and i and j the electrons of the pth and qth molecules, respectively. Because each term of Eq. (12.11) contains either the nuclear coordinates or the electronic coordinates of each molecule, but not both, we can only get contributions to the integral from the term $c_2 \varphi_s \sigma^{s(0)}$ of Eq. (12.10). Contributions from the first term of (12.10) are annihilated [8] either by the orthogonality of the electronic functions φ and φ^r (in integrals of the terms of $\mathbf{V}_{pq}$ containing the nuclear coordinates of the molecule concerned) or by the orthogonality of the nuclear vibration functions of the ground and excited states (in terms of $\mathbf{V}_{pq}$ containing the electronic coordinates). Consequently, the only intermolecular effects of a vibration-induced transition are those due to the small mixed-in component of the perturbing electronic state. In a band system in which both the pure-electronic transition and a vibration-induced transition appear side-by-side, the crystal spectrum of the former will be governed by the properties of the electronic state that is the terminus of the spectral transition, but the latter will reflect only the properties of a second electronic state, from which intensity is stolen by vibrational interaction. This, as will be shown, accounts for some curious features of the spectra.

Expansion of the Potential V_{pq}

On account of the weakness of dipole effects in weak systems, the expansion of the potential must be taken to higher terms. As is well known, if the dimensions of the molecules are not too great compared to their mean separations, it proves to be convenient to expand their intermolecular energy in a two-center expansion about molecular origins, located at molecular centers of inversion, if present.[9]

We introduce an intermolecular axis system xyz with the z axis along the line joining the molecular centers (if molecular centers of symmetry exist; otherwise we join suitable molecular origins) and with x and y axes perpendicular to it. Additionally, there are systems of axes imbedded in each molecule, using whatever symmetry properties the molecules possess. These axes will be called L_p, M_p, and N_p for the pth molecule. Taking naphthalene as the example, N will be the normal to the plane of the molecule, and L and M lie, respectively, along the longer and shorter in-plane axial directions. The first term in the expansion is the dipole-dipole component of the interaction potential given in the intermolecular coordinates by expression (12.12).

$$-e^2 R_{pq}^{-3} (2z_p z_q - x_p x_q - y_p y_q) \qquad (12.12)$$

where R_{pq} is the distance between the molecules. By a transformation of coordinates this dipole-dipole term may be expressed in the (L, M, N) systems. A representative term of the transformed expression is given in Eq. (12.13). This refers to the interaction of a dipole along the L axis in molecule p with an M dipole in molecule q.

$$-e^2 R_{pq}^{-3}\left(2(L_p z)(M_q z)-(L_p x)(M_q x)-(L_p y)(L_q y)\right)\times L_p M_q \quad (12.13)$$

The expressions in parentheses represent the cosines of the angles between the indicated coordinates. The dipole-dipole interaction is completed by including with (12.13) terms referring to dipoles along the remaining axes of the molecules.

To introduce a more compact notation suitable for higher terms we define the tesseral harmonics (unnormalized) as follows:

$$\begin{aligned}
\Upsilon_l^{m(c)} &= 1/2(\Upsilon_l^m + \Upsilon_l^{-m}) = P_l^m(\cos\theta)\cos m\varphi \\
\Upsilon_l^{m(s)} &= (1/2i)(\Upsilon_l^m - \Upsilon_l^{-m}) = P_l^m(\cos\theta)\sin m\varphi
\end{aligned} \quad (12.14)$$

and the corresponding multipole moment components are:

$$\begin{aligned}
Q_l^o &= r^l P_l^o(\cos\theta) &&= r^l \Upsilon_l^o \\
Q_l^{m(c)} &= r^l P_l^m(\cos\theta)\cos m\varphi &&= r^l \Upsilon_l^{m(c)} \\
Q_l^{m(s)} &= r^l P_l^m(\cos\theta)\sin m\varphi &&= r^l \Upsilon_l^{m(s)}
\end{aligned} \quad (12.15)$$

The polar angles θ and φ are measured respectively downward from the N molecular axis and clockwise from the L axis in the LM plane. The dipole-dipole interaction can now be written in the form shown in Eq. (12.16), in terms of the multipole moments in tesseral harmonics:

$$e^2 R_{pq}^{-3} \sum_{i,j} a_{ij} Q_1^i Q_1^j \quad (12.16)$$

The first of the Q's refers to molecule p and the second to q and the indexes i and j run over the values 0, 1(c), and 1(s), leading to a sum of nine terms. The coefficients a_{ij} include the geometrical factors measuring the orientation of the molecular axes to the intermolecular system (x, y, z), and each of the three Q_1^i is a dipole-length operator, the matrix components of which in a basis of molecular wave functions are *transition*-dipole lengths for the molecular transitions. Consequently, the product operators (12.12) have as matrix components in the basis of crystal wave functions, the dipole-dipole interaction energy of the transition-dipole moments of the two molecules p and q. It can be shown that the generalization of (12.16), in which later terms of the expansion of $\mathbf{V}_{pq}$ are included, has the form (12.17)

$$\mathbf{V}_{pq} = e^2 R_{pq}^{-3} \sum_i \sum_j a_{ij} Q_1^i Q_1^j + e^2 R_{pq}^{-4} \sum_i \sum_i \{ b_{ij} Q_1^i Q_2^j + b'_{ij} Q_2^i Q_1^j \}$$
$$+ e^2 R_{pq}^{-5} \sum_i \sum_j c_{ij} Q_2^i Q_2^j + \text{terms in } R^{-6},\ R^{-7}, \ldots \qquad (12.17)$$

The indexes i and j in the several terms of Eq. (12.17) run over all the values 0, 1(c), 1(s), 2(c), and 2(s) up to the order of the harmonics concerned. The coefficients a, b, c, . . . depend upon the geometrical constants of the lattice, through the Wigner coefficients for the transformation from the intermolecular-axis system to molecular axes. These are given in full by Hirschfelder, Curtiss, and Bird.[9] Since each of the eQ's is a component of a multipole electric moment referred to a system of *molecular* axes, we can see that the integral $\mathcal{J}_{pq}^{rs}$ will include a contribution from a chosen term of $\mathbf{V}_{pq}$, as, for example, shown in Eq. (12.18).

$$e^2 R_{pq}^{-l-m-1} c_{ij} (\varphi_p | Q_l^i | \varphi_p^r)(\varphi_q | Q_m^j | \varphi_q^s) \qquad (12.18)$$

This is true only if the indicated components of multipole-transition moments for the transitions $\varphi^r \leftarrow \varphi$ and $\varphi^s \leftarrow \varphi$ are both non-zero. Because of the higher inverse powers of R for the higher multipole interactions, it turns out that, if a transition is dipole-allowed, its dipole transition moment is the only one that needs to be considered, unless it should happen accidentally to be very small. In general, only the lowest multipole transition moment has to be included, a fact that cuts down the effective number of terms in (12.17) to one or two in any one integral $\mathcal{J}_{pq}^{rs}$.

In weak transitions the dipole transition moment is very small, and it is necessary to include the next nonvanishing multipole moment in the calculations. If the transition is $u \leftarrow g$, this is the octupole moment, and the interaction terms of significance are the octupole-octupole, octupole-dipole, and dipole-dipole.

Calculations of Effects in Weak Systems

Before describing the details of the calculations we shall mention some general features of the theory to be applied. Our example throughout will be the weak system of naphthalene at 3,200 A illustrated in Fig. (12.1). The pure electronic band of this system was shown by McClure [10] to be polarized along the longer in-plane axis; its vibration-induced bands are short-axis polarized.

These findings are fully supported by high-resolution studies of the vapor spectrum of naphthalene. In the vapor,[11] the total intensity corresponds to an oscillator strength $f \sim 0.002$, while that attributable to the pure-electronic transition is $f \sim 0.0002$ to 0.0004.

We shall mention the pure-electronic spectrum in the crystal first. Intermolecular forces influence the system in two ways, the first being by interaction between the upper state of the pure-electronic transition in one molecule and the upper state of the same transition in other molecules. This is the first-order effect, the result being a splitting into two components with different polarizations. In this order there is no change in the total intensity, and we should be able to observe the split pure-electronic transition only with some difficulty or not at all if first-order effects were alone important. To explain the large intensification of the pure-electronic transitions in the crystal it is necessary to take account of second-order terms. These deal with the mixing of the upper state of the transition in one molecule with the upper states of *different transitions* in other molecules. The transition in question in thus enabled to acquire to a fractional extent the properties of these other transitions, notably their larger intensity. There are also some energy displacements caused by second-order terms, but these are usually small compared with first-order shifts. These phenomena have already been fully discussed before, and no new points of principle arise in connection with very weak systems. In naphthalene the situation is such that the weak transition interacts strongly, with the transition at 2,750 A, a short-axis system of oscillator strength $f \sim 0.1$, and with the strong system at 2,200 A, oscillator strength $f \sim 1.7$. Under the circumstances found in naphthalene the first-order terms in the pure electronic transition are octupole-octupole in character, and the second-order terms are octupole-dipole, between the octupole-transition moment of the very weak transition and the dipole-transition moments of the stronger 2,750 A and 2,200 A transitions.

Conditions in the vibration-induced bands are different. Since, as we have shown, the only intermolecular resonance

effects are those attributable to the mixed-in state, we may
ignore entirely the true electronic parentage of the upper state
of the vibration-induced bands and regard them as separate
electronic states with transition moments given by the observed
intensity and with polarization the same as that of the mixed-in
state. The *vibrational* mixing is with the upper state of the 2,750 A
system, so that we have in one and the same crystal spectrum
bands produced by vibrational mixing and others due to crystal-
induced mixing. The vibration-induced bands will not be greatly
changed in the crystal. The mixed-in transition must have at
least a fairly large intensity to be effective in appearing in the
vibrationally perturbed bands; dipole-dipole effects will therefore
predominate in intermolecular-resonance effects in the vibration-
induced bands, and even these must be weak in proportion to
the very low observed intensity of about $f = 0.002$. The effects
will be limited to 10 cm^{-1} splitting or less, even in the most favorable
molecular orientations.

Calculations for Vibration-induced Bands

It is easily verified in accordance with what has been said in
the preceding paragraph that only dipole effects are important
in these bands. The basic data for a calculation are the dipole-
dipole interaction sums for naphthalene and the experimental
value of the transition moment, which is 0.067 A. The dipole
sums, calculated by the Ewald-Kornfeld method, are given in
Table 12.1. The square of the transition-dipole length is
4.5×10^{-3} A^2. The first-order splitting, using the values in
Table 12.1, is $2 \times 4.5 \times 10^{-3} \times 1,360 = 12.2$ cm^{-1} for a long-
axis polarized transition, with b component at lower frequencies,
and for a short-axis transition $9.0 \times 80 \times 10^{-3} = 0.7$ cm^{-1},
again with b component lower. A careful experimental study
shows that the splitting is about 1 cm^{-1} with the b lower.[12] This
small splitting is incompatible with expectation for long-axis polarization and agrees with that for a short-axis band. The conclusion
that the vibration-induced spectrum is short-axis polarized is
unambiguous from the crystal and is in agreement with vapor
and mixed-crystal studies. Second-order effects have only a very

Table 12.1. Dipole-Dipole Sums for Crystalline Naphthalene (cm^{-1} A^{-2})

Set [a]	L—L [b]	M—M	N—N	L—M	L—N	M—N
1	575	−778	202	328	−213	656
2	1,360	80	−1,490	1,160	1,620	−351

[a] The entries under set 1 are for interactions of translationally equivalent molecules and under 2 for inequivalent molecules.

[b] L—L refers to the interactions of dipoles along the L molecular axes of both molecules, both pointing along the positive direction. The other interactions are referred to analogously.

slight influence on the splitting and leave the conclusion unaffected.

First-Order Calculation of the Pure-electronic Transition

For the purpose of this calculation we shall assume that all the intensity of the pure-electronic transition and its progression members is concentrated in the O—O band. This intensity in the solution spectrum is $f = 0.0002-0.0004$. We shall adopt the larger value, giving a transition-dipole length of 0.034 A. It is also necessary to use values of the active components of the transition-octupole moment. These quantities are not known, and we shall regard them as parameters, to be chosen to fit the observed crystal splitting. In each of transitions of species $B_{2u} \leftarrow A_g$ (long-axis polarized) and $B_{1u} \leftarrow A_g$ (short-axis polarized), there are two active components of the octupole transition moment, respectively, given in expressions (12.19).

$$Q_3^{1(c)} = 3/2L(5N^2-R^2)$$
$$Q_3^{3(c)} = 15L(L^2-3M^2)$$
$$Q_3^{1(s)} = 3/2M(5N^2-R^2)$$
$$Q_3^{3(s)} = 15M(3L^2-M^2)$$

$$(12.19)$$

To make calculations we require values of lattice sums for the interaction between octupole components in one molecule and octupole components in all others, and for octupole components interacting with dipole components. The required values are listed in Tables 12.2 and 12.3.

Table 12.2. Dipole-Octupole Sums for Crystalline Naphthalene $(cm^{-1}\,A^{-4})^{a}$

Set	$Q_1^{1(c)}-Q_3^{1(c)}$	$Q_1^{1(c)}-Q_3^{3(c)}$	$Q_1^{1(s)}-Q_3^{1(s)}$	$Q_1^{1(s)}-Q_3^{3(s)}$
1	-3.9	-1.7	-10.6	$+1.5$
2	$+15$	$+3.2$	$+71.0$	$+0.5$

Set	$Q_1^{1(c)}-Q_3^{1(s)}$	$Q_1^{1(c)}-Q_3^{3(s)}$	$Q_1^{1(s)}-Q_3^{1(c)}$	$Q_1^{1(s)}-Q_3^{3(c)}$
1	2.5	-2.5	2.5	-2.3
2	45.5	-6.2	-25.2	-1.1

[a] In mixed interaction types the value shown is a mean value. Thus $Q_1^{1(c)}-Q_3^{1(c)}$ stands for the mean interaction for the dipole in molecule p and the octupole in q, and for the reversed arrangement.

Table 12.3 Octupole-Octupole Sums for Crystalline Naphthalene $(cm^{-1}\,A^{-6})^{a}$

Set	$Q_3^{1(c)}-Q_3^{1(c)}$	$Q_3^{3(c)}-Q_3^{3(c)}$	$Q_3^{1(c)}-Q_3^{3(c)}$	
1	-0.30	0.0020	0.008	
2	0.27	-0.0041	0.467	

Set	$Q_3^{1(s)}-Q_3^{1(s)}$	$Q_3^{3(s)}-Q_3^{3(s)}$	$Q_3^{1(s)}-Q_3^{3(s)}$	
1	1.45	-0.0007	0.047	
2	5.02	-0.0063	0.018	

Set	$Q_3^{1(c)}-Q_3^{1(s)}$	$Q_3^{3(c)}-Q_3^{3(s)}$	$Q_3^{1(c)}-Q_3^{3(s)}$	$Q_3^{3(c)}-Q_3^{1(s)}$
1	-0.39	0.0160	-0.048	-0.064
2	-3.55	-0.0076	-0.424	-0.043

[a] In mixed interaction type the value shown is a mean value. Thus $Q_3^{1c}-Q_3^{1c}$ stands for the mean interaction for the octupole in molecule p and the octupole in q, and for the reversed arrangement.

The results of calculations of first-order splitting are given in Fig. 12.2. The splitting shown by the origin band in the crystal is 151 cm^{-1}, with a component lower. However, since we have assumed that all the intensity of the origin band and its progression members is concentrated at one frequency, we must compare the calculated splittings with the sum of all the splittings observed. Much the largest splitting is the 151 cm^{-1} found in the origin band itself; the others are equal in total to about 35 cm^{-1}, and we therefore use the value of 186 cm^{-1} for comparison with first-order theory. According to Fig. 12.2 this splitting is compatible with a range of pairs of values of O_1 and O_3. First-order theory provides no basis for making a choice within the range of acceptable values. Moreover, it would be possible in the first-order approximation to account for the observed splitting if the pure-electronic transition were short-axis polarized. This possibility may be eliminated by considering second-order effects.

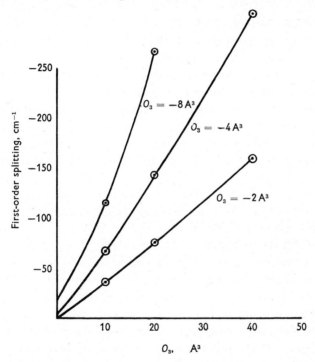

Fig. 12.2. First-order crystal splitting in naphthalene for a weak, long-axis polarized transition of $f = 0.0004$, including dipole and octupole terms. Combinations of moments are selected that give splittings with the a component at lower frequency. The observed splitting is about -180 to -200 cm^{-1}.

Second-order Calculations

Second-order terms affect mainly the intensities with which the various lines in the crystal spectrum appear. Experimentally

178   D. P. CRAIG AND S. H. WALMSLEY

the weak band system as a whole has an intensity ratio of about 4 or 5 to 1 in favor of the b crystal axis.[13] No quantitative results exist for the polarization behavior of individual bands. From the appearance of the spectrum it seems probable that the b component of the origin band is the strongest of the whole system, slightly stronger even than the b component of the vibration-induced band $O+438$ cm^{-1}. In the vapor spectrum, $O+438$ is at least five times stronger than the origin band, and in the oriented-gas model its b component in the crystal spectrum would be fifty times stronger than the origin b component on account of the different orientations of the molecular axes in the crystal. It is thus clear that a transfer of intensity takes place in the crystal resulting in an increased intensity in the b component of the origin band. Among the experimental facts concerning intensities there is the large polarization ratio of the pure-electronic (origin) band ($b/a > 10/1$) and the much smaller ratio in the $0+438$ vibration induced band ($b/a \sim 4/1$). The main purpose of second-order calculations is to investigate how far this behavior can be accounted for.

The starting data for the second-order calculations are the properties of the three lowest absorption systems observed in the vapor spectrum. Besides the 3,200 A system there are the 2,750 and 2,200 A systems; each splits into a and b components in the crystal, and mixing occurs within the two sets of similarly polarized bands. The starting data used are listed in Table 12.4.

The main qualitative features of the intensity transfers can be accounted for using a long-axis assignment and are incompatible with the short-axis assignment. The dependence of intensity on octupole-moment components is not sensitive enough to permit an accurate determination. It is probable,[8] however, that O_1 is in the range -9 to $-7A^3$ and O_3 in the range 12 to 15 A^3. Some uncertainty inevitably attaches to these values, as will be explained. Table 12.5 lists results for the long-axis assignment for $O_1 = -9$ A^3 and $O_3 = 12$ A^3 and Table 12.6 for the short-axis assignment using the values $O_1 = 0$ and $O_3 - 95$ A^3, both of which pairs of values give agreement with the observed splitting. For the short-axis assignment the associated second-order terms give

Table 12.4. Low Transitions of Naphthalene

	3,200-A system	2,750-A system	2,200-A system
Origin frequency	32,020 cm^{-1}	35,000 cm^{-1}	45,500 cm^{-1}
Oscillator strength	Allowed component, 0.0004 Induced component, 0.0016	0.1	1.7
Transition dipole length	Allowed, 0.034 Induced, 0.067	0.53 A	1.86 A
Polarization	Not assumed	Short-axis polarized $B_{1u} \leftarrow A_g$	Long-axis polarized $B_{2u} \leftarrow A_g$
Vibrational structure assumed	Allowed, 1 combination with 702 cm^{-1} Forbidden, none	5 members of 1,400 cm^{-1} progression with intensities proportional to 0.168, 0.280 0.249, 0.187, 0.118	None

results grossly in conflict with experiment, showing that this assignment is incorrect. Table 12.5 shows that, although a considerable intensity transfer has occurred, its amount in absolute terms is insufficient to bring the origin b component up to that in the $O+438$ band. However, the polarization ratio in the origin band $a/b = 1/12$ shows the required reversal from the oriented gas value of 4.2 : 1, and the ratio in the $O+438$ (1 : 3.5) band is in good agreement with observation. On the other hand, the short-axis assignment leads to the expectation that every band of the system, both pure-electronic and vibration-induced, would be stronger in a polarization than in b. This is quite incorrect.

The agreement between theory (for long-axis assignment) and experiment is good except in the absolute intensity of the b com-

Table 12.5. Calculated 3,200 A Spectrum of Crystal Naphthalene

Long-axis assignment: $O_1 = -9$ A^3, $O_3 = 12$ A^3

Calculated splittings: 0—0 -144 cm^{-1} (expt. -151)

0+438 0.7 cm^{-1}

0+702 -26 cm^{-1}

	Absolute b component f values	Polarization ratio, a/b
0—0	0.0006	1 : 12
0+438	0.0035	1 : 3.5

Table 12.6. Calculated 3,200 A spectrum of Crystal Naphthalene

Short-axis assignment: $O_1 = 0$, $O_3 = 95$ A^3

Calculated splittings: 0—0 -149 cm^{-1}

0+438 11 cm^{-1}

	Absolute b component f values	Polarization ratio, a/b
0—0	0.0025	1.2 : 1
0+438	0.0002	2.1 : 1

ponent of the origin band. This part of the calculation is very sensitive to the value taken for the rather small energy separation between the 3,200 A and 2,750 A systems. This separation depends on the differential red shift of these systems between vapor and crystal; this has not been allowed for in our calculations. Also, it must be remembered that there may be some residual error due to cutting off the multipole expansion at the octupole-octupole term. In general, we should include all terms up to a chosen inverse dependence on the molecular separation, so that the dipole-32 $\times$ pole term ought to be included, as well as the octupole-octupole term. In naphthalene this cannot be a serious source of error because the octupole-octupole moment is only of significance in the first-order splitting, and there dipole interactions of all types are negligible. In general, however, consideration would have to be given to such terms of the interaction potential.

We may summarize as follows: The novel features of very weak transitions in the spectra of molecular crystals are (1) the feeble effects on vibration-induced bands compared to pure electronic ones, and (2) the prominence of intensity perturbations. These two principal characteristics may be explained by taking account of the annihilation of all but weak dipole effects in vibration-induced transitions and by including higher multipole terms in the theory of weak pure-electronic transitions.

References

1. A. S. Davydov, *J. Exptl. Theoret. Phys.* (*U.S.S.R.*) **18**, 210 (1948)
2. J. Frenkel, *Phys. Rev.* **37**, 17 (1931).
3. R. E. Peierls, *Ann. Physik.* **13**, 905 (1932).
4. D. S. McClure, *Solid State Phys.* **8**, 1 (1959).
5. D. P. Craig and J. R. Walsh, *J. Chem. Soc.* **1958**, 1613.
6. D. S. McClure and O. Schnepp, *J. Chem. Phys.* **23**, 1575 (1955), and references therein.
7. D. P. Craig, L. E. Lyons, and J. R. Walsh (to be published).
8. D. P. Craig, L. E. Lyons, S. H. Walmsley, and J. R. Walsh, *Proc. Chem. Soc.* **1959**, 389.
9. Hirschfelder, Curtiss, and Bird, "Molecular Theory of Gases and Liquids," p. 843, John Wiley & Sons, Inc., New York (1954).
10. D. S. McClure, *J. Chem. Phys.* **22**, 1668 (1954).
11. D. P. Craig, J. M. Hollas, M. F. Redies, and S. C. Wait, *Proc. Chem. Soc.* **1959**, 361.
12. J. R. Walsh, Ph.D. thesis, University of Sydney (1958); D. P. Craig, L. E. Lyons, and J. R. Walsh (to be published).
13. D. P. Craig and L. E. Lyons, *J. Chem. Phys.* **20**, 1499 (1952).

Emission Spectra in Crystalline Naphthalene

H. Sponer

Introduction

An understanding of the energy levels of naphthalene crystal has been achieved essentially by correlating levels of naphthalene in a dilute mixed crystal (durene) with levels in naphthalene vapor and then comparing them with data of the pure-crystal absorption and fluorescence spectra.[1-4] The most extensive published data on naphthalene vapor absorption in the 3,220- to 2,900-A region are still those of de Laszlo.[5] We have taken (1948) absorption spectra of light and heavy naphthalene in this region (unpublished) and in the 2,900- to 2,500-A region.[6] The spectrum at 3,200 to 2,900 A has the appearance of a forbidden transition. The symmetry assignment of the upper term underwent some changes and is now generally accepted to be $^1B_{3u}$. Interacting vibrations in a transition B_{3u}—A_{1g} must be of g character. Closer examination of the vapor spectrum suggested the existence of two "subsystems" of different rotational structure, indicating two different transition-moment directions in this region.* The pure-electronic transition at 32,020 cm^{-1} has a negligible transition moment in the long molecular axis x. Excitation of b_{1g} vibrations will give $^1B_{2u}$ symmetry for the resulting vibronic states and short-axis y polarization; b_{2g} vibrations will lead to vibronic states of B_{1u} symmetry with polarization perpendicular to the molecular plane (z axis.)

Correlation between Vapor and Crystal Levels

It is not intended to go into details of the vapor band structure

* At the presentation of this paper a note (D. P. Craig, J. M. Hollas, N. F. Redies, and S. C. Wait, jr., *Proc. chem. Soc.* **1959** 361) containing the same distinction had gone unnoticed. The author is indebted to Dr. Craig for calling attention to this work.

in this chapter, since a few examples will suffice to describe the comparison. The $0-0$ level at 32,019 cm^{-1} belongs to the system of bands with a wider and simpler structure. It has a main sequence of a 64-cm^{-1} rotational separation. On this band there appears superimposed the vibration 507 in the band 31,513/449 on the long wavelength side and as 501 in the band 32,520 on the short wavelength side. Further bands at 31,252 and 32,722 contain the symmetric vibrations 762 and 703, respectively. All these bands show some finer structure in the 64 interval. For simplicity, the whole set of bands built upon the 0,0 at 32,019 by superposition of symmetric vibrations will be called system 1. It is a system of weak bands.

System 2 contains one quantum of a b_{1g} vibration, which makes the "accidentally forbidden" transition allowed and has symmetrical vibrational modes superimposed on it. Hence in this system (B_{2u} part of the spectrum) a progression of strong bands starts from the bands 32,457/400 and 32,931/872, which are apart by 438 and 910 cm^{-1}, respectively, from the origin at 32,019. The great enhancement of the B_{2u} component over the B_{3u} portion of the spectrum is largely due to interaction with the close-lying higher electronic state $^1B_{2u}$. All bands in system 2 show extended fine structure that is more complicated than that in bands of system 1. A larger interval of about 59 is accompanied by a narrow finer structure, with a 10-cm^{-1} interval occurring frequently.

The vapor systems 1 and 2 can be retraced in the naphthalene crystal spectra. They correspond to the now often called K and M, meaning "crystal" and "molecular", series. This distinction applies only to extremely weak singlet transitions in molecular crystals. In naphthalene there is an "accidental" cancellation of matrix elements in the transition-moment calculation. In benzene the transition is strictly forbidden by symmetry. It is the latter molecule in which these characteristics were first discovered, and its near-ultraviolet absorption spectrum was first interpreted as a forbidden transition.[7] In the same paper there was also discussed the absorption spectrum of crystalline benzene obtained at $-259°$C by Kronenberger.[8] The spectrum had been taken with unpolarized light. Comparison with the vapor spectrum revealed the interesting fact that the crystal spectrum had a 0,0 band with extended structure and, directly imposed on it, a progression of the symmetric 923 vibration. Reasons for the presence and extended structure of the zero band in the crystal were suggested already at that time.* They contain the idea occurring later in the exciton theory of Davydov,[9] who used the naphthalene crystal as his model. Subsequent important theoretical contributions and applications have come from McClure, Fox and Schnepp, and others and have been reviewed by McClure.[10] The naphthalene crystal belongs to the monoclinic space group $C_{2h}{}^5$ with two molecules per unit cell. The axes are $a = 8.29$ A, $b = 5.95$, $c = 8.68$. The molecules lie with their long axes closely parallel to the c axis; their short axes make an angle of 27.8° with the b axis. The molecular centers are at inversion centers of the crystal.

Since we are concerned here chiefly with luminescence spectra of naphthalene crystals, the absorption data will be recalled only as necessary information for the discussion of luminescence phenomena. Figure 13.1 shows the level scheme for the first transition. Polarized absorption was obtained using chiefly the ab plane.[2, 11, 12] McClure's analysis placed the zero transition in the mixed crystal at 31,554 cm^{-1}. It has vanishing intensity in the short-axis polarized absorption and is strong in the long-axis polarized spectrum. It corresponds to the 32,019 in the vapor. Its analogue in the pure-crystal spectrum would be the first member of the series which should show factor splitting. This is represented[2] in the bands 31,476 and 31,642, the first of which is weakly present along the a axis and the second of which is strong along the b axis. The splitting of 166 cm^{-1} is in accordance

* From ref. 7, p. 218: "We interpret it as the 0,0 band whose appearance is made possible in violation of the selection rules by the action on the benzene molecules of crystal forces. Actually this absorption extends from 37797 to 37907 cm^{-1}. Thus its long wave edge lies 31 cm^{-1} towards the red from the theoretical 0,0 band. It is not quite clear whether this shift is due to excitation of a crystal frequency in the initial state or whether it is caused by a resonance phenomenon between the electronic excitation of molecular units in the crystal . . ."

with theoretical expectation. The first M band occurs in absorption at 31.976 cm^{-1} in both polarization directions (stronger along b than a). According to expectation it shows no splitting. Its analogue in the vapor spectrum is the strong band at 32,457 cm^{-1}.

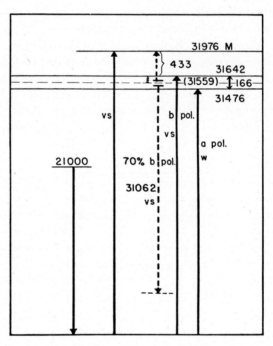

Fig. 13.1. First absorption and fluorescence region and phosphorescence emission of naphthalene crystal.

As mentioned before, the vibrationally induced bands and the bands directly superimposed on the weak 0,0 band show different rotational structure in the vapor. When using crystals and low temperatures the rotations change into librations, i.e., they become a hindered rotation, and since all molecules in the lattice execute librations instead of genuine rotations, we refer to them as lattice vibrations. Raman and Nedungadi [13] were the first to explain the polarization properties of low-frequency Raman lines in sodium nitrate in this fashion. The symmetry types of low frequency Raman lines in aromatic crystals were treated particularly by Mathieu, Kastler, and Cabannes.[14] For naphthalene, Kastler has given three pairs of Raman frequencies, each corresponding to a symmetric and asymmetric hindered rotation about one of the three molecular axes in the crystal. We observe combinations of them in the absorption and fluorescence crystal spectra. This fine structure is the main characteristic of the vibrationally induced bands, which do not contain the large factor group splitting of the 0,0 band. The latter is replaced here by a small splitting.

Emission Processes in Naphthalene Crystals

a. Fluorescence. All observers agree that the main fluorescence starts with a strong band at 31,062 cm^{-1}. The explanation of this "level" was not fully understood at the time of the conference. Fluorescence in the vapor begins at 32, 456 with a fairly strong band, and the main fluorescence starts from the 31,513 level.[15, 16] The first belongs to the short-axis polarized system, which is vibration-induced. The second band has a symmetric 506 vibration excited in the ground level. The absence or presence of the zero transition is plainly seen in the two systems appearing in the fluorescence of naphthalene in durene along the c' and b crystal axes.[3] The emission of shortest wavelength of the vibration-induced system is equal to 0,0—509.

In the crystal absorption,[2, 17] the b-polarized component 31,642 cm^{-1} is about one hundred times stronger than the a component. When using higher-energy excitation, the 31,476 cm^{-1} band appears in fluorescence polarized along the a axis, and the higher component is missing. No spectrum is found built upon the two component levels. Instead, the main fluorescence starts with the 31,062 band. It is a strong spectrum in which a 520 vibration is prominent. This emission is b-polarized. It was interpreted as M series, i.e., a vibration-induced spectrum. Emission from the higher factor group component is suppressed, because it sensitizes the zero level of the "molecule" series (31,559) by radiationless energy transfer. It does not sensitize the lower component 31,476, because emissions from the two levels are polarized perpendicularly to each other. Fluorescence from the M zero-level 31,559 will be polarized in the direction of the upper Davydov component, i.e., along b. The zero line of this transition would have the frequency of the upper component minus one-half (166). Fluorescence starting from this level to the vibrationless ground state is not observed, because it has to be allowed by a vibration. Consequently, the shortest-wavelength emission should equal the calculated zero line minus the value for the interacting vibration, which is a little over 500. This leads to the strong fluorescence spectrum beginning at 31,062 that was just mentioned. The same conclusions had been reached before independently by Wolf [18] and Zmerli [19] from their experiments.

In spite of the fact that a non-totally symmetric 500 cm^{-1} vibration had not been reported in the Raman spectrum, this interpretation seemed convincing at this time because the spectrum was easily analyzed as a vibration- induced M of naphthalene.

Recent results of Prikhotjko and Shpak [20] and of Wolf [21] indicate however, that the 31062 level must belong to an impurity, recognized by them as β — methylnaphthalene. One proof is that 31062 is an absorption line ruling out its origin from a vibratinoal level. We convinced ourselves that even at 4.2°K it appeared as a sharp absorption line. Consequently, the main part of the crystal series, called ν_b, series by Zmerli [19], has to be assigned to β — methylnaphthalene with 31062 as 0,0 transition. The mehylsubstitution changes it into an allowed spectrum. It is sensitized by the higher exciton level (31642) of naphthalene, thus weakening the genuine naphthalene fluorescence which begins with the band 30,964.[21] We interpret this band as $0-1$ band of the M series of naphthalene whereas the 0,0 band is forbidden.*

b. Delayed Fluorescence in Naphthalene Crystals. If the strong fluorescence of naphthalene crystal originating at 31,062 cm^{-1}, and sensitized by the higher Davydov component at 31,642 cm^{-1}, belongs to the impurity of β — methylnaphthalene, then

---

* This paragraph has been rewritten at proofreading because new observations were made in the meantime. See A. F. Prikhotjko and M. T. Shpak, *Optika i Spektroskopiya* **6,** 119 (1959); H. C. Wolf, *Naturwiss.* **48,** 43 (1961).

the same should apply to the delayed fluorescence [20], [21]. Occurrence of delayed fluorescence must necessarily be connected with a long-living storage mechanism of the excitation energy in the crystal. Two storage processes are known to occur: formation of exciton traps, and formation of metastable states. Both of them lie energetically below the exciton bands. At higher temperature a delayed return from the trapped state to the exciton state might be possible, but it cannot happen at 4°K. A thermal release from the metastable triplet into an excited singlet level is even at room temperature not possible. However, transitions into higher quantum levels of excited trap states or of metastable states might become feasible if a second exciton does come close enough to the location of such long-lived states. The now highly excited states (double excitation energy) can go over to the lowest excited level by internal conversion in the usual way, but the fluorescence will appear "delayed." Or, in case impurities of lower energy are present, the singlet excitation energy may be used for exciting the impurity. Apparently, such a case is realized in naphthalene crystal.

Similar considerations may apply if the high excitation state, which was reached in two steps, lies above the conductivity band for free electrons and consequently photoionization may set in. The free electrons may then be trapped, and after release from the traps could reunite with holes with light emission [20]. Again, at 4°K thermal reliberation from the traps is quite improbable since there is no reason that the traps are very shallow. However, light irradiation or exciton waves approaching these traps closely might liberate the electrons in a similar fashion as from color centers in inorganic phosphors. Discussion remarks expressing related ideas have been during the meeting.

c. **Phosphorescence in Naphthalene Crystals.** In addition to the delayed fluorescence, which has a lifetime of the order of 10^{-3} sec, three more emissions from naphthalene crystals have been observed by our group with a phosphoroscope,[22] namely, at 19,137, 20,974, and 27,762 cm^{-1}. The last spectrum appears at liquid N_2 and He temperatures. It is the only spectrum that does not sharpen up at 4°K. It never appears simultaneously with the delayed fluorescence. It does not appear in EPA. But it is often found on the same plate with the 19,137. The 20,974 is usually observed together with the delayed fluorescence. On some plates both the 20,974 and 19,137 were observed.

In crystals with exciton movement, of which naphthalene is an example, singlet excitation energy is easily transferred to low-lying levels of impurities, thereby weakening fluorescence and phosphorescence emission of the main substance. It appears to be almost impossible to avoid the last traces of impurities in naphthalene. In order to decide whether the 19,137 belongs to naphthalene or to an impurity, Dr. H. Renner of our group used samples, which in the crystalline phase showed the 19,137 phosphorescence, for experiments in which this naphthalene was adsorbed on different surfaces like Al_2O_3 and SiO_2 and for other experiments in which the naphthalene was used in a so-called "inclusion" compound. For the latter purpose Schardinger β and γ dextrins were used. Without going into details it will be mentioned here only that the 19,137 spectrum disappeared under these experimental conditions, whereas the 20,974 phosphorescence remained. It is the true phosphorescence spectrum of naphthalene. The 19,137 and with it very probably the 27,762 belong to an impurity.

References

1. D. S. McClure, *J. Chem. Phys.* **22**, 1668 (1954).
2. D. S. McClure and O. Schnepp, *J. Chem. Phys.* **23**, 1575 (1955).
3. D. S. McClure, *J. Chem. Phys.* **24**, 1 (1956).
4. H. C. Wolf, *Z. Naturforsch.* **10a**, 244 (1955).
5. H. G. de Laszlo, *Z. physik. Chm.* **118**, 369 (1925).
6. H. Sponer and C. D. Cooper, *J. Chem. Phys.* **23**, 646 (1955).
7. H. Sponer, G. Nordheim, E. Teller, and A. L. Sklar, *J. Chem. Phys.* **7**, 207 (1939).
8. A. Kronenberger, *Z. Physik* **63**, 494 (1930).
9. A. S. Davydov, *J. Exptl. Theoret. Phys. (U.S.S.R.)* **18**, 210 (1948).
10. D. S. McClure, *Solid State Phys.* **9**, 1 (1959).
11. A. Prikhotjko, *J. Phys. (U.S.S.R.)* **8**, 257 (1944).
12. A. Prikhotjko, *Exptl. Theoret. Phys. (U.S.S.R.)* **19**, 383 (1948).
13. C. V. Raman and T. M. K. Nedungadi, *Nature* **143**, 679 (1939).
14. A. Kastler, *Z. Elektrochem.* **54**, 501 (1950).

15. P. Pringsheim, *Ann. acad. sci. tech. Varsovie* **5**, 29 (1938).
16. O. Schnepp and D. S. McClure, *J. Chem. Phys.* **20**, 1375 (1952).
17. W. Obreimov and K. Shabaldas, *J. Phys. (U.S.S.R.)* **7**, 168 (1943).
18. D. Griessbach, G. Will, and H. C. Wolf, *Z. Naturforsch.* **11a**, 791 (1956); H. C. Wolf, *Advances in Solid State Phys.* **9**, 1 (1959).
19. Adnan Zmerli, *J. chim. phys.* **1959** 387.
20. H. Sponer, Y. Kanda, and L. A. Blackwell, *J. Chem. Phys.* **29**, 721 (1958).
21. N. W. Blake and D. S. McClure, *J. Chem. Phys.* **29**, 722 (1958).
22. Presented at Symposium on Molecular Structure and Spectroscopy, Ohio State University, Columbus, Ohio (June, 1956).

14

Absorption and Luminescence Spectra and the Spectral Dependence of Photoemission and Photoconduction in Aromatic Hydrocarbon Crystals

L. E. LYONS

1. Photoemission of Electrons

Photoemission of electrons from crystals of aromatic hydrocarbons occurs almost as readily as it does from metals. This was first observed on anthracene by Pochettino.[1] Thresholds were reported by previous workers[2] for only three substances. Recent work[3] has extended the list to other compounds. The thresholds are compared with the experimental or theoretical ionization potential of the gaseous molecules in Table 14.1.[4]

Table 14.1. The Difference W in the Energy of Ionizing a Gaseous Molecule and a Crystal of the Same Substance

	Threshold of emission from crystal	Gaseous ionization potential expt.	theory	$-W$ (threshold— ionization potential)		$-W$ (calc.)
Tetracene	5.26		6.92		1.7	
Anthracene	5.65	6.86	7.23	1.3	1.6	> 1.0
1:2-Benzanthracene	5.68		7.35		1.5	
1:2:5:6-Dibenzanthracene	5.69		7.42		1.5	
Chrysene	5.73		7.72		2.0	
Pyrene	5.81		7.58		1.8	
Phenanthrene	6.45		8.02		1.5	
Naphthalene	6.76	8.12	(8.12)	1.4		> 0.8

The only gaseous ionization potential so far reported for the substances of the table is that for naphthalene. The value for

anthracene[5] is experimental but depends upon the validity of
certain spectral identifications. The other ionization potentials
are theoretical, with a parameter evaluated for naphthalene.

There is little doubt that an energy difference W, of something
more than 1 ev, exists between the threshold and the ionization
potential. An explanation of this and some calculations have been
given previously.[6] The value originally calculated for W was said at
the time to be an underestimate, as Fox also has stated.[7] The
general nature of the explanation has been confirmed by the later
work. The polarization of the crystal by the positive charge
remaining after the electron is emitted causes the ionization
energy to be lower in the crystal than in the gas.

2. Photoconduction

The spectral dependence of photoconductance in anthracene-
type crystals varies with the electrode arrangements. For a cell
with two bar electrodes on the illuminated surfaces and for
optical transitions that are moderately intense, there is a similarity
between the $I_S-\nu$ and the $\varepsilon-\nu$ curves (I_S the photocurrent in a
surface cell, ε is the molar-extinction coefficient, and is the
frequency of the exciting light). The resemblance was explained
as a surface effect, and although the exact details of the surface
effect are still in doubt, it seems agreed that a surface explanation
is correct. The breakdown of the similarity, as there is with
naphthalene when weak transitions are considered, is thus able
to be understood as due to the penetration of the light into the
crystal to a deeper region than any affected by the surface
phenomena. The photocurrents observed are therefore bulk photocurrents, i.e., those in which the surface is unimportant.

Other deviations from similarity between $I_S-\nu$ and $\varepsilon-\nu$ curves
occur where the shape of the electrodes is changed and with it
the directional properties of the electrical field in the crystal.
These deviations from similarity were attributed[8] to whether or
not the electrodes were placed on the side of the crystal which
was illuminated or on that which was not, i.e., the front or the
back. It was stated that when the electrodes were on the front,
the $I_S-\nu$ curve was quite unlike the $\varepsilon-\nu$ curve, the maxima in

one corresponding to the minima in the other. This claim was fully investigated by Mackie,[9] who found that when the electrodes on the front surface were bar electrodes and the light fell on a surface that consequently experienced a relatively uniform electrical field, then the I_S—ν curve maintained its similarity to the ε—ν curve. If, however, the electrodes were intermediate between long bars and points, then the front surface of the crystal experienced a nonuniform field, the value of I_S fell, and also the similarity was lost.

A comparable loss in similarity between the I_S—ν and ε—ν curves was reported [10, 11] several years ago in the case of photocurrents I_B measured in a sandwich cell, the light entering through a semitransparent electrode. Mackie [9] has worked further on this point and studied the pronounced space charge already known to be present in such experiments. The charge had a big effect on (a) the I_B—t curve, (b) the I_B—V curve, and (c) the back photocurrent in the absence of an applied field, all of which effects had previously been studied.[10,11] The I_B—t curve was used to measure the space charge in a given crystal. In this way he correlated space-charge effects with the spectral dependence of I_B. Light that was absorbed more or less uniformly throughout the crystal gave rise to less space charge than light that was absorbed near one electrode, and as a result there appeared a peak in the I_B—V curve at longwavelengths. The fall in I_B at wavelengths longer than the peak was due to light being transmitted right through the crystal and a decrease in the number of quanta absorbed. A definite, though relatively small, current was registered at wavelengths much longer than that of the peak. The effects of space charge were reduced by increasing the applied field. The reduction when the illuminated electrode was positive could be taken to the point when the space-charge effect was negligible. Under these circumstances I_B was determined solely by the number of quanta absorbed: below a threshold wavelength, which varied with the thickness of the crystal and was found where the optical density of the crystal was about 0.7, the I_B—ν curve was a straight line. Figure 14.1 shows the effect on the spectral dependence of increasing the field. Since the effect of space charge is always to reduce I_B, its removal results in a much larger current than is otherwise observed.

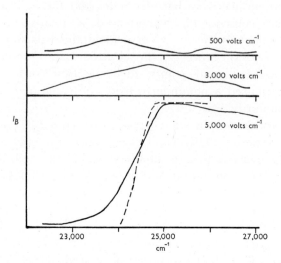

Fig. 14.1. The spectral dependence of the bulk photocurrents in anthracene with increasing field. Positive electrode illuminated. The broken curve shows the absorption of the same crystal.

A second method of reducing the effect of space charge was found in the irradiation of the sample simultaneously by ultra-violet and by infrared light. Infrared quanta of energy about 0.8 to 0.9 ev were found to be effective in detrapping some of the charges that gave rise to the space charge. The extinction coefficient of anthracene crystals for infrared radiation in this range was measured as about 0.5. Crystals at the beginning of an experiment were found to contain a certain number of trapped charges that could be freed by infrared radiation.

It was easier to follow the distribution of space charge in a sandwich cell where the field varied only in one dimension. In the surface cell for electrode arrangements giving a nonuniform field in the crystal-surface effects on I_S—t, I_S—v, and I_S—V curves were observed that resembled the behavior of the sandwich cell. Therefore space-charge effects were held to be responsible for the phenomena observed in the surface cell.

We can conclude, therefore, that both I_B—v and I_S—v curves are understood in principle. The details of the mechanism causing the similarity for uniform-surface fields of I_S—v and ε—v curves, however, have not yet been established.

Two further effects of space charge must be mentioned:

a. The presence of space charge must have influenced the recorded measurements[12] of d-c dark conductivity, giving lower values than actually obtained. On anthracene, at least, we are not aware of any work in which this disability has been completely removed. The explanation of deviations from Ohm's law, which became less at high fields, was not understood at the time of a recent review.[13] It is undoubtedly similar to that given to our I_S—V curves for nonuniform surface fields, namely, that space charge is present.

b. Any theoretical treatment that is built on the basis of Poisson's continuity equation and diffusion relations will not apply to the results on sandwich cells that have been reported so far, unless allowance is made for the variation in field within the sample. This variation generally will be a function of time (although a steady state may be reached), and consequently a full theory is very difficult. Experiments in which the light is propagated perpendicularly to the field direction and experiments in which the light is but feebly absorbed afford the best hope of theoretical quantitative explanation. Such experiments are planned.

The existence of a "conduction band" is a traditional assumption in solid-state physics, and indeed we do not desire to question it. If, however, it is thought to mean that light above a quantal energy of, say, 5 ev will produce a much bigger current in anthracene crystals than light below that energy, recent work by Morris[3] shows such a conclusion to be false. Photoconduction in surface cells takes place in both anthracene and naphthalene at wavelengths as low as 1,600 A, in very much the same way and at much the same magnitude as in the ordinary ultraviolet. Photoconduction persists even below the photoemission threshold. There is no large increase in current at any photoconduction threshold between 1.3 and 8 ev. It seems likely, then, that from 1,600 to above 10,000 A, apart from the surface effect discussed previously, photocurrents in the anthracene crystals so far examined depend chiefly on the number of quanta of light absorbed, the mechanism being more or less constant throughout. There seems, too, considerable evidence that the photoconduction is dominated by the trapping not only of the electrons but also of the more mobile positive charges. Trapping would certainly affect the observation of any pronounced photoconduction threshold at a conduction band.

The existence of a photocurrent shows that the crystals absorb light feebly all through the visible and into the infrared. To what is this absorption due? The ionized excitons and free conduction states that were discussed previously[6] on the basis of an almost classical physics must exist in some form. Calculations of photo-emission thresholds have been sufficiently successful to make us expect that the lowest ionized exciton level will occur possibly as low as 1 ev or even less. It is, however, not correct to regard these crystal levels as single. They will undoubtedly be broadened, and the broad level is that likely to be observed at room temperature because of the interaction with phonons. It seems conceivable that sufficient broadened levels of both bound and free charges exist to give rise to continuous absorption in the range considered. The production of free carriers was previously mentioned[10] as yielding continuous absorption.

In Fig. 14.2 various (unbroadened) energy levels are shown in a simplified scheme. The existence of zones of levels instead of single levels is understood. The diagram suggests two ways in which the influence of infrared radiation of about 0.8 ev could give rise to increased currents. In Fig. 14.2 the conduction level is shown below 3 ev, but it must be emphasized that there is no observation on such a level. Similarly, the dephts of the trapping levels below the corresponding untrapped levels have been drawn in a way convenient for making the diagram and do not necessarily indicate measured quantities. Transitions A are those to the neutral exciton level of lowest energy with the accompanying edge levels. Such transitions occur to a number of crystal levels, depending on the number of molecules in the unit cell. For simplicity only one is shown. These levels are discussed elsewhere in this paper.

The photoconduction has been shown to be due largely to the movement of positive holes. If we ignore the movement of electrons, we can ignore the transition type D (Fig. 14.2), which refers to the detrapping of a negative carrier. Transitions of types E and C

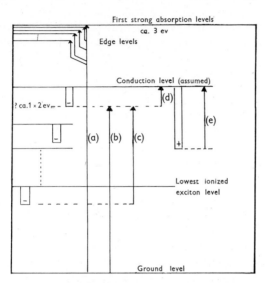

Fig. 14.2. Schematic diagram of some theoretical and observed energy levels in molecular crystals such as anthracene. (a), (b), (c), (d) and (e) denote various types of transitions.

both would increase positive hole conduction. In type E a positive carrier is detrapped. In type C a positive carrier that has been moving around a trapped negative charge becomes freed, although the negative charge remains trapped. Transitions of type B result in the production of a trapped negative and a free positive charge. Such transitions might well occur thermally if not optically. The lower limits of the energy of such a transition are fixed by the temperature coefficient of the dark conductivity, which is about 0.8 ev in the expression $= {}_0 \exp(-E/kT)$. The upper limit is presumably fixed by the largest wavelength of radiation that is known to produce conductivity (unless, indeed, two quanta are necessary to produce one carrier, but such an assumption does not seem at present to be required, although it is conceivable).

From such considerations the value 1.2 ev has been estimated for anthracene.

Recombination of charges must occur in the crystal, and thus the possibility of luminescence was envisaged.[10] From our present considerations luminescence could occur all through the visible, and the maximum could be determined solely by the temperature, if the levels in fact form a near continuum.

3. Neutral Excited States

The luminescence from anthracene containing a small quantity of tetracene changes its character as the temperature is lowered to 4°K, at which temperature the usual result is that the energy transfer to the tetracene has been greatly reduced.[15] As the temperature is gradually changed from 4 to 300°K, there are particular temperature ranges over which the changes are most pronounced. The temperature dependence of the luminescence from anthracene free of tetracene has also been studied[16] over the same range. Once again there are certain ranges of temperature over which the changes are most rapid. These ranges show a striking similarity to those in which there is a change in the energy-transfer process. Therefore, it seems likely that the explanation of the temperature dependence of the anthracene luminescence will also show why the energy transfer is affected. The transfer to the tetracene is affected by the effect of temperature on the host lattice. There is thus a need to understand anthracene luminescence. The origins of the absorption and luminescence transitions in anthracene crystals of about 3 ev are known only approximately. The amount of the splitting between the a and b crystal states is far from clear. There certainly seems to be a separation between the origins of absorption from those of luminescence, a separation attributed by Sidman[17] to trapped-exciton states and by McClure[18] to a Franck-Condon effect. There is also a considerable body of evidence[19] for the existence of a whole series of origins. Edge bands often occur in both absorption and luminescence. The number of edge bands is now thought [16] to include bands at 25,370, 25,310, 25,275, 25,170,

25,110, 25,070, 25,030, 24,985, 24,930, 24,870, 24,815, 24,770, 24,715, 24,670, as well as others.

The luminescence from anthracene crystals consists of three or four main regions, intervals between which are approximately 1,400 cm^{-1}, which is about the frequency of a totally symmetrical molecular vibration. As the temperature is lowered to 4°K, there is an apparent shift of the whole spectrum to lower energies by about 550 cm^{-1}. This shift has been attributed to a decrease in the intensity of certain bands and corresponding increase in others. The effective origins of the luminescence shift to higher energies as the temperature is raised. A theory has been proposed to account for this.

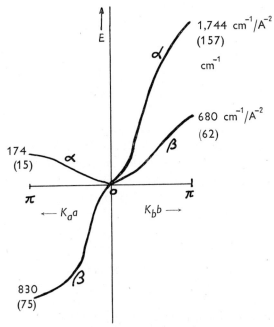

Fig. 14.3. Exciton bandwidths in anthracene. (Splitting of α and β states at $k = 0$ not shown).

What energy levels occur in the relevant region of the spectrum? The exciton levels considered previously in connection with the spectrum of anthracene crystals have been those in which the exciton wave vector $k \approx 0$. There is, in fact, a zone of levels for each crystal state, and these levels have been calculated, and some of the results are shown in Fig. 14.3, in which the numbers in parentheses refer to the values in cm^{-1} relevant to the 3-ev transition. When it is remembered that the $k = 0$ levels of the α and β crystal states are separated, with the β lying at the lower energy, the total energy spread of the bands is several hundreds of cm^{-1}. Optical transitions to any level in these zones can take place provided there is a phonon of wave vector p that is absorbed or emitted simultaneously. Both energy and momentum are conserved. However, the energy of an exciton (relative to that for $k = 0$) differs from that of a phonon of similar wave vector. If the vibrations of the crystal that are thus considered are totally symmetric in the unit cell group, then the polarization of the bands of lowest energy will be b, which approximates the result obtained experimentally.[20] Edge bands of higher energy have a greater component which is a polarized.

The levels just discussed are not trapped levels but depend on lattice vibrations. Such vibrations are important in the spectrum in another way also. The general shape of the luminescence spectrum makes it clear that a Franck-Condon type of effect is operative. The equilibrium value of a crystal coordinate is different in the excited and ground state. The maximum luminescence occurs approximately 400 cm^{-1} from the origin. Such a value represents perhaps 10 quanta of a lattice vibration.

The trapped levels of Frenkel[21] to which Sidman referred would be largely depopulated at room temperature. It is possible by assuming that the observed luminescence occurs from excitons in various depths of traps to arrive at a very simple explanation of the temperature dependence of the energytransfer process in anthracene containing tetracene. At low temperatures the excitons are in deep traps and are therefore relatively immobile. As the temperature rises the excitons occupy more shallow traps and become more mobile and are therefore more likely to produce an excited tetracene center. At sufficiently high temperatures the excitons would be quite mobile. Thermal equilibrium between trapping levels is assumed in this picture. It is not possible at present to assert that this picture is true, especially as the influence of defects has not been evaluated.

Both the discussion of trapped excitons and the preceding discussion of free excitons point to the necessity of a further study of exciton-phonon interaction. Such a development is likely to constitute the next stage of work in this field.

References

1. A. Pochettino, *Atti accad. naz. Lincei* **15**(1), 355; **15**(2), 17 (1906).
2. A. L. Hughes and L. A. DuBridge, "Photoelectric Phenomena," 1st ed., McGraw-Hill, New York (1932)
3. L. E. Lyons and G. C. Morris (to be published).
4. F. A. Matsen, *J. Chem. Phys.* **24**, 602 (1956); "Proceedings of the Third Conference on Carbon," p. 22, Pergamon Press, Ltd., London (1959).
5. L. E. Lyons and G. C. Morris, *J. Mol. Spectroscopy* (1960).
6. L. E. Lyons, *J. Chem. Soc.* **1957**, 5001; and unpublished work.
7. D. Fox, *Phys. and Chem. Solids* **8**, 439 (1959).
8. J. Ferguson and W. G. Schneider, *Can. J. Chem.* **36**, 1633 (1958).
9. J. C. Mackie, M.Sc. thesis, University of Sydney (1959); L. E. Lyons and J. C. Mackie (to be published).
10. L. E. Lyons and G. C. Morris, *J. Chem. Soc.* **1957**, 3648.
11. D. M. Compton, W. G. Schneider, and T. C. Waddington, *J. Chem. Phys.* **27**, 160 (1957).
12. H. Mette and H. Pick, *Z. Physik* **134**, 566 (1953): N. V. Riehl, *Zhur. Fiz. Khim.* **29**, 959 (1955); D. C. Northrop and O. Simpson, *Proc. Roy. Soc.* (*London*) **A234**, 124 (1956); H. Inokuchi, *Bull. Chem. Soc. Japan* **29**, 131 (1956).
13. C. G. B. Garrett, in N. B. Hannay (ed.), "Semiconductors," Monograph Series No. 140, p. 634, Reinhold Publishing Corporation, New York (1959).
14. G. C. Morris, Ph.D. thesis, University of Sydney (1957).
15. L. E. Lyons and J. W. White, *J. Chem. Phys.* **29**, 447 (1958); J. Ferguson and W. G. Schneider, *Can. J. Chem.* **36**, 11070 (1958).
16. L. E. Lyons and J. W. White (to be published).
17. J. Sidman, *J. Chem. Phys.* **25**, 115 (1956).
18. D. S. McClure, *J. Chem. Phys.* **25**, 481 (1956).
19. A. P. Prikhotjko and I. Ya. Fugol, *Optika y Spektroskopiya* **4**, 335 (1958).
20. I. Ya. Fugol and S. Z. Shulga, *Optika y Spektroskopiya* **5**, 34 (1958).
21. J. Frenkel, *Physik. Z. Sowjetunion* **9**, 158 (1936).

15

Paramagnetic Resonance of Phosphorescent Naphthalene Molecules*

C. A. HUTCHISON, JR.

It is now well known that a very anisotropic, sharp-line, paramagnetic resonance spectrum may be observed in naphthalene molecules that have been optically excited into a triplet state.[1] This spectrum is observed when naphthalene molecules are oriented in solid solution in durene[2] (symmetrical tetramethyl

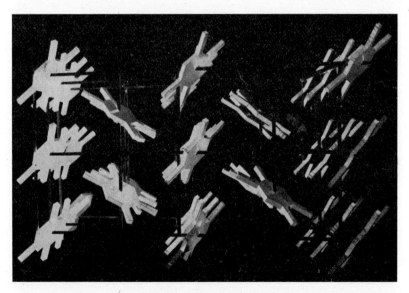

Fig. 15.1. Model of solid solution of naphthalene in durene.

benzene) with a concentration of approximately 0.2 mole per cent, as shown in Figs. 15.1, 15.2, and 15.3. There are two crystallographically inequivalent durene molecules in the struc-

* This work was supported by the U.S. Atomic Energy Commission.

Fig. 15.2. Model of solid solution of naphthalene in durene.

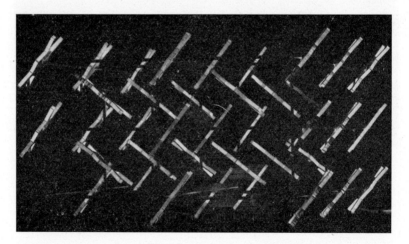

Fig. 15.3. Model of solid solution of naphthalene in durene.

ture.[3] Naphthalene enters the structure substitutionally for durene.

We denote the long axis of naphthalene or durene by x, the short axis by y, and the normal to the plane by z. When naphthalene is substituted for durene, the x, y, and z axes of naphthalene are parallel, respectively, to the same axes of one or the other of the two types of durene, as will be seen later. Also the structure is such that the planes of the two types of naphthalene are nearly perpendicular and their y axes are nearly parallel.

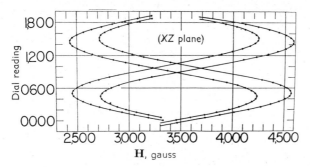

Fig. 15.4. Magnitudes $|\mathbf{H}|$ of magnetic field at which resonance is observed at 9,700 mc sec^{-1} when $\mathbf{H}$ is rotated in the xz plane of one of the two types of naphthalene molecules.

Figures 15.4, 15.5, and 15.6, show the experimental values of the magnitude $|\mathbf{H}|$ of magnetic field at which resonance peaks are observed at the boiling point of liquid N_2 as $\mathbf{H}$ is rotated in the

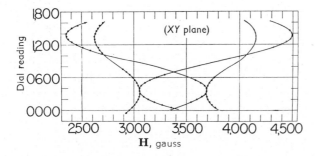

Fig. 15.5. Magnitudes $|\mathbf{H}|$ of magnetic field at which resonance is observed at 9,700 mc sec^{-1} when $\mathbf{H}$ is rotated in the xy plane of one of the two types of naphthalene molecules.

three principal magnetic planes of one of the naphthalene molecules, i.e., the *xz* plane, the *xy* plane, and the *yz* plane. Two
absorption peaks originate from each type of molecule. It is clear

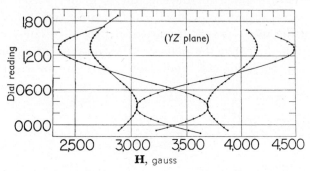

Fig. 15.6. Magnitudes $|\mathbf{H}|$ of magnetic field at which resonance is observed
at 9,700 mc sec^{-1} when $\mathbf{H}$ is rotated in the *yz* plane of one of the two types
of naphthalene molecules.

from the structural information given previously that in the *xz*
plane, for example, the resonance patterns of the two types of
molecule must be nearly the same and displaced from each other
by $\pi/2$ in angle of rotation. The *xz* patterns are seen in Fig. 15.4
to be so displaced. When the field is along the *y* axis of one
naphthalene, it is nearly along the same axis of the other. Hence
the two two-line patterns nearly coincide in this orientation of
$\mathbf{H}$, as seen in Figs. 15.5 and 15.6.

Inasmuch as durene is a molecular crystal with only relatively
weak forces binding the molecules together, it is assumed that the
main perturbation on the triplet-state electrons responsible for
the anisotropy is intramolecular in origin. The free molecule
has orthorhombic symmetry. The most general splitting of the
energies of the three states of any triplet in an orthorhombic
field is given by the eigenvalues of the hamiltonian[4]

$$\mathcal{H} = \mathbf{H}g\mathbf{S} + DS_z^{\,2} + E(S_x^{\,2} - S_y^{\,2})$$

In this hamiltonian, $S = 1$, which corresponds to the triplet state's
having two parallel spins. This spin gives rise to three states
with strong field quantum numbers $M_s = 1$, 0, -1. In the

present experiments the alternating magnetic field is polarized perpendicular to the static magnetic field, and the two transitions for which $\Delta M_s = 1$ are seen. g is a tensor describing the magnetic splitting of the three energies; in the present case, g is found to be isotropic, with the value 2.0030. The anisotropy arises from the molecular splitting described by D and E, and the resultant energies depend upon the angles that $\mathbf{H}$ makes with the x, y, and z axes. D is a parameter describing the axial component of the molecular splitting in the absence of a magnetic field, and in the case of molecules such as benzene, it would be the only molecular-splitting parameter. D/hc is found to have the value 0.1006 cm^{-1}. E measures the deviation from axial symmetry and is here found to be 0.0138 cm^{-1}. These values of the parameters describe the experimental data within their error at 9,700 mc sec^{-1} and 23,000 mc sec^{-1}. It is clear that in the absence of a magnetic field the degeneracy is removed to give energies 0, $D+E$, and $D-E$ and that in the presence of the field the two $\Delta M = 1$ transitions occur at different magnitudes of the field for fixed frequency.

Now, of course, the question occurs as to the source of the zero-field splitting. Spin-orbit coupling could in principle do the job, but it is well known to be very small in such systems. The very long experimental phosphorescence lifetimes support the theoretical calculation of very small spin-orbit couplings, since their perturbation is one that flips over electron spins and thus produces triplet-singlet emissions. The zero-field splitting arises from spin-spin magnetic-dipole interactions between the two electrons with parallel spins in the triplet state. If two parallel spins are placed in π orbitals on adjacent C atoms in the naphthalene rings, their magnetic dipole-dipole energy is seen to vary in an obvious manner with the orientation of the spins with respect to the molecular axes. This energy of orientation is of order 0.1 cm^{-1}, the observed splitting. The square of the Bohr magneton divided by the C—C bond distance is of the order of 0.16 cm^{-1}.

These agreements with the experimentally observed splittings are not just fortuitous. Contrary to the case of the O_2 molecule, two electrons with parallel spins cannot be put on the same atom at the same time in the π-electron approximation without violating the Pauli principle. It has been shown that more careful consideration of excited states[5] that permit both electrons on the same C simultaneously, lead to a very small dipole-dipole energy in spite of its r^{-3} dependence. Moreover, because of the fact that we are dealing with a triplet state, it may be shown that an antisymmetry requirement[6] on the space part of the wave function keeps the electrons apart, and thus zero-field splittings from magnetic dipole-dipole interactions do not arise from very close approaches of the two electrons.

Consequently, the good agreement of theoretical caluclations[7] of the zero-field splittings by dipole-dipole interaction with the experimental results gives strong evidence of the origin of the anisotropy.

Moreover, it should be pointed out that it has been found that the π-electron configuration mixture required to get the magnitudes and relative signs of D and E (the experiments show that they are of opposite signs) is the L_a state,[7,8] in essential agreement with what is expected a priori for the lowest triplet state.[9] This state is one consisting mainly of the configuration 5—5′ in which one electron is promoted from the highest filled orbital into the lowest unfilled orbital. With this is mixed a smaller amount of the configuration 4—4′ in which an electron in the next to the highest filled orbital is promoted to the next to the lowest unfilled orbital.

We now turn to a discussion of the hyperfine effects of the protons. The isotropic hyperfine splittings for the negative ions of aromatic molecules that are rapidly tumbling in solution have been successfully interpreted[10] by assuming that the isotropic splitting a, due to an aromatic proton, is proportional to the electron spin density on the adjacent carbon atom $a = Q\rho$, where ρ is the spin density. The universal semiempirical constant Q has the value -22.5 gauss per spin or -63 mc sec^{-1} per spin, the same for all aromatic C—H bonds.[11] The above equation has been derived theoretically on the basis of the mixing of π and σ configurations by exchange.[10] In the oriented system that we are discussing here, we have the opportunity of investigating the anisotropic hyperfine effects that arise from dipole-dipole interaction, between the π electrons on the adjacent C atom and the proton, which averages to zero in the case of the free radicals in solution.

In Fig. 15.7 is shown an axis system that may be used in the description of the hyperfine effects in a single C—H fragment.

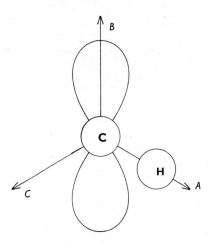

Fig. 15.7. Axis system for discussion of hyperfine interaction.

The C axis is perpendicular to both the A axis, which lies along the C—H bond, and the B axis, which is along the π orbital. The combined dipole-dipole and isotropic interaction energies may be taken to be the diagonal elements of the hamiltonian

$$\mathcal{H} = AS_A I_A + BS_B I_B + CS_C I_C$$

where $S = 1$, $I = 1/2$ is the spin of the proton, and A, B, and C are the hyperfine splittings when the spins are along the respective axes. In the case of a strong magnetic field along a direction that makes angles α, β, and γ with the A, B, and C axes, respectively, the hyperfine splitting is then

$$(A^2 \cos^2 \alpha + B^2 \cos^2 \beta + C^2 \cos^2 \gamma)^{1/2}$$

The dipole-dipole interaction between an electron polarized in various directions in the π orbital and the proton may be calculated,[12] and when this effect is added to the isotropic effect, the result is given by

$$A \cong -30 \text{ mc sec}^{-1}$$
$$B \cong -60 \text{ mc sec}^{-1}$$
$$C \cong -90 \text{ mc sec}^{-1}$$

Experimentally,[13] these values have been found to be

$$A = -30.0 \text{ mc sec}^{-1}$$
$$B = -61.5 \text{ mc sec}^{-1}$$
$$C = -92.5 \text{ mc sec}^{-1}$$

These are the splittings for unit electron spin on the adjacent C atom.

We shall treat our naphthalene molecule as an aggregate of eight such C—H fragments. In a strong magnetic field we may have any situation from all eight protons parallel to the field to all eight antiparallel. Using the values of A, B, and C we can then calculate the hyperfine shift for any arbitrary configuration of proton spins, any arbitrary direction of $\mathbf{H}$ with respect to molecular axes, and any arbitrary distribution of spin over the π system of the molecule.

Consider for example the case when H is parallel to the x axis of the molecule. Suppose we use simple Huckel orbitals and consider only the 5—5' configuration. This gives a normalized spin density 0.18 on each of the α protons, and 0.07 on each of the β protons, and 0 in the 9,10 positions in the $^3B_{2u}$ state, which we assume to be the state under study. With $\mathbf{H}$ along x the splitting by the α protons with the higher spin density has the large value -92.5 mc sec^{-1} per unit spin density on the C. The β C—H bond directions are close to $\mathbf{H}$, and the spin density is low, both facts leading to much smaller splittings from the β protons. Hence the four α protons, all equivalent in their effects, lead to five hyperfine shifts of $4 \times 1/2 \times 0.18 \times 92.5 = 2\rho_\alpha A$, $1\rho_\alpha A, \ldots, -2\rho_\alpha A$, with relative probabilities 1, 4, 6, 4 and 1 respectively. The four equivalent β protons further produce much smaller splittings of each of these components into five components resulting in the 25 lines shown in Fig. 15.8. In Fig. 15.9 is shown an oscilloscope pattern of the first derivative of the absorption when H is along x. The pattern is seen to be similar to the calculated one. The five peaks from the α protons are resolved, but the further structure is not. The durene used in this case was completely deuterated. This makes the resolution somewhat better than for the case when light durene is used. Other H's in the naphthalene, D in durene, and crystal strains lead to the lack of resolution.

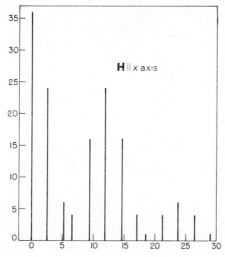

Fig. 15.8. Hyperfine lines to be expected with **H** along x axis.

In a similar manner the hyperfine pattern for the cases of **H** parallel to y or z may be calculated. The qualitative results are in good agreement with the experimental observation. When H is along the y axis, a fortuitous combination of the trigonometry and normalized spin densities leads to near equality of the splittings of all eight protons. The pattern is then almost a pattern of nine equally spaced peaks with a binomial-coefficient distribution of intensities. The observed single peak has the correct width relative to the x axis pattern and is gaussian.

If we assume that the experimental values, $A = -30.0$ mc sec^{-1}, $B = -61.5$ mc sec^{-1} and $C = -92.5$ mc sec^{-1} obtain in our case also, we may then infer that $\rho_\alpha = 0.209$ from the x axis data.

It is not possible to get a quantitative idea of the value of ρ_β from our results because the effects of ρ_α are always involved and in fact dominate. It is to be noted that the value of ρ_α is close to

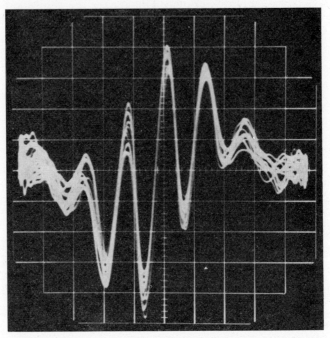

Fig. 15.9. Experimental hyperfine pattern with **H** along x axis.

that observed in the naphthalene negative ion. There is undoubtedly a negative spin density on the 9,10 C's which will need to be investigated by means of C^{13} effects. The complete elucidation of the hyperfine structure effects must await further studies on isotopically substituted molecules.

We might be led to believe that the triplet state that we are observing is not the $^3B_{2u}$ state that we have been postulating[9] but perhaps the $^3B_{3u}$ state that has an appreciable spin density in the 9,10 positions and that has been suggested as a possibility on the basis of optical work.[14] However, this state has a larger spin density on the β position than on the α position. This difficulty might be surmounted by saying that although the planes of the naphthalene molecules are parallel to those of the durenes, the naphthalenes are rotated about the normal to their plane by $\pi/2$ with respect to the durenes for which they substitute, thus leading again to hyperfine patterns similar to those that are observed.

Such possibilities are eliminated by two further experimental results. When a single D is substituted for one of the α H's, the resulting hyperfine pattern consists of four peaks with intensities 1, 3, 3, 1, and when 1,4-dideuteronaphthalene is examined, a three-line spectrum with intensities 1, 2, 1 is observed. It is clear that this fact is inconsistent with a $^3B_{3u}$ state in a molecule oriented as just described. The only possibility seems to be that the naphthalenes are oriented as originally described. It will be

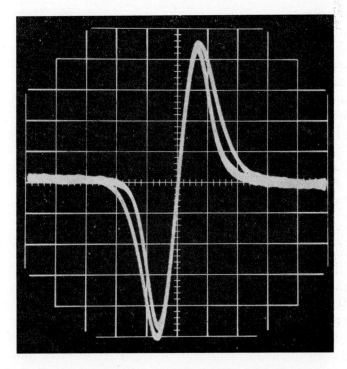

Fig. 15.10. Experimental resonance-absorption line with **H** along x axis of completely deuterated naphthalene.

of great importance to investigate naphthalene with the 9,10 positions labeled with C.[13]

We have also examined completely deuterated naphthalene. In this case because of the larger spin of D and its smaller magnetic moment, we have many more lines much more closely crowded together. The experimental result with **H** along the x axis is shown in Fig. 15.10. When the experimental observations on the five-line pattern are used to calculate the pattern expected for the changed spin and moment, the result is in agreement with the observation.

While investigating the completely deuterated naphthalene, it was observed that the resonance signal found in this case was extraordinarily intense relative to that observed in ordinary naphthalene. Therefore we examined the decay of the resonance signal after the cessation of ultraviolet irradiation. The mean life at the boiling point of liquid N_2 of the resonance of light naphthalene in light durene was found to be 2.1 ± 0.1 sec and of heavy naphthalene in heavy durene 16.9 ± 0.7 sec. The lifetime of ordinary naphthalene in a rigid glass (EPA) has been found to be 2.6 ± 0.2 sec at 77°K. The lifetimes for both light and heavy naphthalene are found to be approximately independent of whether light or heavy durene is used to make the crystals. The lifetime of the mono-α-deuteronaphthalene is found to be the same as that of light naphthalene within the error of the measurement. 1,4-dideuteronaphthalene has a lifetime of approximately 3 sec.

It has been suggested [15] that the hyperfine interaction might be the lifetime-limiting perturbation in this case and that the heavy naphthalene triplet might have longer life because of the smaller hyperfine interaction. The effect of the D on the lifetime might also be purely a mass effect. The large observed effect of D substitution could possible arise from the effect of mass on the rate of the radiationless transition from the triplet state to the ground state. The rate of this radiationless triplet-singlet transition might be controlled either by a tunneling process or by the rate of passage over the potential barrier. In either case the larger D mass would result in a longer triplet-state lifetime.

The group working at Amsterdam [16] has, in some very beautiful experiments, extended the observation of magnetic resonance to the phosphorescent states of other molecules in solution in a glass by the use of the transitions in which $\Delta M_s = 2$. This transition is allowed because of the dipole-dipole interaction. This transition is not as anisotropic as the $\Delta M_s = 1$ transition, and the resonance is observable in randomly oriented systems. We are working on the problem of resonance absorption in randomly oriented molecules using zero magnetic field. In this case we have just the zero-field molecular splitting described above and hence no anisotropy except in the intensity. The zero-field splitting is 0.1 cm^{-1}, and so the absorption is still in the microwave region. There should be no problem of sensitivity.

Work is also in progress to find suitable single-crystal systems for the investigation of other organic molecules in high-field experiments. We are also attempting a determination of the signs of D and E, inasmuch as the theoretical calculations give the signs of these parameters.

We have examined single crystals of pure deuteronaphthalene for resonance of conduction electrons created by multiple-photon absorption, but without success.

References

1. C. A. Hutchison, Jr. and B. W. Mangum, *J. Chem. Phys.* **29**, 952 (1958).
2. D. S. McClure, *J. Chem. Phys.* **22**, 1668 (1954).
3. J. M. Robertson, *Proc. Roy. Soc. (London)* **A141**, 594 (1933); **A142**, 659 (1933).
4. K. W. H. Stevens, *Proc. Roy. Soc. (London)* **A214**, 237 (1952).
5. H. M. McConnell and Sternlicht (in private communication).
6. H. M. McConnell, *Proc. Nat. Acad. Sci. U.S.*, **45**, 172 (1959).
7. M. Gouterman and W. Moffitt, *J. Chem. Phys.* **30**, 1107 (1959); M. Gouterman, *J. Chem. Phys.* **30**, 1369 (1959); H. F. Hameka, *J. Chem. Phys.* **31**, 315 (1959).
8. N. S. Ham and K. Ruedenberg, *J. Chem. Phys.* **25**, 1, 13 (1956); **29**, 1199 (1958).
9. R. Pariser, *J. Chem. Phys.* **24**, 250 (1956).
10. H. M. McConnell, *J. Chem. Phys.* **24**, 764 (1956); H. M. McConnell and D. B. Chesnut, *J. Chem. Phys.* **28**, 107 (1958); H. M. McConnell, *Ann. Rev. Phys. Chem.* **8**, 105 (1957); R. Bersohn, *J. Chem. Phys.* **24**, 1066 (1956); S. I. Weissman, *J. Chem. Phys.* **25**, 890 (1956); B. Venkataraman and G. K. Fraenkel, *J. Chem. Phys.* **24**, 737 (1956).

11. H. M. McConnell and H. H. Dearman, *J. Chem. Phys.* **28**, 51 (1958).
12. H. M. McConnell and J. Strathdee, *Mol. Phys.* **2**, 129 (1959).
13. T. Cole, C. Heller, and H. M. McConnell, *Proc. Natl. Acad. Sci U.S.* **45**, 525 (1959).
14. R. Williams, *J. Chem. Phys.* **30**, 233 (1959).
15. H. M. McConnell, (in private communication).
16. J. H. Van der Waals and M. S. De Groot, *Mol. Phys.* **2**, 333 (1959); M. S. de Groot and J. H. Van der Waals (to be published).

Dispersion Forces in Molecular Crystals

D. S. McClure

1. Introduction

In the Davydov theory of electronic spectra of molecular crystals,[1] the intermolecular resonance between identical molecules is the only type of coupling considered. However, the well-known Van der Waals, or London, dispersion forces [2] provide the binding energy of molecular crystals, and it is worth investigating to what extent they also affect the spectra. The London forces may also be applied to impurity molecules in a molecular crystal, while the resonance forces vanish for this case.

It should be possible also to calculate some of the important contributions to the heat of solution of an impurity molecule as well as the heat of formation of the crystal. It may also be possible to learn something about the mode of packing of molecules in a crystal and the frequencies of lattice vibrations by studying the anisotropy of the dispersion forces.

Our aim in this paper is limited to exploring only a few of these properties. We shall also confine ourselves to the use of the multipole expansion for expressing the intermolecular potential. There is a real question as to the validity of this expansion in the case of molecular crystals where the extent of the molecules in space is comparable to the distance between neighbors in the crystal. Nevertheless, we shall use it, since this is the first approach to the problem and results may be obtained easily. It has been used successfully by Craig [3] in the calculation of Davydov splitting in molecular crystals, so that to some extent its validity has been tested.

The pair-wise interactions between two molecules in fixed orientations relative to each other and far enough apart so that their charge distributions do not overlap appreciably can be expressed as the sum of the classical multipole interactions and the London dispersion force. The first of these contributions arises when the molecules are viewed as static distributions of charge and contribute interaction energies of the first order in quantum mechanical perturbation theory. The dispersion forces arise when the correlated motion of electrons in the two molecules is taken into account and are present only in the second order of perturbation theory. If we consider the molecules to be nonrigid, the classical multipole interactions include induction forces. These interaction energies may be summarized as follows:

For rigid uncharged molecules, the interaction potential includes terms of the types[2]

Dipole-dipole: $p_1 p_2/R^3$

Dipole-quadrupole: $(p_1 Q_2 + p_2 Q_1)/R^4$

Quadrupole-quadrupole: $Q_1 Q_2/R^5$

For nonrigid molecules there are additional terms of the types

Induced dipole-induced dipole: $(p_1^2 \alpha_2 + p_2^2 \alpha_1)/R^6$

Induced quadrupole-induced quadrupole: $(Q_1^2 \alpha_2 + Q_2^2 \alpha_1)/R^8$

Dispersion forces between nonpolar molecules arise from the above interaction potentials when electron correlation is taken into account. The dipoles and quadrupoles appearing in the formulas for this case are not the static multipoles but the virtual multipoles due to electronic transitions.

This paper will be limited mainly to an investigation of the dipole-dipole dispersion term for the case of a nonpolar impurity molecule in a nonpolar molecular crystal. The static dipole vanishes in these cases, and the static quadrupole is usually the first nonvanishing term of the multipole series. Evidence for the importance of some of these higher multipole terms is presented later. In the following section, we calculate some crystal properties which depend only on the equilibrium configuration.

2. Theory of the Band Shift and of the Heat of Solution

The hamiltonian function for a crystal with one impurity molecule, can be written

$$\mathscr{H} = \mathscr{H}_1 + \sum_{h=2}^{N} \mathscr{H}_h + \sum_{h=2}^{N} \mathscr{H}_{h1} + \sum_{ik} \mathscr{H}_{ik} \qquad (16.1)$$

where $\mathscr{H}_h$ and $\mathscr{H}_1$ are the unperturbed hamiltonian operators for the electrons of the hth host molecule and the impurity molecule; $\mathscr{H}_{h_1}$ is the interaction term between host and impurity; and $\mathscr{H}_{ik}$ is the interaction term between host molecules. For the interaction operators we shall substitute the dipole-dipole term

$$\mathscr{H}_{ik} = \mathbf{p}_i \boldsymbol{\theta}_{ik} \mathbf{p}_k \qquad (16.2)$$

where

$$\boldsymbol{\theta}_{ik} = [3(\mathbf{r}_{ik})(\mathbf{r}_{ik}) - (r_{ik})^2]/r^5{}_{ik}$$

The latter is the geometric factor, in this case a dyadic.

The wave functions that diagonalize this hamiltonian to a reasonable approximation are made up of products of single-molecule functions. In the zero order these are of the form:

Ground state:
$$\psi^0 = \varphi_1^0 \prod_{i=2}^{N} \varphi_i^0$$

Impurity excited:
$$\psi^k = \varphi_1^k \prod_{i=2}^{N} \varphi_i^0 \qquad (16.3)$$

Impurity and lattice excited:
$$\psi_h^{km} = \varphi_1^k \varphi_h^m \prod_{i \neq h} \varphi_i^0$$

This last is not a good wave function, since there will be many that differ from it only in the position of the excited host-crystal molecule h. The ψ_h^{km} must therefore be combined into orthogonal linear combinations, such as

$$\psi_q^{km} = \varphi_1^k \sum_h a_h^q \varphi_h^m \prod_{i \neq h} \varphi_i^0 \qquad (16.3a)$$

The a_h^q must be determined from the corresponding secular equations involving the hamiltonian, Eq. (16.1). We shall not carry this out, since it is sufficient if we only assume that a set of coefficients a_h^q exists and that they form an orthogonal matrix; i.e., $\sum_q (a_h^q)^2 = 1$, $\sum_q a_h^q a_i^q = 0$, etc. We shall also ignore the complications that arise when two electronic states of the lattice lie close together.

The effect on the kth state of the impurity molecule of the dispersive coupling to the crystal is tiven by

$$-\Delta E_2^k = \sum_n \sum_m \sum_q [|\mathscr{H}^k_{nmq}|^2/(E_n + E_{mq} - E_k)] \qquad (16.4)$$

where

$$\mathscr{H}^k_{nmq} = (\varphi_1^k \prod_i \varphi_i^0 | \mathscr{H}' | \varphi_1^n \sum_h a_h^q \varphi_h^m \prod_i \varphi_i^0)$$

and $\mathscr{H}'$ consists of the intermolecular coupling terms of Eq. (16.1). The E_n and E_k are energies of the impurity molecule measured from its ground state; E_{mh} is the energy of the qth state in the m band of the host crystal; $E_{mq} \approx E_m$, where E_m is the molecular energy level. We neglect the dependence of the energy denominator on q since the bandwidths in molecular crystals are small, and we can therefore factor the energy denominator out of the sum over q. In the absence of appreciable overlap between molecular wave functions, the above matrix element summed over q reduces to

$$p_{kn}^2 \, p_{omh}^2 \sum_q (\sum_h \theta_{1h} a_h^q)^2 \qquad (16.5)$$

The terms $\sum \mathscr{H}_{ik}$ between lattice molecules do not contribute to this; $p_{kn} = (\varphi_k | p_1 | \varphi_n)$, $p_{omh} = (\varphi_0^h | \mathbf{p}_h | \varphi_n^h)$, and θ_{1h} is now the value of the geometric factor for unit dipoles, a scalar. The p's are expressed as multiples of the unit dipole.

The summations in Eq. (16.5) reduce to

$$\sum_h \theta_{1h}^2 \sum_q (a_h^q)^2 + 2 \sum_{i>h} \theta_{1h} \theta_{1i} \sum_q a_h^q a_i^q = \sum_h \theta_{1h}^2$$

due to the orthogonality propertis of the a_h^q. The change in energy of the state k due to the dispersion forces finally becomes

$$-\Delta E_2^k = \sum_{n \neq k} \sum_m [p_{kn}^2 p_{omh}^2 \sum_h \theta_{1h}^2/(E_n + E_m^h - E_k)] \qquad (16.6)$$

The change of the energy of the absorption band, $0 \to k$, of the impurity molecule is $\Delta E_2^k - \Delta E_2^0$, where ΔE_2^0 is obtained from Eq. (16.6) by letting $k = 0$ and noting that $E_0 = 0$ by definition.

In order to evaluate expressions like (16.6) another approximation will be introduced. The electronic polarizability $\alpha_0(\nu)$ of a molecule in its ground state in the limit of very low frequencies may be written

$$\alpha_0(0) = \sum_m (2p_{om}^2/E_m) \qquad (16.7)$$

If the transitions making important contributions to the value of $\alpha_0(0)$ are confined to a narrow range, we can define an average energy for this range, and calling it I, write

$$\sum_m p_{om}^2 = \tfrac{1}{2}\alpha_0 I \qquad (16.8)$$

Similar averages of the energies in the denominator of Eq. (16.6) will be used. The average excitation of the impurity molecule will be designated I and that of the host molecules I^h.

The energy shift of the ground state can then be approximated by

$$-\Delta E_2^0 = 1/4 [II^h/(I+I^h)]\alpha\alpha^h \sum_h \theta_{1h}^2 \qquad (16.9)$$

where I^h and α^h refer to host-crystal molecules I and α to the impurity. So that we may obtain an expression for the excited state analogous to Eq. (16.9) we must separate (16.6) into sets of terms having comparable energy denominators (in order to be able to collect the latter into an average energy). The term in $\sum_n$, in which $n = 0$ has the energy denominator $E_m - E_k$ while the other terms have $E_n + E_m^h - E_k$. If we separate this term, substitute Eq. (16.8) for the p_{omh}^2 and substitute the average energy values, we find

$$-\Delta E_2^k = [\tfrac{1}{2}p_{0k}^2 \alpha^h I^h \sum_n \theta_{1h}^2/(I^h - E)]$$
$$- [\sum_{n \neq k, 0} \tfrac{1}{2}p_{kn}^2 \alpha^h I^h \sum_n \theta_{1h}^2/(I + I^h - E_k)] \qquad (16.9a)$$

At this point we shall consider two simplifying approximations: Replace $\sum_{n \neq k, 0} p_{kn}^2$ by $\sum_n p_{kn}^2 - p_{0k}^2$ and then assume that $\sum_n p_{kn}^2 \cong \sum_n p_{0n}^2$. Next replace $\sum_n p_{0n}^2$ by $\tfrac{1}{2}\alpha_0(0)I$. This results in the use of the ground-state polarizability through

$$\sum_{n \neq k, 0} p_{kn}^2 \cong \tfrac{1}{2}\alpha_0 I - p_{0k}^2.$$

b. The polarizability of a molecule in its excited state k can be written

$$\alpha_k(0) = 2 \sum_{n \neq k} [p_{kn}^2/(E_n - E_k)] \cong [2 \sum p_{kn}^2/(I - E_k)] - 2(p_{k0}^2/E_k)$$

From this we obtain

$$\sum_{n \neq k, 0} p_{kn}^2 = [\tfrac{1}{2}\alpha_k(0) + (p_{k0}^2/E_k)](I - E_k)$$

This substitution results in the use of excited-state polarizabilities. From a practical point of view, b is less desirable than a, since little is known about the α_k, but from a theoretical point of view use of the latter is more correct.

The two corresponding equations for ΔE_2^k can be written directly. The bandshift formulas obtained by taking $\Delta E_2^k - \Delta E_2^0$ are (letting $E_k = E$)

$$\Delta E_2^k - \Delta E_2^0 = (II^h/I + I^h - E)\{[\tfrac{1}{2}p_{0h}^2\alpha_h/(I^h - E)]$$
$$+ [\tfrac{1}{4}E\alpha_0\alpha_0^h/(I + I^h)]\} \sum_h \theta_{1h}^2 \qquad (16.10)$$

This equation is strictly analogous to Eq. 12 of Longuet-Higgins and Pople[4] for liquid solutions. It differs only in the way it is necessary to take account of the geometry of the surrounding molecules. For the other substitution

$$\Delta E_2^k - \Delta E_2^0 = \{[II^h/(I + I^h - E)][(I^h/E)][\tfrac{1}{2}p_{0k}^2\alpha^h/(I^h - E)]$$
$$- [\tfrac{1}{4}(I - E)\alpha_k\alpha_0^1/I][\tfrac{1}{4}II^h/(I + I^h)]\alpha_0\alpha_0^h\} \sum_h \theta_{1h}^2 \qquad (16.10a)$$

If as a reasonable guess we say $\alpha_k = (I\alpha_0/I - E)$, Eq. (16.10a) goes over approximately into (16.10).

An additional refinement would be to use polarizabilities appropriate to the transition energy E. However, in order to get some rough numbers for comparison with experiment, Eq. (16.10) will be used.

An important modification of Eq. (16.10) is to express it in terms of the differently oriented transitions within the molecules. The rectangular molecular axes of the host crystal molecules may be designated L, M, N, and molecular transitions are confined to these directions if the symmetry is high enough. A subscript may be attached to differentiate between two or more molecules in a unit cell. The axes of the impurity molecule will be designated $L'M'N'$. In a number of important cases, these directions coincide with those of one of the host-crystal molecules, and we shall assume this to hold in the following. The factors $\alpha_0 \alpha_0^h \sum_h \theta_{1h}^2$ and $p_{0k}^2 \alpha_0^h \sum_h \theta_{1h}^2$ in Eq. (16.10) become modified to

$$\alpha_0 \alpha_0^h \sum_h \theta_{1h}^2 \rightarrow \sum_x (\alpha_0)_x \sum_y \sum_h (\theta_{1h})_{xy}^2 (\alpha_0^h)_y$$
$$p_{0k}^2 \alpha_0^h \sum_h \theta_{1h}^2 \rightarrow (p_{0k})_x^2 \sum_y \sum_h (\theta_{1h})_{xy}^2 (\alpha_0^h)_y \qquad (16.11)$$

x and $y = L$, M, or N where the transition $0 \rightarrow k$ is assumed to be x polarized. The notation will be simplified from this point on by dropping some of the subscripts. In making these changes we assume that the average energy denominators are the same for all polarizations. The quantity $p_x \sum_y \sum_h \theta_{xy}^2 \alpha_y^h$ in the second of Eqs. (16.11) may be regarded as the reaction field of the crystal acting on the dipole p_x, and the term $p_x^2 \sum_y \sum_h \theta_{xy}^2 \alpha_y^h$ is the energy of interaction between this field and the dipole. The quantity $\sum_y \sum_h \theta_{xy}^2 \alpha_y^h$ is a reaction field for unit dipoles and will be referred to simply as a reaction field. Since it occurs so frequently the following abbreviations will be used:

$$a_{xx} = \sum_y \sum_h \theta_{xy}^2 \alpha_y^h$$
$$a_{xy} = \sum_z \sum_h \theta_{xz} \theta_{zy} \alpha_z^h \qquad (16.11a)$$

The cross terms such as a_{xy} will appear later in the theory of the orientation forces.

The equation for the bandshift of an L-polarized transition $0 \rightarrow k(L)$ can now be written from Eq. (16.10) as

$$\Delta E_2^k - \Delta E_2^0 = (II^h/(I+I^h-E)\{[\tfrac{1}{2} p_L^2 a_{LL}/(I^h-E)]$$
$$+ [\tfrac{1}{4} E \sum_x \alpha_x a_{xx}/(I+I^h)]\} \qquad (16.12)$$

Numerical calculations of the bandshift require values of the θ, the α, and the α^h. The θ may be obtained by direct summation over the nearest and next-nearest neighbors in the crystal, since they fall off as R^{-6}. Values of $\sum_h \theta_{xy}^2$ for the naphthalene crystal using the 14 nearest neighbors are given in Table 16.1.[5] There are six molecules having orientations equivalent to the one at the origin and eight having inequivalent orientations.

The reaction-field constants require values of the three principle polarizabilities of the molecule. These should be obtainable

Table 16.1. Values of the Orientation Factors and Reaction-field Constants for Naphthalene Crystal (Summation extends over 14 nearest Neighbors)

Orientation factors $(\text{cm}^{-1}\,\text{A}^{-2})^2$		Reaction fields, A^{-3}	
$\Sigma\theta_{LL}^2$	1.313×10^6	a_{LL}	1/162
$\Sigma\theta_{MM}^2$	0.221	a_{MM}	1/210
$\Sigma\theta_{NN}^2$	1.323	a_{NN}	1/125
$\Sigma\theta_{LM}^2$	1.513	a_{LM}	1/6,250
$\Sigma\theta_{N}^2$	2.328	a_{LN}	1/430
$\Sigma\theta_{NM}^2$	2.493	a_{NM}	1/1,850

from the three refractive indexes of the crystal by suitably correcting for the internal fields. The equations obtained are complicated and cannot easily be solved, as they contain products of all three molecular polarizabilities. Preliminary results suggest that they will be useful for checking approximations to the α, even if not for the actual calculations. Values of α were obtained by ignoring the effect of the internal fields. The dielectric tensor was transformed by the appropriate similarity transformation into the molecular coordinate system, and the values of α were assumed to be derivable from the diagonal components of the transformed tensor by way of

$$4\pi N\alpha_L/3 = (\varepsilon_{LL}-1/\varepsilon_{LL}+2), \quad \text{etc.} \qquad (16.13)$$

The average of the three α values for a molecule when computed this way agrees with the value of the polarizability calculated from the molar refractivity of the liquid via

$$R = V_m[(n^2-1)/(n^2+2)] = 4\pi N\alpha(\text{av})/3 \qquad (16.14)$$

and are probably fairly close to their correct values. Values of polarizabilities derived in this way are given in Table 16.2 for

Table 16.2. Approximate Values of Molecular Polarizabilities

	$\alpha_{LL},\ A^3$	α_{MM}	α_{NN}	α_{av}
Naphthalene	21.3	17.1	13.0	19.8 [a]
Anthracene	33.1	28.5	21.8	
Phenanthrene	33.0	27.6	22.1	
Azulene (assumed to be the same as for naphthalene)				

[a] From molar refraction of liquid naphthalene.

several aromatic hydrocarbons. The reaction fields computed from the orientation factors and polarizabilities are given for naphthalene in Table 16.1. The reaction fields can be expressed in units of A^{-3} by multiplying the $\sum \theta^2$ by $(8.63 \times 10^{-6})^2$ and using α^h in A^3.

The product of the α of the impurity molecule and the reaction field of the crystal is a dimensionless number. The smaller the volume corresponding to $1/a_{LL}$, etc., the greater is the reaction field. These volumes are seen to be on the order of ten times the polarizability; thus the band-shift energies will be on the order of one-tenth the average energy of excitation, according to Eq. (16.12). Some calculated values of bandshift are given in Table 16.3, where they are compared with the experimental values.

Table 16.3. Comparison of Observed and Calculated Band Shift (A positive number means the band shifts to the red, going from vapor to crystal).

	Calculated, cm^{-1}	Observed, cm^{-1}
Anthracene in naphthalene (1st band)	1,000 cm^{-1}	1,703 cm^{-1}
Anthracene in phenanthrene (1st band)	700	1,480
Azulene in naphthalene (1st band) [a]	240	−375
Azulene in naphthalene (2d band)	650	709

[a] The discrepancy for azulene is undoubtedly connected with the presence of a permanent dipole in this molecule. This dipole is probably reduced in the first excited state.

The results shown in Table 16.3 are fairly encouraging. About 60 to 70 per cent of the bandshift is accounted for by the dipolar dispersion forces. The term in Eq. (16.12) containing the transition dipole is found to be rather unimportant, contributing only about 10 per cent for the case of anthracene in naphthalene. The lack of agreement for azulene can be explained by the fact that this molecule has a permanent dipole whose value changes from one excited state to another. The present calculation does not take this into account.

It is also possible to return to Eq. (16.9) and compare the ΔE_2^0 values to the heat of solution of the impurity in the crystal. If the molecules were rigid, ΔE_2^0 evaluated at the equilibrium position would be the heat of solution, except for contributions from higher multipoles. Part of ΔE_2^0 should be canceled by the work done against repulsion forces, since the molecules are not rigid. Thus we expect ΔE_2 plus higher multipole terms to be greater than the observed heat of solution. We shall estimate the heats of solution to be of the order of heats of formation, since no heat-of-solution data are available. In the case of naphthalene, $\Delta E_2^0 = 0.334$ ev. Summing Eq. (16.9) over the entire crystal amounts to multiplying ΔE_2^0 by Avagadro's number and dividing by 2, to avoid counting pair-wise interactions twice. The result is ΔE_2 (crystal) $= 3.8$ kcal/mole. The heat of sublimation of naphthalene is 15 kcal/mole, so that in order to agree with the predicted inequality, the dipolar dispersion forces must account for less than one-fourth of the heat of formation of the crystal.

3. Theory of the Orientation Forces

Since the dipole-dipole dispersion force accounts for most of the bandshift, it is worth investigating its orientation dependence to determine its effect on the lattice vibrations. It may be possible to explain the excitation of lattice vibrations when an impurity molecule makes an electronic transition.

Some examples that show the extent to which lattice vibrations are excited during transitions in impurity molecules are shown in Figs. 16.1 to 16.3. In some of these examples, the 0—1 lattice-vibration transition is stronger than the 0—0 band. There is also one example of a lattice vibration destroying electronic selection rules within the molecule. This is the example of the $^1A_{1g} \rightarrow {}^1B_{3u}$ transition at 4 ev of naphthalene in a durene crystal. Hutchison[6] has shown that naphthalene in durene occupies, within a degree, the same position that the durene molecules do. The transition is forbidden in the c-direction of the durene crystal, since this is the short molecular axis (transition is allowed along long axis). The symmetry of the crystal field is low enough so that in the crystal this polarization is formally allowed. The 0—0 band does appear weakly; however, the 0—1 band of the 15-cm^{-1} lattice mode appears more strongly. Therefore this is a case of vibrational electronic interaction in which a lattice mode is responsible for the perturbation. Evidently, it enables the crystal field to become more effective in mixing electronic states than it is in the equilibrium position. The 15-cm^{-1} mode is probably an oscillation about the normal to the naphthalene plane. The moment of inertia about this axis is the largest, and the restoring forces are probably the smallest, since the oscillation moves the molecules toward a cleavage plane of the durene crystal.

The nature of the lattice vibrations was clarified by Kastler and Rousset[7] and Fruhling,[8] who worked out the theory of Raman scattering from molecular crystals and interpreted Raman data for several crystals. According to their interpretation the Raman active normal modes for a crystal such as naphthalene having two molecules per unit cell are simply the symmetric and antisymmetric librations of the molecules about their principle axes of inertia.

Table 16.4. Raman Active Lattice Modes of Naphthalene Crystal[7]
(L = long axis; M = short; N = normal to plane.)

Libration axis	L		M		N	
Symmetry	S	A	S	A	S	A
Frequency, cm^{-1}	109	127	76	74	54	46
$k \left(\dfrac{\text{dyne-cm}}{\text{radian}} \right) \times 10^{12}$	9.16	12.40	12.10	11.50	8.30	6.02
$I \times 10^{40}$ g-cm^2	267		667		935	
$\sqrt{\overline{\delta\phi_0{}^2}}$ degrees	1.69		1.35		1.37	
$\sqrt{\overline{\delta\phi_1{}^2}}$ degrees	2.93		2.34		2.36	

Their assignment of the vibrations of the naphthalene crystal is given in Table 16.4. We also give there the force constant for the libration obtained from

$$\nu = 1/2\pi \sqrt{(k/I)} \qquad (16.15)$$

The force constants for librations of an impurity molecule in a molecular crystal do not appear to change by more than 10 per cent between the low-lying excited states and the ground state, since the frequencies are about the same in all states. The evidence for this statement is presented in Table 16.5, where such libration frequencies are compared for several states in a number of mixed-crystal systems.

Table 16.5. Comparison of Vibration Frequencies of Impurity Molecules in a Molecular Crystal in Ground and First Excited States (Some of the lattice lines listed may be combinations)

	Ground state	1st excited state
Anthracene in naphthalene [a]	30, 50	26, —
Tetracene in naphthalene [b]	19, 49, 121	24, —, 115
Tetracene in anthracene [b]	41	39
Azulene in naphthalene [c,d]	15, 39, 59, 78	—, 38, 48, 60, 79, 93
Naphthalene in durene [e]	39, 98	15, 27, 38, 62, 89, 111

[a] J. W. Sidman, *J. Chem. Phys.*, **25**, 115 (1956).
[b] J. W. Sidman, *J. Chem. Phys.*, **25**, 122 (1956).
[c] J. W. Sidman and D. S. McClure, *J. Chem. Phys.*, **24**, 757 (1956).
[d] The second excited state is considered rather than the first.
[e] D. S. McClure, *J. Chem. Phys.* **24**, 1 (1956); also Fig. 16.3.

The reason for the excitation of vibrations during an electronic transition must therefore be a change in equilibrium position of the

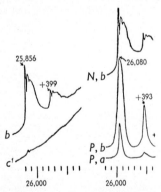

Fig. 16.1. Origin of the absorption at 4°K to the first band of anthracene in a single crystal of naphthalene (left) and phenanthrene (right). The lattice fine structure is clearly visible on the high-frequency side of the 0—0 band at 25,856 cm⁻¹ in naphthalene, polarized along *b*. The broad symmetrical shape of the 26,080 band in phenanthrene is probably due to the excitation of many low-frequency lattice modes that cannot be resolved.

excited molecule in the crystal. The change could come about because of changes in the direction of the reaction field upon excita-

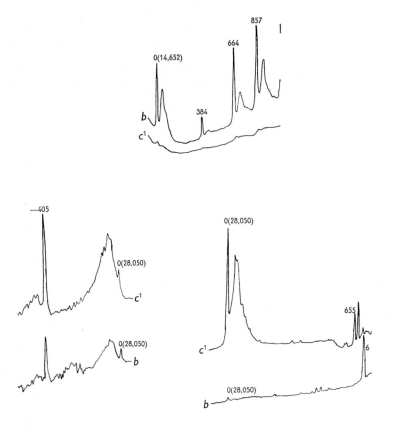

Fig. 16.2. Above: Absorption of first excited state of azulene in naphthalene.
Lower right: absorption to second excited state. Lower left: fluorescence
from second excited state. In all cases the prominent group of lines near the
0—0 band is lattice vibration structure.

tion. This possibility will be explored. First, however, we shall
apply the Franck-Condon principle to the data of Figs. 16.1 to
16.3 to see how much of a displacement must be postulated.

The rms displacement during a libration, using the harmonic
oscillator approximation, is

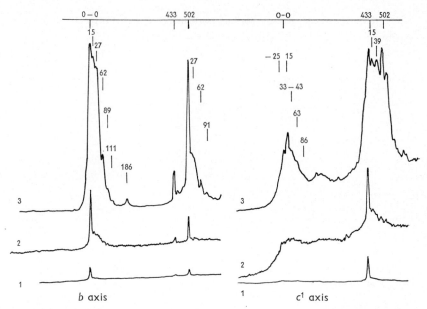

Fig. 16.3. The three tracings, 1, 2, and 3, are taken from photographs of the spectrum of naphthalene in durene at 20°K of increasing concentration × path length. The 0—0 band is symmetry permitted in the *b*-axis direction, but forbidden along *c'*. At higher *c* × 1, however, the 0—0 band does appear, but the 15 cm^{-1} lattice mode is stronger. Lattice structure is also shown added to the molecular vibration bands.

$$\overline{\delta\phi_n^2} = (1/\beta)(n + \tfrac{1}{2}) \tag{16.6}$$

for the *n*th oscillator level. $1/\beta = (h/4\pi^2 c \bar{\nu} I)$ where ν is the vibration frequency in cm^{-1} and I the moment of inertia. Values of the rms displacement for naphthalene are given in Table 16.4. The displacement of the equilibrium position required in order to excite lattice modes strongly will be of the order of the rms displacement, or a degree or two in the case of naphthalene.

The Franck-Condon overlap integrals $R_{00}, R_{01}, \ldots, R_{0n}$ are needed for an exact calculation. These are the overlap integrals between the zero-point level of the ground state and the *n*th level of the excited state. The intensity of a lattice-vibration band relative to the 0—0 band is

$$I_n/I_0 = R_{0n}^2/R_{00}^2 \tag{16.17}$$

Assuming the same bandwidth, the values of the peak absorption coefficient could be substituted here. The R_{0n} are given by

$$R_{0n} = \int_{-\infty}^{\infty} \psi_0^0(x)\psi_n^e(x-\delta x) \ dx \tag{16.18}$$

where the displacement upon excitation is δx. In the harmonic approximation we obtain

$$R_{00} = \exp -[(\delta x)^2 \beta/4]$$
$$R_{01} = (\sqrt{\beta}/2) \, \delta x \, \exp -[(\delta x)^2 \beta/4]$$

The intensity ratio becomes

$$I_1/I_0 = (\beta/2) \, \delta x^2 \cong (\beta/2) \, \delta\phi^2$$

Using the value of β_L for naphthalene, the values of $\delta\phi$ for $I/I_0 =$ 1.0, 0.5, 0.1 are 3.4°, 2.4°, 0.76°. These are of the same order of magnitude as the values of $\sqrt{\delta\phi_n^2}$ of Table 16.4.

The data of Figs. 16.1 to 16.3 show that I/I_0 is in the range from 0.1 to 1.0, and we must now see if the change of the dispersion forces upon excitation could account for a force of the magnitude required for the corresponding displacements. The torque can be computed from the displacement by using the harmonic-oscillator-force constant

$$T = -k \, \delta\phi$$

The values of k given in Table 16.4 and the values of $\delta\phi$ given above show that the torque causing displacement from equilibrium must be on the order of 10×10^{-12} dyne-cm/rad $\times 1°/57.4° = 0.17 \times 10^{-12}$ dyne-cm

The forces we seek must come from terms in the energy that are linear in the angles of displacement. We begin by calculating the energy of a molecule in a rotated position in the lattice. Suppose a transition occurs in the L direction of the molecule when it is rotated out of its equilibrium position into a new position L', M', N'. The moments induced in the lattice by this transition arise from the components of the molecular transition moment p_L in the directions M' and N as well as L'. Thus there are three „inducing" moments $p_L \cos LL'$, $p_L \cos ML'$, $p_L \cos NL'$. Each of these will induce moments in the three directions of each molecule of the lattice. For a particular lattice molecule, the moments induced in it are

$$p_L{}^h \text{ (ind)} = p_L\alpha_L(\theta_{LL}{}^h \cos LL' + \theta_{ML}{}^h \cos ML' + \theta_{NL}{}^h \cos NL')$$
$$p_M{}^h \text{ (ind)} = p_L\alpha_M(\theta_{LM}{}^h \cos LL' + \theta_{MM}{}^h \cos ML' + \theta_{NM}{}^h \cos NL')$$
$$p_N{}^h \text{ (ind)} = p_L\alpha_N(\theta_{LN}{}^h \cos LL' + \theta_{MN}{}^h \cos ML' + \theta_{NN}{}^h \cos NL')$$

$$(16.19)$$

where the first subscript on $\theta_{xy}{}^h$ refers to the molecule at the origin and the second to the molecule out in the lattice, and cos ML', etc., are the direction cosines of the new axes, e.g., L' in the fixed coordinate system. The energies of interaction of the induced moments with the moments at the origin are, apart from a factor

$$E_{LL}{}^h = p_L \cos LL' \, p_L{}^h \text{ (ind)} \, \theta_{LL} = p_L{}^2\alpha_L \cos LL'(\theta_{LL}{}^2 \cos LL'$$
$$+ \, \theta_{LL}\theta_{ML} \cos ML' + \theta_{LL}\theta_{NL} \cos NL')$$
$$E_{ML}{}^h = p_L \cos ML' \, p_L{}^h \text{ (ind)} \, \theta_{ML} = p_L{}^2\alpha_M \cos ML'(\theta_{ML}\theta_{LL} \cos LL'$$
$$+ \, \theta_{ML}{}^2 \cos ML' + \theta_{ML}\theta_{NL} \cos NL')$$

$$(16.20)$$

and seven analogous components. Their sum may be written

$$E_L{}^h(L', M', N') = cp_L{}^2 \sum_z \cos zL' \sum_y \cos yL' \sum_x \alpha_x\theta_{zx}\theta_{yx} \quad (16.21)$$

where $((x,y,z) - (L, M, N)$. The constant c arises from the appropriate part. Eq. (16.9) or (19.9a). These energy contributions must be summed over all molecules in the crystal. Introducing the definitions (16.11a) the total energy becomes

$$E_L = cp_L{}^2 \sum_z \cos zL' \sum_y \cos yL'a_{yz}$$
$$E_M = cp_M{}^2 \sum_z \cos zM' \sum_y \cos yM'a_{yz} \quad (16.22)$$
$$E_N = cp_N{}^2 \sum_z \cos zN' \sum_y \cos yN'a_{yz}$$

where the energy expressions have been written for each of the possible transition directions.

Each of these expressions may be simplified by writing it for the case of small rotations, ϕ_L, ϕ_M, ϕ_N, about each of the three axes:

$$E_L = c p_L^2 (a_{LL} + 2a_{LN}\phi_M + 2a_{LM}\phi_N)$$
$$E_M = c p_M^2 (-2a_{MN}\phi_L + a_{NN} - 2a_{LM}\phi_N) \quad (16.23)$$
$$E_N = c p_N^2 (2a_{MN}\phi_L - 2a_{LN}\phi_M + a_{NN})$$

The dispersion energy acting on the ground state of the impurity molecule may be written as a function of angle by modifying Eq. (16.9) by means of Eq. (16.23):

$$-\Delta E_2^0 = \tfrac{1}{4}[II^h/(I+I^h)][\textstyle\sum_x a_{xx}\alpha_x + 2a_{MN}(\alpha_N - \alpha_M)\phi_L$$
$$+ 2a_{LN}(\alpha_L - \alpha_N)\phi_M + 2a_{LM}(\alpha_L - \alpha_M)\phi_N] \quad (16.24)$$

The torques acting on the impurity molecule are therefore

$$T_L = \partial E_L^0/\partial\phi_L = 2a_{MN}(\alpha_N - \alpha_M), \quad \text{etc.} \quad (16.25)$$

Equation (16.25) is reminiscent of the formulas for Raman intensities of librational transitions.[7] These torques are opposed by others that we have not previously considered, and the equilibrium position results.

The angular dependence of the dispersion energy in the excited state is obtainable from Eqs. (16.10) and (16.23). We shall use the second of Eqs. (16.10) for the sum over the p_{kn}^2 and suppose that $0 \to k$ is L-polarized.

$$-\Delta E_2^k =$$
$$[II^h/(I+I^h-E)]\{(I^h/E)[\tfrac{1}{2}p_L^2/(I^h-E)](a_{LL}+2a_{LN}\phi_M+2a_{LM}\phi_N)$$
$$+ \tfrac{1}{4}[(I-E)/I](\textstyle\sum_x a_{xx}\alpha_x+2a_{MN}(\alpha_N-\alpha_M)\phi_L+2a_{LN}(\alpha_L-\alpha_N)\phi_M$$
$$+ 2a_{LM}(\alpha_L-\alpha_M)\phi_N)\} \quad (16.26)$$

The α's in this formula apply to the excited state.

The additional forces acting on the ground state may be represented by a set of force constants k_L, etc., such that the corresponding potential energy is $\tfrac{1}{2}k_L\phi_L^2$. These terms include the terms in ϕ_L^2, etc., omitted from Eq. (16.23), but also include repulsion energies between atoms on different molecules, etc. The equilibrium position in the ground state is determined by the total potential

$$\partial V(\text{tot.})/\partial\phi_L = 0, \quad \text{etc.}$$

giving

$$\phi_L{}^0 = \tfrac{1}{2}[II^h/(I+I^h)][a_{MN}(\alpha_N-\alpha_M)/k_L], \quad \text{etc.} \quad (16.27)$$

These values of $\phi_L{}^0$, etc., define the equilibrium position in the ground state.

We assume that the k_L, etc., do not change between the ground and first few excited states. It is an experimental fact that the lattice frequencies do not change by over a few per cent. The equilibrium position in excited states, is therefore determined by the potential

$$V^k = -\varDelta E_2{}^k + \tfrac{1}{2}k_L\theta_L{}^2 + \tfrac{1}{2}k_M\theta_M{}^2 + \tfrac{1}{2}k_N\theta_N{}^2$$

giving

$$\phi_L{}^{k(L)} = \tfrac{1}{2}[I^h(I-E)/(I+I^h-E)][a_{MN}(\alpha_{Nk}-\alpha_{Mk})/k_L] \quad (16.27a)$$

The angular displacement around the L axis for an L-polarized transition is therefore

$$\varDelta\phi_L{}^L = \phi_L{}^{k(L)}-\phi_L{}^0 \quad\quad\quad\quad (16.28)$$

If the approximation mentioned in connection with Eq. (16.10a) is used, i.e., that $(I-E/I)\alpha_k = \alpha_0$, then

$$\varDelta\phi_L{}^L = [a_{MN}(\alpha_{N0}-\alpha_{M0})/k_L][EII^h/(I+I^h)(I+I^h-E)] \quad (16.29)$$

Evaluating this expression for naphthalene gives a displacement of 4×10^{-4} radian around the L axis, which is a factor of 100 too small to account for the appreciable lattice-mode excitation observed. The rotation around the short axis M is the most favored, according to the data of Tables 16.1 and 16.2. The value of $\varDelta\phi_L{}^M = 0.013\ p_L{}^2+0.0036$ radian. For a transition with a large dipole moment, say 1 A, $\varDelta\phi = 0.017$ radian, or nearly a degree. However, the transitions observed in mixed crystals are often weak, and therefore the excitation of the lattice does not depend on the contribution from the transition moment. It therefore appears that the calculated change of equilibrium position brought about by the change in dispersion forces is too small by a factor of 10 or more to account for the lattice modes observed in the spectra.

The approximations made during the course of the calculation are probably not severe enough to account for all of this discrepancy. Rather, the basic assumptions must be modified. Evidently, it is necessary to find forces that depend more strongly on angle than the dipole-dipole dispersion forces. The interaction of the permanent quadrupoles would be a possibility. However, at the distances between molecules in molecular crystals, the multipole expansion itself probably must be abandoned. A treatment similar to that of Davies and Coulson's[9] calculation of the dispersion forces between polyenes would be much better, although very complicated for the aromatic hydrocarbons. In this calculation, the interaction between individual atoms of each molecule is considered. The principal coupling, however, comes from only a few π-electron transitions, and the corresponding „radiation patterns" of these transitions can be visualized rather easily. The attractive forces come from the constructive interference of these radiation patterns, and when only a few transitions are involved, a simple physical picture of the attraction results. The angular dependence of these attractive forces is much stronger than for the forces between point dipoles.

This procedure could probably be carried out for the aromatics if the radiation patterns of the transitions could be reduced to a simple form and if some of the details of molecular structure could be ignored. A possibility for doing this would be to use Platt's free-electron model of the electronic states of the molecule.[10]

The apparently good agreement between observed and calculated bandshifts must be regarded as somewhat fortuitous. Since $\Delta E_2{}^0$ was not nearly large enough to explain the heat of solution, $\Delta E_2{}^k$ must also be too small, but their difference is about right, because the neglected contributions are the same in the two states. The bandshift calculations that are done for liquid solution[4] must also be in good agreement with experiment by virtue of a similar accident. The calculations of the displacement point to the multipole expansion being the source of the error.

References

1. A. S. Davydov, *J. Exptl. Theoret. Phys. (U.S.S.R.)* **18**, 210 (1948).
2. F. London, *Trans. Faraday Soc.* **33**, 222 (1930); H. Margenau, *Rev. Mod. Phys.* **11**, 1 (1939).
3. D. P. Craig and J. R. Walsh, *J. Chem. Soc.* **1958**, 1613; D. P. Craig and P. C. Hobbins, *J. Chem. Soc.* **1955**, 539, 2309; D. Fox and O. Schnepp, *J. Chem. Phys.* **23**, 767 (1955).
4. H. C. Longuet-Higgins and J. A. Pople, *J. Chem. Phys.* **27**, 192 (1957).
5. Some of the values of θ_{xy} were obtained from J. R. Walsh, Ph.D. thesis, Univ. of Sydney (1958). This outstanding thesis proved very valuable to the writer in preparing this paper.
6. C. A. Hutchison, Talk Given at the Conference on Electronic Conduction in Organic Solids, Duke Univ. (Apr. 20–22, 1960).
7. A. Kastler and A. Rousset, *J. phys. radium* (8) **2**, 49 (1941).
8. A. Fruhling, *Ann. phys.* **6**, 401–480 (1951).
9. P. L. Davies and C. A. Coulson, *Trans. Faraday Soc.* **48**, 777 (1952).
10. J. R. Platt, *J. Chem. Phys.* **17**, 484 (1949).

17

Electronic States of Aromatic Solids

DAVID FOX

Introduction

In this paper, we compare the behavior of charge carriers and excitons in conventional semiconductors with that in aromatic crystals. Although a considerable amount of quantitative theoretical work has been done on the exciton states of the simpler aromatic solids,[1] the treatment of the conducting states has been mainly qualitative and speculative.[2-4]

The discussion here will be based on semiclassical models which may be derived from more detailed quantum mechanical considerations. The latter treatment may be found in the references.

Exciton States

In many of the simpler aromatic compounds, the absorption spectra of the crystals and of the corresponding free molecules are very similar. This observation suggests that the final state of an optical transition in the solid is essentially a molecular excited state. However, there are features of the crystal spectra which can be explained qualitatively and quantitatively if one assumes that the molecular excitation is not confined to one molecule but is coherently shared by all molecules of a perfect crystal.

In such a state—an exciton—the excitation has a definite energy and crystal momentum; its position in the crystal is completely uncertain. The energy contains not only a molecular excitation term, but also a kinetic energy contribution, dependent on the momentum. The range of kinetic energies, for excitons with different momenta, is as large as 1 ev in some crystals. In spite of this variation in energy, the low-temperature absorption spectra are quite sharp, because a selection rule forbids the transition unless the momenta of the created exciton and of the absorbed photon are equal.

In a classical description of an exciton in a molecular crystal, one may consider the excitation to be mobile, with the electrons involved in the excited state of a particular molecule remaining behind as the excitation passes. In contrast, the classical picture of the Wannier exciton [5] in a conventional semiconductor (germanium, silicon, etc.) is that of an electron and hole bound together to form a hydrogen-like atom which moves freely through the crystal, carrying along the excitation energy. The difference between the two pictures arises from the difference in the mechanisms for the transfer of the energy through the crystal. In a more general formulation of the exciton problem, originally proposed by Frenkel,[6] some of the kinetic energy terms are matrix elements in which there is a transfer, between the initial and the final state, of both the excitation and the charges involved in this excitation from one molecule to the next. Such charge exchange cannot be important if the electronic wave functions of neighboring atoms or molecules are isolated from one another, as is the case in crystals like anthracene. On the other hand, where the overlap is large, the charge exchange is very important, but then the use of atomic or molecular orbitals in building crystal wave functions becomes inaccurate. Wannier has shown that in such cases one may reformulate the problem, obtaining the well-known model of a bound electron-hole pair moving through the conventional semiconductor.

Another group of kinetic energy terms consists of matrix elements in which there is an intermolecular transfer of the excitation, but no charge exchange, between the initial and final states. Such terms can be important even if the molecular orbitals are completely isolated from one another. The excitation is transferred primarily through an electric interaction between the transition dipole moments of the molecules. These transition moments are the same as the matrix elements involved in optical absorption, so the interaction is large (and the effective mass of the exciton is small) if the absorption is strong. The Wannier model is most accurate where the binding between the electron and hole is weak, so that the exciton radius is large. With the electron far from the hole, the optical transition dipole moment will be small, so that in crystals like germanium this second mechanism for motion of the excitation may be neglected. On the other hand, aromatic molecules generally have fairly strong optical absorptions, so the second mechanism is important; excitons corresponding to the second anthracene transition have a range of kinetic energies of the order of one electron volt. (It has often been stated that the interactions between molecules of aromatic crystals are all very weak; the transition dipole interaction is certainly an exception.)

Conducting States

The one-electron-band model is well known. Each electron or hole is assumed to move freely through the perfect crystal, in a Bloch state of definite crystal momentum. If the crystal is nearly perfect, one may think of each charge carrier as spending most of its time in a momentum state, occasionally being scattered from one such state to another.

A somewhat similar model may be applied to the *perfect* aromatic molecular crystal. The free electron will spend most of its time in the neighborhood of one molecule or another, and very little time in the interstitial regions; its wave function will be a linear combination of excited molecular orbitals. Because these orbitals are almost completely isolated from one another, the effective mass of the charge carrier will be large. Similar considerations apply to free hole states.

In the case of the excitons, the strong excitation transfer mechanism in aromatic crystals makes up for the weak pair transfer, so that the exciton effective mass may still be small. No such alternative mechanism is known for the conducting states. With a large effective carrier mass, the range of kinetic energies will be of the order of, or much smaller than, kT at room temperature. These kinetic energies may then be smaller than the perturbation energies, so that the model of a free carrier occasionally scattered by imperfections is not valid. With a sufficiently large effective mass in the perfect crystal, a better picture is provided by the hopping model, in which one assumes that the carrier spends a long time on some molecule; the perturbations arising from the presence of other molecules cause an occasional jump to a neighbor. For inter-

mediate values of the effective mass, it is possible that neither the
hopping nor the conventional band picture is valid.

To find the excitation energy for the lowest conducting state in
the hopping model, one may start with a neutral crystal, remove
an electron from one molecule, and place it on another a great
distance away.[2,3] Considering this charge transfer to take place in
several steps, we first remove the electron from its original molecule to a point far from the crystal; this requires the addition of
energy I, the molecular ionization potential. Bringing the electron
back to the crystal and placing it on the second molecule regains
energy A, the molecular electron affinity. We now have a widely
separated ion pair, and each ion polarizes the surrounding molecules. The energy W of interaction of each ion with the polarization is the same for the two ions, to a first approximation. The
excitation energy is then $I-A-2W$. There are other terms, but
these are small compared with those considered here. (They are
probably fairly small even with intermediate values of the effective
mass.)

Either the electron on the negative ion or the hole left behind
on the positive ion may now carry current, by hopping to adjacent
molecules. The two charges are sufficiently far apart that they act
independently of one another.

Hopping Neutral Excitations

The argument given above, to show that one may retain the
momentum-state picture for excitons in molecular crystals, does
not apply to those cases in which the optical transition moments
are very small. Here the kinetic energy terms, arising from interaction of these moments, may be much smaller than the perturbation energies. In such a case, one should use a hopping model for
the excitation. This is certainly so for excitations to the molecular
triplet state, where the optical transition is highly forbidden. The
hopping model is also applicable to such excitations as the 0—0
component of the first benzene transition, except possibly in a good
crystal at very low temperatures. (This transition is forbidden in
the free molecule, but it is weakly allowed in the crystal.)

Another excitation in which the hopping model is useful is one in which an electron is transferred to an adjacent molecule, leaving a hole behind.[2] The attraction between the two charges prevents further separation, if no additional energy is supplied. To move this excitation through the crystal, one must also transfer the charge pair. The matrix element for this process is extremely small, and the hopping model should be used, probably even at low temperatures.

Speculations on the Molecular Triplet State

In each of several aromatic crystals, the observed value of the activation energy for dark conductivity, E, turned out to be $\frac{1}{2}E_t$. Here E_t is the energy of the triplet state of the isolated molecule, measured from the ground state, and E is defined by the first of the relations

$$\sigma = \sigma_0 \exp\left(-E/kT\right) = \sigma_0 \exp\left(-E'/2kT\right) \qquad (17.1)$$

with T the absolute temperature, k the Boltzmann constant, σ the dark conductivity, and σ_0 a constant. The quantity E', introduced to simplify the later discussion, is defined as $2E$.

The similarity between the last member of Eq. (17.1) and the expression for the dark conductivity of a conventional intrinsic semiconductor led many authors to assume that E' was the band gap in aromatic crystals. The observed equality between E' and E_t led to the further assumption that the molecular triplet state was involved in the conduction. Since this state is nonconducting, the involvement must be indirect.

The validity of the first assumption depends on whether the conductivity is intrinsic; this point has been dealt with by Garrett.[4] We shall present arguments against the assumption that the triplet state plays a role in conduction. These arguments will be divided into two parts: in the first, the crystal will be considered to be essentially in thermal equilibrium, while the remaining discussion will be based on the unlikely possibility that there are significant deviations from equilibrium.

a. In thermal equilibrium, the population of each conducting state depends on the energy of that level, but not on the mechanisms of transitions between states. The observed value of E' there-

fore cannot be explained in terms of the excitation of one of the
nonconducting states (in particular, the triplet state of a molecule),
followed by a transition to the conducting state. If the equality of
E' and E_t is not a coincidence, it must arise from a relationship
between the structures of triplet and conducting states. It has been
suggested that it takes the same energy to raise an electron from the
highest filled to the lowest unfilled molecular orbital (with the
final spin state a triplet) as it does to place that electron in the same
unoccupied state of a distant molecule. When the latter transfer is
effected, either the electron or the hole left behind on the first
molecule is free to move from one neighbor to another. The population of charge carriers would then have the temperature dependence indicated in Eq. (17.1), with the "band gap" E' numerically
equal to E_t.

It may be proper, as an approximation, to use the same molecular wave function, in the two cases, for the state which the
electron enters. However, even if the wave functions were identical, the two excitation energies would not be the same. First, if we
consider spinless electrons, the transfer of an electron to a distant
molecule involves, among other energy terms, the Coulomb energy
of separation of the electron from the positive charge left behind.
This contribution, which is not negligible, does not appear in the
energy of the triplet state. Second, when the spin is taken into
account, we note that each of the two ions produced by the
charge transfer is in a *doublet* state; the wide separation of the
ions prevents these states from interacting to form a singlet and
a triplet. Since the singlet and triplet molecular states differ
greatly in energy, there is no reason to expect equality between
the energy of the molecular triplet and that of the two ionic
doublets.

b. Let us assume that for some unknown reason, each set of
measurements was carried out on a sample in which there was an
equilibrium number of triplet excitations, but an abnormally low
number of charge carriers. For such a nonequilibrium case, one
can set up a rather artificial model in which the current is indirectly
determined by the population of the triplet states. This number,
however, varies with temperature as $\exp(-E_t/kT)$, not as

exp $(-E_t/2kT)$.* If, for this or any other reason, the current were proportional to the triplet population, one should find E, and not E', equal to E_t. (In anthracene at room temperature, the factor exp $(-E_t/kT)$ is so small that there is a negligible probability of finding even a single molecule in the triplet state.)

If even the triplet states are not in equilibrium, there should be no relationship between E' and E_t.

References

1. See, for example, A. S. Davydov, *J. Exptl. Theoret. Phys.* (U.S.S.R.) **18**, 210 (1948); D. P. Craig and P. O. Hobbins, *J. Chem. Soc.* **1955**, 539, 2309; D. P. Craig, *J. Chem. Soc.* **1955**, 2302; D. Fox and O. Schnepp, *J. Chem. Phys.* **23**, 767 (1955).
2. L. E. Lyons, *J. Chem. Soc.* **1957**, 5001.
3. D. Fox, *J. Phys. Chem. Solids* **8**, 439 (1959).
4. C. G. B. Garrett *in* N. B. Hannay (ed.) *"Semiconductors,"* Monograph Series No. 140, p.p. 634-675, Reinhold Publishing Corporation, New York (1959).
5. G. H. Wannier, *Phys. Rev.* **52**, 191 (1937).
6. J. Frenkel, *Phys. Rev.* **37**, 17, 1276 (1931).

* The factor of $1/2$ in the exponent in the case of an intrinsic semiconductor appears because the possible distributions of electrons in the conduction band are independent of the distributions of holes in the valence band. This factor appears also in the case of an equilibrium distribution of ion pairs. However, in molecular excitations, once one determines a distribution of electrons among the excited states of the various molecules, the distribution of "holes" in the ground states is completely determined. In such a case, the factor of $1/2$ does not appear. These conclusions are based on some rather general statistical arguments, not restricted to solids. It is required only that the Fermi level be far, compared to kT, from any of the one-electron states.

18

Ionic Organic Photoconductors

R. C. NELSON

The class of ionic organic photoconductors consists principally of dyes; the colored ion may be either positively or negatively charged. The first report of their photoconductivity is to be found in the work of Petrikaln,[1] who found that a number of common dyes showed a substantial response to light. More recently the study of these materials has been pursued by Vartanyan,[2] and after him, by Nelson, by Weigl, and by H. Meier.

A certain confusion is evident in an inspection of the literature on this topic. Although different workers may agree roughly on the broad qualitative aspects of the behavior of these substances, they usually disagree markedly on quantitative matters. This is undoubtedly due to the fact that it is customary, and often necessary, to investigate the properties of films deposited from solvents. In certain cases, of which rhodamine-B is a good example, it is easy to form films having consistently replicable properties by this method. On the other hand, the writer [3] has noticed the difficulty of forming replicable films of cyanine dyes, where it is not uncommon for the dye to exist in solution in two or three different states of aggregation, so that the sort of film that results depends sensitively on temperature and rate of evaporation of solvent. Other details, such as the degree of evacuation of the cell containing the film, the nature of the electrodes, and in some cases, the history of previous illumination of the film may also affect its properties. In general, it is not safe to assume that it is sufficient to name the dye of which the film is composed to specify its properties.

Because a large number of dyes are readily available in a fairly pure state and because it is easy to prepare films by solvent evaporation, a considerable number of photoconductive dyes are listed in the literature, perhaps sixty or seventy. Few of these have been investigated in detail, and the principal generalization that can be made is that there is a tendency for anionic dyes to be *p*-type conductors and cationic dyes *n*-type, as judged by the enhancement or quenching, respectively, of conduction by oxygen.[4]

Relatively little is known about the photoconductivity of anionic dyes, and the remainder of this discussion deals with cationic dyes only.

A class of cationic dye that has often been investigated is the triphenylmethanes. Films of these dyes produced by solvent evaporation have rather uniform properties, the dyes themselves are easy to handle, and their behavior can be studied with simple equipment because of the relatively large photoconductances and long time constants. Some important generalizations have been found in studies of triphenylmethane dyes that probably apply also to other cationic dyes.

Photoconductivity is excited by light absorbed in the lowest electronic optical transition of the solid dye film.[5] This point seems to be well established for all dyes for which action spectra have been observed. The lowest electronic state of the solid triphenylmethane dye can be related to the lowest electronic excited state of the dye ion, greatly broadened and shifted toward the red.

It can be shown that the long-wave absorption threshold of the dye film gives a measure of the energy of the photoconductive excited state with respect to the ground state. For example, in basic fuchsin the external photoelectric effect has been measured by Fleischmann,[6] giving the energy of an electron in the ground state of the solid dye as -5.2 ev. Using the electron-beam-retardation method,[7] the writer has measured the work done in adding an excess electron to the solid dye, presumably to the conductive excited state, the value being -3.2 ev. The difference in these energies, 2.0 ev. should then be approximately the separation of the ground state and the photoconductive excited state. The threshold for photoconductivity is found to be at 1.8 ev, indicating that within the limitations of the data, all the threshold energy is used in raising an electron to the conductive excited state.

It has been shown that the optical properties of triphenylmethane dye films depend on the nature of the dye cation but not on that of the associated anion.[8] The same is true of the work done in adding an electron to the dye solid, as measured by the electron-beam-retardation method.[9]

The photoconductive properties of the triphenylmethane dyes are of some interest. The most favorable experimental material is basic fuchsin.[10] A long time, about 2 hours, is required to reach a steady state in constant illumination. The limiting process is not the formation of charge carriers, but the rate of formation of some structural modification in the film that gives rise to a memory effect. If the film is darkened after a steady state has been reached, the photoconductivity decays according to a second-order, or bimolecular, law. When the cell is reilluminated at the same intensity, a steady state is reached quickly, the limiting rate now being that of formation of charge carriers. If the light intensity is now increased, the achievement of a steady state of higher conductance is once again very slow. The decay in the dark is again bimolecular, but the rate constant is found to be smaller and inversely proportional to the conductance at the new steady state. The result of all this is that the film appears to have a property that may loosely be described as the ability to remember the highest level of illumination to which it has recently been exposed. In addition, there is a rather complicated set of dependences of rates and conductances on temperature, characterized by a single activation energy.

The cyanine dyes and related types have also been much studied; they are of interest because of their use as photographic sensitizers. Since they tend to form films of very complex structure, they are not easy to work with. The writer has made some progress, however, with pinacyanole, and has been able to show that at least four distinct structural modifications, which have characteristic optical absorption bands, are to be discovered in pinacyanole films and has found methods of preparing films that are reproducible and have interesting properties.[11] In such films the rates are rather fast: one type has a decay of photoconductivity that can be described by two rate constants, one $\sim 10^{-5}$ sec and the other of about 10^{-2} sec. Broadly speaking, the differences between the cyanines and the triphenylmethanes as photoconductors are more noticeable than the similarities.

We may indeed divide cationic photoconductors into two types.

that correspond roughly in behavior to more or less typical triphenylmethane and cyanine films. However, there is not anything of fundamental significance in this correspondence; attempts to find descriptive terms for the types seem to lead to inconsistencies at the present state of knowledge, and for the moment, they will be designated simply as "type 1" and "type 2". Some characteristic differences between the types are indicated in Table 18.1. The

Table 18.1.

	Type 1	Type 2
Time constant	10^3 sec	10^{-5} sec
Photoconductance (typical cell)	10^{-7} mho	10^{-11} mho
Dark resistance at 70°C (typical cell)	10^{10} ohm	$\geq 10^{12}$ ohm
Memory effects	Prominent	Absent
Effect of temperature on photoresponse	0.42 ev	0.12 ev
Photoconductive threshold	7.700 A	7,700 A

data given are specifically for a type-1 malachite-green film and a type-2 pinacyanole film, but it is to be understood that the use of some particular dye is largely a matter of convenience. For instance, films of either type may be prepared from pinacyanole, using the proper procedures, and a type-1 pinacyanole film has properties not excessively different from those of a type-1 malachite-green film.

A while ago the writer proposed a model to account for the temperature dependences in the triphenylmethane dyes that was essentially a classical band model in which every molecule is also a trap.[9] This model seems appropriate to type-1 films in general; when it is extended to type-2 films, however, it makes erroneous predictions.

In consequence, what might be called a modification of the first scheme was proposed for type-2 films, but it was a modification that changed the essential character of the model. In the modified form, the band property disappears, and the excited electron is no longer in a state that is common to a whole aggregate of molecules, but can now be assigned at a given instant to a single molecule or ion in which it is an excess electron over the normal number, which it sees as a potential well and from which it can move by tunneling through a barrier into an adjacent molecule or ion. It was shown that in semiclassical approximation the model has the property of photoconductivity and that the calculated mobility is not implausible in order of magnitude.

Since these two models are essentially different in character, it should be possible to devise experiments which would distinguish between them. If type-1 films are band-model photoconductors and type-2 films are not, we should expect to be able to find clear evidence of this in relatively simple situations, and two types of experiments have been carried out that seem to substantiate this hope.

The first of these has to do with the existence or nonexistence of intrinsic semiconductivity in dye films. It is well known that in an intrinsic semiconductor the conductance is proportional to exp $(-E/2kT)$, where E is the bandgap, and the factor $\frac{1}{2}$ in the exponential is a consequence of the assumption fundamental to the band model, that an electron in a band is to be associated with a whole aggregate or crystal rather than with a specified site. There are a number of dyes that have bandgaps of about 1.5 ev, as inferred from the optical threshold, and for these it should be possible to observe intrinsic semiconductivity if the band model is applicable. Malachite green does indeed show such an effect. The optical threshold is found at 1.6 ev.[5] In addition to the optical energy for the formation of a charge carrier, there is a further requirement of 0.4 ev of thermal energy, which, when added to half the optical energy, gives a total requirement of 1.2 ev. This is in good agreement with the value found by measuring dark conductance as a function of temperature. Similar results have been found in a few other cases, and certainly some type-1 films show intrinsic semiconductivity.

In the case of the nonclassical model, the considerations that led to the factor of $\frac{1}{2}$ in the exponential no longer apply; we expect to find conduction proportional to exp $(-E/kT)$, and at temperatures at which the films are reasonably stable, 70°C or less, the intrinsic semiconductivity should be too small to measure. A few type-2 pinacyanole cells have been prepared that realize this expectation within experimental error. The chief difficulty lies in the correction for the conductance of the glass blank upon which the film lies, but good cells can be said to have a conductance at 70°C, which is less than 1 per cent of that shown by a malachite-green film in the same blank. Since the optical thresholds are the same and since such evidence as is available suggests that the mobility of carriers in the pinacyanole is greater than that in malachite green, there is reason to suspect that type-2 films may not fall in the class of band-model intrinsic semiconductors. This conclusion is somewhat reinforced by the fact that type-1 pinacyanole films can be prepared and do show intrinsic semiconductivity of the same order of magnitude as that of malachite green.

The second type of experiment has to do with effects at a junction between a dye film and cadmium sulfide. The writer observed some years ago that there is a photovoltaic effect at such an interface,[12] and a detailed consideration of the system shows that the phenomena to be expected at a junction between cadmium sulfide and a band-model film are markedly different from those predicted for the junction with a nonclassical localizable-state photoconductor.

These preparations seem to be free of a barrier layer and show no significant rectification. Under such circumstances we do not expect a junction between two band-model photoconductors to have very exciting properties. The basic expectation would probably be a small photovoltage depending on a non-Maxwellian distribution of photoelectrons for its existence. Something of this sort is observed at a junction between cadmium sulfide and a type-1 film. In the particular case of malachite green, the photovoltage is of the order of 0.03 volt for a film of moderate thickness in strong light. Since the photoconductive time constant of malachite green is rather long, there is a persistent effect on the resistance of the cell following illumination, but the photovoltage is transient and disappears in less than 10^{-3} sec when illumination is stopped. When the dependence of photovoltage on the wavelength of illumination is examined, it is found that the photovoltaic effect arises from light absorbed by the cadmium sulfide.

This is presumably to be ascribed to the fact that the quantum yield of carriers in cadmium sulfide is many orders of magnitude greater than in malachite green, but the mechanism involved is not clear.

In the case of a junction between cadmium sulfide and a type-2 film, we predict that strange things will happen if the nonclassical model is valid. This arises from the fact that we consider each mobile electron to be in general an excess or supernumerary electron in the molecule in which it is momentarily localized and hence to have a well-defined energy that is in good approximation under ordinary conditions, independent of the total number of such electrons. If this is true, we should be able to make a meaningful measurement of this energy by the electron-beam-retardation method, since we should expect it to be immaterial to its energy whether an excess electron is in a molecule by reason of its having been injected into it from outside or by having diffused into it from the site at which it was originally separated from a hole.

When the junction between a type-2 film and cadmium sulfide is illuminated, we find an open-circuit potential difference of the order of a few tenths of a volt. From the spectral dependence of the effect, we find that it is produced by light absorbed by the dye only and that the action spectrum is substantially identical with that for photoconductivity of the dye. The dye becomes positive, and since it is an n-type conductor, we surmise that the photovoltaic effect arises because electrons tend to pass from the dye into the cadmium sulfide. If this is the case, these electrons in the cadmium sulfide should have a status similar to that of a roughly equal number injected into it by an electron beam; that is to say, it should be possible to measure their energy by the electron-beam-retardation method. After doing this, we have values for the energies of electrons on both sides of the interface obtained by the same method. In terms of our model for type-2 films and our working hypothesis as to how the photovoltaic effect arises, they are realistic values, and hence we are led to predict that the open-circuit photovoltage at the junction should be numerically equal to the difference in energies of the electrons on the two sides as we have measured them. This is, in good approximation, what is observed. If we neglect a transient higher voltage, which appears immediately upon illumination and which can be accounted for in a natural way as due to the initial shift of the Fermi level in the cadmium sulfide with the transfer of the first few electrons into it, the measured photovoltage at a cadmium sulfide-pinacyanole interface is 0.43 to 0.48 volt, and the measured energy differences fall in the same range.

Another consequence is that since we have not had to take into account the light intensity to arrive at the expected photovoltage, it should be independent of light intensity and equal to the difference in energies at any illuminance at which it is possible to make a measurement. This effect is also observed. Within about 0.03 volt, the photovoltage at a good pinacyanole-cadmium sulfide junction remains constant over a range of light intensities of 100 : 1, starting at the lowest illuminance at which a measurement can be made.

At present three other dyes have been worked with that form type-2 films, and although the results are not quite as satisfactory for these materials because the technique of making pure type-2 films has not been worked out for them, in each case the photovoltage saturates at a fairly low light intensity and at a value that is within a few hundredths of a volt of that predicted by the energy measurements.

There is in addition a third reason for believing that type-2 films are not classical band-model photoconductors. This reason is associated with the existence of a remarkable phenomenon observed to take place with type-2 films on glass. In the course of some experiments involving the exploration of such a film with a spot of light while observing its photoconductive response, it was found that there was a very marked delocalization of the effect of illumination, in contrast to type-1 crystal violet films in which the effect of illumination is highly localized.[13] This effect was eventually traced to the fact that the dye film was "sensitizing" conduction in the glass itself. This was found to be a bulk or volume conductivity, with currents through pyrex 1 mm thick that were comparable in magnitude to the photocurrents in the dye films.

A study of the phenomenon suggested very strongly that electrons were transferred into the glass from the dye film.[14]

Glass is, of course, almost the archtype of insulators, and a fair working definition of an insulator is that it is a medium that sets a boundary to the phenomena in a band-model conductor. There is no evidence of any such effect arising from films that are known to be characteristically of type 1, for which the band model appears to be valid. While the interpretation of this effect is as yet uncertain, a reasonable conjecture might be that the transfer of an electron from dye to glass is a tunneling process similar to that which has been invoked to account for diffusion of electrons in the dye film itself. If this is so, it is not impossible that a charge-carrier situated in a molecule at the interface sees very little asymmetry between the two processes of transfer back into the dye or forward into the glass.

In conclusion, it may be said that there is considerable evidence that a single model is not adequate to describe phenomena in cationic photoconductors and that, while the band model does well enough for what we have called type-1 films, another sort of model must be used for films of type-2. The writer's nonclassical model, while as yet in a rather crude state of formulation, gives evidence of being able to account for the remarkable properties of type-2 films.

Acknowledgement. The writer wishes to express his appreciation of the support of the C. F. Kettering Foundation, which for a number of years has made it possible for him to pursue his interest in this field.

References

1. Z. Petrikaln, *Z. physik. Chem.* (B)**10**, 9 (1930).
2. A. T. Vartanyan, *Zhur. Fiss. Khim.* **20**, 1065 (1946); **22**, 769 (1948); **24**, 1361 (1952).
3. R. C. Nelson, *J. Opt. Soc. Am.* **46**, 10 (1956).
4. H. Meier, *Z. wiss. Phot.* **53**, 1 (1958).
5. J. W. Weigl, *J. Chem. Phys.* **24**, 883 (1956).
6. R. Fleischmann, *Ann. Physik* **5**, 73 (1930).
7. R. C. Nelson, *J. Opt. Soc. Am.* **46**, 1016 (1956).

256   R. C. NELSON

8. J. W. Weigl, *J. Chem. Phys.* **24**, 364 (1956).
9. R. C. Nelson, *J. Chem. Phys.* **30**, 406 (1958).
10. R. C. Nelson, *J. Chem. Phys.* **22**, 892 (1954).
11. R. C. Nelson, *J. Opt. Soc. Am.*, October 1961.
12. R. C. Nelson, *J. Opt. Soc. Am.* **46**, 13 (1956).
13. R. C. Nelson, *J. Chem. Phys.* **23**, 1550 (1955).
14. R. C. Nelson, *J. Opt. Soc. Am.* **50**, 1029 (1960).

The Electrical Conductivity of Solid Free Radicals and the Electron Tunneling Mechanism*

D. D. ELEY and M. R. WILLIS

Introduction

The potential box model [1-3] used to describe the semiconducting properties of organic substances indicated that under favorable circumstances a solid free radical would behave as a semiconductor with very small or zero energy gap. This proved to be the case, measurements by an a-c method on polycrystalline samples of $\alpha\alpha'$-diphenyl-β-picryl hydrazyl (DPPH) giving an energy gap of 0.26 ev. The validity of the a-c method has been challenged,[4] but subsequent measurements by the d-c method,[5] using evaporated films, have confirmed the original findings.

The role of odd electrons in the conduction process in crystals of substances having only partial radical character is less well understood. Indeed, since the existence of partial radical character is in many cases still unexplained, the problem remains a complex one. Free electrons are known to exist in some polycyclic hydrocarbons, e.g., violanthrone and violanthrene,[6] but the semiconducting properties are in no way anomalous.[7] On the other hand, those molecular complexes that are so highly conducting[3, 8] are in most cases paramagnetic.[9,10] Similarly, there appears to be some correlation between the semiconductivity and the concentration of free electrons in pyrolyzed polymers.[11] Thus, further information is required on the properties of unpaired electrons as conducting species.

* This paper is the fifth in a series on the semiconductivity of organic substances. Parts 1 to 4 have been published by the Faraday Society.

[257]

The idea of conduction by electrons without activation has implications in biophysics. The conductivity of dry proteins[12] is rather low to explain the rates of many metabolic processes in terms of electron transfer. The suggestion has been made[13] that a protein in a suitable environment may lose a hydrogen atom during the course of a reaction, creating a free radical. This is equivalent to creating a positive hole in the conduction band and would result in a lowering of resistance.

In this chapter conductivity measurements on two solid free radicals (Coppinger's radical[14] and Banfield and Kenyon's radical[15]) are reported. The results are considered in relation to the electron-spin-resonance signal and the solid-state optical-absorption spectra. The potential box model is used to interpret the results. The theory of quantum tunneling is applied to this model to explain the effect of applied fields. An attempt to create positive holes in a protein is also described.

Preparation of Materials

Coppinger's Radical (2, 6, 3′, 5′-tetra-tert-butyl-4′-phenoxy-4-methylene-2, 5-cyclohexadiene-1-one radical). This compound is also known as galvinoxyl.

where X = tertiary butyl.

Initial experiments were performed on a sample obtained from J. E. Bennett of Shell Research Laboratories, Cheshire, which had been prepared by oxidation of the precursor (compound AN2, obtained from the Ethyl Corporation).

Later experiments were made on a sample obtained from Dr. St. Pierre of the General Electric Co. It was prepared by the method of Kharasch and Joshi[16] and gave a melting point of 156 to 157°C.

Banfield and Kenyon's Radical [1 : 3 dimethyl-1(phenylimine oxide)-butylidene-3-N'-phenyl-N' oxynitrogen].

$$CH_3 - C - CH_2 - C - CH_3$$

with structure showing:

$$
\begin{array}{c}
\text{CH}_3 \\
| \\
\text{CH}_3 - \text{C} - \text{CH}_2 - \text{C} - \text{CH}_3 \\
| \qquad\qquad \text{O} \diagup| \\
\text{C}_6\text{H}_5 - \text{N} - \text{O} \qquad \text{N} - \text{C}_6\text{H}_5
\end{array}
$$

A sample of the precursor was obtained from J. B. Mathews of Shell Research Laboratories. It was oxidized using ammoniacal silver oxide.[15] To avoid any effects of atmospheric oxygen the reaction was performed under nitrogen. When purified by recrystallization from petroleum ether, the deep red crystals melted with decomposition at 88 to 90°C. Owing to the strong tendency of free radicals to form a complex with some solvents, the methods of purification described in the literature were strictly adhered to.

Gelatine. An ion-free sample was obtained from A. G. Ward of the British Gelatine & Glue Research Association.

Hydrogen. Commercial hydrogen was purified by diffusion through a heated palladium thimble.

Experimental

Semiconductivity Measurements. Polycrystalline specimens were compressed between nickel electrodes of area 7 mm² *in vacuo.* Hydrostatic pressure of 80 kg cm⁻² was applied with a Ni-monic 90 spring to overcome intercrystalline resistances. The resistance was measured using a valve voltmeter capable of measuring resistances up to 10^{15} ohms. The measuring technique has been described in detail elsewhere.[12]

Current/Voltage Relationships. These were measured under the conditions described above. Extra batteries were incorporated in the bridge circuit to provide higher applied fields. To minimize errors due to Joule heating effects, thermal equilibrium was established at the highest voltage used, and measurements of resistance with decreasing voltage were made rapidly. The temperature at which the experiment was performed was selected so that a wide range of voltages all gave a measurable potential across a single standard resistor in series with the specimen.

Solid-State Spectra. Coppinger's radical forms homogeneous films by vacuum evaporation onto optically flat silica and also gives good films by deposition from ether solution. Specimens prepared by both these methods gave similar results.

Banfield and Kenyon's radical is less stable thermally and does not give good films from solvents. In this case the KBr disk technique was used.

Measurements of the absorption spectra were made with a Unicam SP-500 model spectrometer.

Hydrogen-Atom Bombardment. The purpose of this experiment was to attempt to remove hydrogen atoms from the surface of a dry protein and to observe any change in conductivity

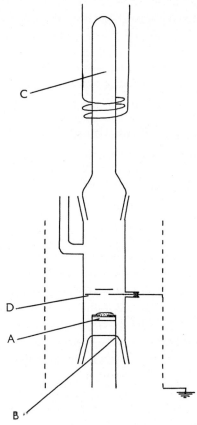

Fig. 19.1. The cell used for the bombardment of gelatine with hydrogen atoms.

that occurred. Gelatine was selected for the purpose, since it has a measurable resistance at room temperature and also is readily deposited as a hard layer by evaporation of a concentrated solution.

The apparatus used is shown in Fig. 19.1. A surface cell was made by laying strips of platinum 0.5 mm apart across a silica disk A. The disk was supported on tungsten rods sealed into a B34 joint B. The metal to glass seals were made using phoenix glass. This increased the resistance of the empty cell considerably. A concentrated gel was prepared by dissolving pure gelatine in warm distilled water and smearing a small quantity between the electrodes. The cell was then assembled and evacuated for 24 h to dry out the specimen. The electrodes were connected to a valve voltmeter and the lower half of the cell surrounded by an earthed metal screen. Hydrogen was admitted to a pressure of 0.1 mm Hg, and an electrodeless discharge struck in the tube C for 5 min using a 39 mc/sec oscillator. An earthed screen D was used to minimize effects due to charged species and to avoid photoconduction. The resistance could not be followed during the bombardment, as the oscillator affected the stability of the bridge. When the oscillator was switched off, the resistance was measured, and its variation with time was followed.

Results

Resistance/Temperature Measurements. The range of temperature over which measurements of resistance were made was limited at the lower end by the very high resistance of the solids at room temperature and at the upper end by the melting or sublimation temperatures. In particular, the low melting point (88°C) of Coppinger's radical only permitted experiments over a short temperature range ($\sim$40°C).

The substances behaved as typical organic semiconductors, obeying the usual law for intrinsic conduction:

$$\kappa = \kappa_0 \exp\left(-\Delta\varepsilon/2kT\right)$$

where κ is the conductivity, $\Delta\varepsilon$ the energy gap, and k the Boltzmann constant. Plots of the variation of the logarithm of resistance

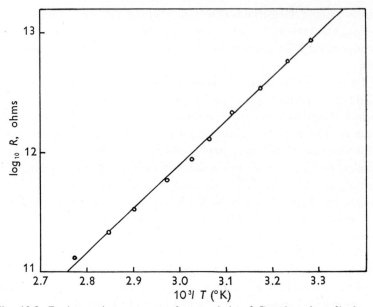

Fig. 19.2. Resistance/temperature characteristic of Coppinger's radical.

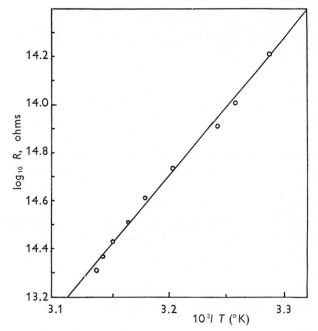

Fig. 19.3. Resistance/temperature characteristic of Banfield and Kenyon's radical.

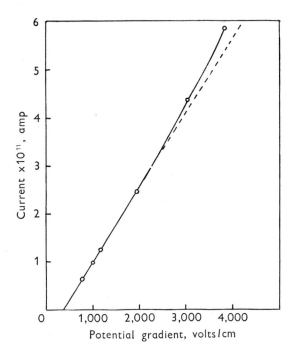

Fig. 19.4. Variation of current with applied field for Coppinger's radical at 63°C.

with reciprocal absolute temperature are shown for Coppinger's radical in Fig. 19.2 and for Banfield and Kenyon's radical in Fig. 19.3. Mean values of κ_0 and $\Delta\varepsilon$ are shown in Table 19.1.

Ohmicity Measurements. Measurements of the variation of the current passing through the specimen with different applied fields are shown in Fig. 19.4 for Coppinger's radical and Fig. 19.5 for Banfield and Kenyon's radical. Both substances show only gradual departures from Ohm's law within the range studied. At very high resistances the grid current of the electrometer causes a slight error and the curves do not go through the zero.

Solid-State Spectra. The solid-state electronic spectra of the two free radicals are shown in Figs. 19.6 and 19.7. The energies of the long-wave absorption thresholds are shown in Table 19.1.

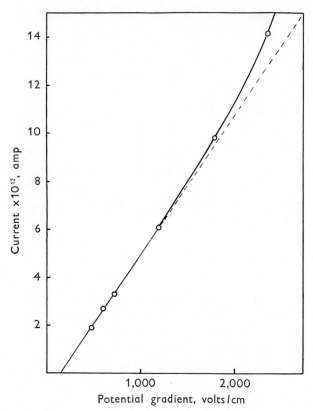

Fig. 19.5. Variation of current with applied field for Banfield and Kenyon's radical at 50°C.

Table 19.1.

Compound	Form	Method	$\triangle\varepsilon$, ev	$\log_{10}\kappa_0$ ohm cm^{-1}	b	Optical threshold ev
DPPH[2]	Polycrystalline[2]	A-C	0.26	$\bar{6}\,1$		
	Film[5]	A-C	0.16	$\bar{8}.78$		
	Film[5]	D-C	0.36	$\bar{7}.03$	5.4×10^{-4}	
Coppinger's radical	Polycrystalline	D-C	1.45	$\bar{1}.15$	4×10^{-4}	~ 1.3
Banfield and Kenyon's radical	Polycrystalline	D-C	2.31	5.0	5×11^{-4}	~ 2.2

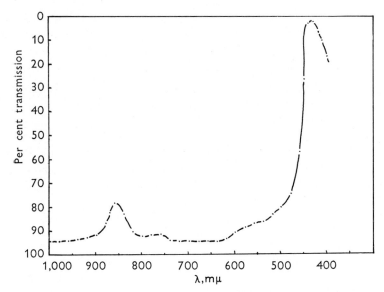

Fig. 19.6. Solid-state absorption spectrum of Coppinger's radical (evaporated film).

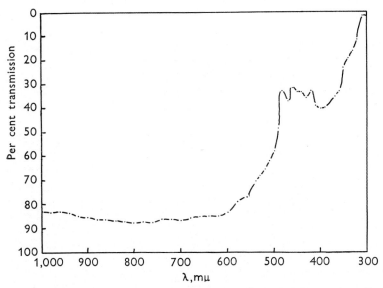

Fig. 19.7. Solid-state absorption spectrum of Banfield and Kenyon's radical (KBr disk).

Hydrogen–Atom Bombardment. The film of gelatine, when thoroughly outgassed at room temperature, had a resistance of 6.6×10^{14} ohms. After there had been an electrodeless discharge in the top half of the cell for 5 min, which was then switched off, the resistance had dropped to 9.3×10^{13} ohms (14 per cent of its former value). The resistance slowly increased with time until it had returned to its former value after 35 min.

Discussion

The numerical results are shown in Table 19.1 together with those published for DPPH. The striking feature of these results is the great difference in behavior between DPPH and the other two radicals. DPPH has a very low energy and low resistance at room temperature. Coppinger's and Banfield and Kenyon's radicals, on the other hand, have large energy gaps and very high resistance at room temperature.

The variation in $\Delta\varepsilon$ for samples of DPPH measured under vastly different experimental conditions indicates that a large part of the observed energy gap is associated with intercrystallite effects. The remainder may well be due to the coulombic energy required to dissociate an exciton.[17] Fundamentally, the conduction occurs without a process of electron activation. For this to take place, the electron must have a very high mobility in the ground state. This would require molecules to be favorably packed in the crystal lattice and the electron to be in a molecular orbital of suitable dimensions.

A comparison of the energy gaps of Coppinger's and Banfield and Kenyon's radicals with the energies of the optical absorption threshold shows quite good agreement, as has been observed for polycyclic hydrocarbons.[18] In this case we can identify the transition with the first doublet state without the usual ambiguity of multiplicity. The rather low extinction coefficient of the first absorption peak in Coppinger's radical ($\lambda = 840$ mμ, extinction coefficient $= 1,820$, in hexane) indicates that the level arises from "electron resonance."[19]

It is evident that mobility of electrons in the ground states of the two radicals examined here is too low to permit observable conduction. We have previously associated mobility with the tunneling probability of electrons through the intermolecular potential-energy barriers. In this case, the orbitals containing the unpaired electrons in the ground state must be unfavorably situated, spatially or energetically, for tunneling to occur. A consideration of the electron-spin-resonance absorption signals tends to support this view. The extremely small line width for DPPH has been

Table 19.2. Electron-Spin-Resonance Absorption

Compound	Form	Line width ΔH, (gauss)
DPPH	Single crystal[20]	1.9
	Polycrystalline[20]	3.7
Coppinger's radical	Polycrystalline[22]	6
Banfield and Kenyon's radical	Polycrystalline[23]	8.9

ascribed to narrowing that occurs when electrons are exchanged between the orbitals of different molecules.[21] The effect is much less marked for Coppinger's radical and Banfield and Kenyon's radical and would thus indicate a lower exchange probability. In the latter, the odd electron has been regarded as localized on the N—0 group.[24] Thus, in order for conduction to occur, the electron must be excited to a higher energy level, from which the potential-energy barrier has a higher permeability.

It would therefore seem that the mobility of a conduction electron (or positive hole) is very strongly influenced by the size and shape of the barrier between molecules. A detailed consideration of the problem of electron tunneling under the influence of an applied field is therefore relevant, and we consider the general case of a molecule containing an even number of π electrons.

The Molecular-Barrier Model. In previous papers [1,2] it was pointed out that the first act will be the excitation of a π electron from the uppermost filled $(n/2)$th molecular orbital to the lowest empty $(n/2+1)$th orbital, involving an energy $\Delta\varepsilon$. This electron may then tunnel to the equivalent empty level in a neighboring molecule, the permeability factor for the barrier determining the mobility μ of the electron. Many, Harnik, and Gerlich[25] pointed

to a similar mechanism as responsible for the wide range of mobility values for organic substances, which run parallel to the $\Delta\varepsilon$
values. The relationship is of the form $\mu\alpha v^{\Delta\varepsilon}$ for the amino acids,
but there is a broad scatter of values when all substances are
considered.[12]

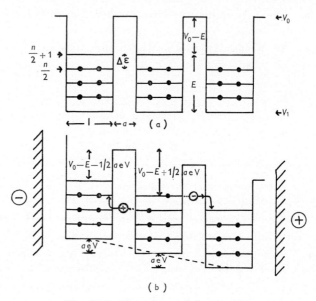

Fig. 19.8. The potential box model.

Figure 19.8(a) shows the potential box model for three adjacent
molecules each containing six π electrons and Fig. 19.8(b) the
situation in a voltage gradient V volts cm^{-1} after excitation of an
electron in the central molecule, leaving a gap in the $(n/2)$th level
that may be regarded as a positive hole. The electron may then
tunnel to occupy the $(n/2+1)$th level in the next molecule, the
total potential energy change for transferring the electron being

$$I - E - aeV - (e^2/Dr)$$

where I is the ionization potential, E the electron affinity of the
organic molecule, aeV the energy change over the barrier width a,
due to the applied field V, and e^2/Dr the coulombic energy of the

ion-pair "exciton." * An electron may similarly enter the vacant level of the central molecule from the left-hand molecule, which is equivalent to a positive hole moving as shown. This process involves a further separation of charge, but it is probable that the term e^2/Dr is small, because of the polarizability of surrounding π electrons giving rise to a high effective dielectric constant D. Also, in this particular step the electron descends the gradient aeV, which tends to offset the coulombic energy.

We assume the numbers of electrons and holes per cubic centimeter, n and p, are given by the band-theory formula

$$n = p = [2(2\pi kT)^{3/2}/h^3](m_e m_h)^{3/4} \exp\left(-\Delta\varepsilon/2kT\right)$$

If we assume the effective mass of the electrons and holes are equal to that for the free electron, this reduces to

$$n = p = 2.48 \times 10^{19} \exp\left(-\Delta\varepsilon/2kT\right) \text{ cm}^{-3} \quad \text{at } 298°K$$

It may be inappropriate to apply this equation to the present case. Since the overlap of wave functions of π electrons is small between different molecules, the band may be regarded as very narrow. We may estimate from Shockley's formula[26] that a band-width of 0.1 ev corresponds to an effective mass of 43, and one of 0.01 ev to 433. Therefore the density of states term may well be greater than 2.48×10^{19}, an upper limit being the number of molecules per cubic centimeter multiplied by the multiplicity of the conducting molecular state[25] of the order of 10^{22}. For the present purpose we shall assume the first figure to hold.

The specific conductivity is then given by

$$\kappa = ne\mu_e + ne\mu_h = \kappa_0 \exp\left(-\Delta\varepsilon/2kT\right)$$

where e is the electronic charge and μ_e and μ_h the mobility of electrons and positive holes. There is considerable interest in evaluating the factors that determine μ or κ_0. In addition, it is possible that deviations from Ohm's law may be due to the tunneling process. For simplicity we shall discuss electron tunneling, but

* Even when the positive hole and electron are located on neighboring molecules, D will not necessarily be unity, as the charges may be largely screened by polarizable π electrons.

the formulas derived are immediately applicable to positive holes. The electron in the first excited level $n/2+1$ see, Fig. 19.8(1), may be regarded as moving between the potential walls with velocity v_e

$$v_e = (n/2+1)h/2lm_e$$

It will "strike" the barrier with a frequency $v_e/2l$, and if it passes through, the barrier will suffer a net displacement $a+l$, where a is the barrier width and l the appropriate molecular dimension. If the probability of passing the barrier in the field direction is T_f, and in the reverse direction T_b, then the "drift velocity" of the electron in the field is

$$v_{de} = (v_e/2l)(a+l)(T_f-T_b)$$

and the current density of electrons is

$$i = n_e e v_{de} = [2(2\pi m_e kT)^{3/2}/h^3][\exp(-\Delta\varepsilon/2kT)]_e$$
$$[(n/2+1)h(a+l)(T_f-T_b)/4l^2 m_e] \quad *$$

The term in square brackets is μV, where μ is the mobility as defined earlier and V is the applied voltage gradient. Since

$$i = \kappa_0 V \exp(-\Delta\varepsilon/2kT)$$

this equation also gives a value for κ_0 now derived for square and triangular barriers.

Square Barriers. Referring to Fig. 19.8(b), we suppose the effect of the applied voltage gradient V is to raise one energy level by $\frac{1}{2}aeV$ and lower the adjacent one by $\frac{1}{2}aeV$, where a is the barrier width. Therefore [27]

$$T_f(T_b) = [16E(V_0-E\pm\frac{1}{2}aeV)/V_0^2]$$
$$\exp\{-2\sqrt{[2m_e(V_0-E\pm\frac{1}{2}aeV)]}a/\hbar\}$$

where the minus sign applies to T_f, the positive to T_b. We neglect the effect of the aeV term on the pre-exponential factor and write

$$T_f-T_b = 16E(V_0-E)/V_0^2$$
$$(\exp\{(-2\sqrt{[2m_e(V_0-E)]}/\hbar)a[1-\frac{1}{2}aeV/(V_0-E)]^{1/2}\}$$
$$-\exp\{(-2\sqrt{[2m_e(V_0-E)]}/\hbar)a[1+\frac{1}{2}aeV/(V_0-E)]^{1/2}\})$$

* A factor 2 much be added when we include $+m$ holes.

Where $aeV \ll (V_0 - E)$, this reduces to

$$T_f - T_b = (32E/V_0^2)(V_0 - E)$$
$$\exp\left(\{-2\sqrt{[2m_e(V_0 - E)]}/\hbar\}a\right) \cdot \sinh\left\{\sqrt{[2m_e/(V_0 - E)]}(a/\hbar)(aeV/2)\right\}$$

We shall evaluate this expression for typical values of the constants, namely, $V_0 = 20$ ev, $E = 10$ ev, $a = 3 \times 10^{-8}$ cm, when $T_f - T_b = 0.49 \times 10^{-3} \sinh 7.28 \times 10^{-9} V$.

With the additional substitution of $n = 20$ (number of π electrons)

$$l = 10 \times 10^{-8} \text{ cm} \qquad T = 298°\text{K}$$

$i = 4.98 \times 10^5 \exp(-\Delta\varepsilon/2kT) \sinh 7.28 \times 10^{-9} V$ amp cm^{-2}
when V is in volts per centimeter.

We expect the $\sinh x$ to be approximated by x up to $x = 0.3$ (deviation of about 1.3 per cent), so Ohm's law should be obeyed to this accuracy to $V \sim 5 \times 10^7$ volts cm^{-1}. In the Ohm's law region

$$i = 3.602 \times 10^{-3} V \exp(-\Delta\varepsilon/2kT) \text{ amp cm}^{-2}$$
$$\kappa_0 = 3.602 \times 10^{-3} \text{ ohms}^{-1} \text{ cm}^{-1}$$
$$\mu = 0.2516K_0 = 0.91 \times 10^{-3} \text{ cm sec}^{-1}/V \text{ cm}^{-1}$$

Triangular Barriers. In this case the transmission coefficients are[28]

$$T_f(T_b) = \exp -\tfrac{4}{3}[\sqrt{2m_e(V_0 - E \pm \tfrac{1}{2}aeV)}/\hbar]a^*$$

where a^* is the width of the barrier at the point of penetration, i.e.,

$$a^* = a(V_0 - E \pm \tfrac{1}{2}aeV)/V_0$$

where a is the width of the barrier at its base. The plus sign refers to T_b and the minus sign to T_f.

As previously, and for $aeV \ll 2(V_0 - E)$,

$$T_f - T_b = \exp\left\{-\tfrac{4}{3}[(2m_e)^{1/2}/\hbar][(V_0 - E)^{3/2}/V_0]a\right\}$$
$$2 \sinh\left\{[\sqrt{2m_e(V_0 - E)}/V_0](a/\hbar)(aeV)\right\}$$

For $V_0 = 20$ ev, $E = 10$ ev, $a = 3 \times 10^{-8}$ cm as before, $T_f - T_b = 7.832 \times 10^{-2} \sinh 7.28 \times 10^{-9} V$. with $n = 20$, $l =$

10×10^{-8} cm, $T = 298°K$ $i = 8.09 \times 10^7$ exp $(-\Delta\varepsilon/2kT)$ sinh $7.28 \times 10^{-9} V$ amp cm^{-2}, when V is in volts per centimeter.

Ohm's law should hold to 1.3 per cent up to $V = 5 \times 10^7$ volts cm^{-1} and in this region

$$i = 5.89 \times 10^{-1} V \exp (-\Delta\varepsilon/2kT) \text{ amp cm}^{-2}$$
$$\kappa_0 = 5.89 \times 10^{-1} \text{ ohms}^{-1} \text{ cm}^{-1}$$
$$\mu = 1.48 \times 10^{-1} \text{ cm sec}^{-1}/V \text{ cm}^{-1}$$

Implications of the Tunnel Theory. The above calculations carried out with typical energy and lattice magnitudes, and assuming the effective mass of the carrier is that of the free electron, give κ_0 values of order 10^{-1} and 10^{-3}. In fact, observed values of κ_0 vary over the range 10^{-8} to 10^6 at least (see, for example, Many, Harnik, and Gerlich[25]), and the calculated values are in the middle of this range. It must be expected that some of this variation in observed values arises from errors in the energy-gap values, although in our experience these may be reproduced with a considerable precision, even on apparently unfavorable substances such as proteins. The equations above relating κ_0 to E, and by implication to $\Delta\varepsilon$, also involve other molecular properties, such as a, l, V_0, and n, and m_e is another possible variable. It is not surprising, therefore, that while a linear relation between $\log_{10}\mu$ and $\Delta\varepsilon$ was observed for a narrow class, amino acids and proteins, inclusion of all substances show a spread of μ of 10^6 for $\Delta\varepsilon = 2.0$ ev.[12]

Perhaps the most striking observation is the high κ_0 values of 10^4 for proteins.[12] These substances may well have exceptionally high path length or l values, but of itself this would lead to low mobilities on the present theory (due to a decreased frequency of electron striking the barriers), and additional assumptions will be required to explain these values.

The κ_0 values of the three solid free radicals presented in this chapter cover a very wide range and fit into the "scatter-diagram" already published of $\log_{10}\kappa_0$ versus $\Delta\varepsilon$ near the upper limiting straight line.[12] The function

$$i = A \sinh bV \exp (-\Delta\varepsilon/2kT)$$

describes the form of the observed data on i/V curves. At low voltages this gives Ohm's law $i = AbV \exp \Delta\varepsilon/2kT$. At very high voltages it gives a relationship

$$l = (A/2)e^{bV} \exp\left(-\Delta\varepsilon/2kT\right)$$

already described by Inokuchi in earlier work in this laboratory.[29] But the observed b values * are many powers of ten greater than

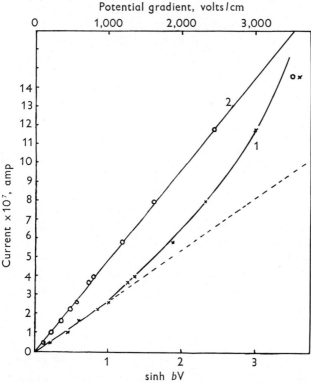

Fig. 19.9. Curve 1, the variation of current with applied field for DPPH; curve 2, the variation of current with $\sinh bV$ (V is the potential gradient in volts per centimeter, and b is the factor required to linearize the data).

those calculated on the theory using the typical values for parameters. Because of the narrow energy bands the effective mass may

* Similar b values are found for single crystals of anthracene, as calculated from Mette and Pick, *Z. Physik.* **134**, 566 (1953).

be much larger than that for the free electron. If $m_e = 100$, this will raise the calculated b value by a factor 10 and lower Ab (which is κ_0) by 4.5×10^{-3} for both square and triangular barriers. Therefore, so far as variations in m_e go, the model predicts that a high κ_0 will be associated with a small departure from Ohm's law, as measured by a small b value. This conclusion does not apply to the present three free radicals, but it does qualitatively agree with a so far unpublished observation that the proteins with high κ_0 values of 10^4 show negligible departure from Ohm's law at 10^3 volts cm^{-1}.

It may be that the deviations from Ohm's law are to be associated with electron tunneling through barriers of an intercrystalline kind. However, if this is so, the theory would require at first sight a low κ_0. In favorable cases, such as metal-free phthalocyanine, single crystals and powders do not differ greatly in κ_0, so there is no evidence that gaps or defects in the powder are a limiting factor for conductivity.

The theory does suggest that a careful correlation of κ_0 with the Ohm's law deviation would be interesting for single crystals. It does not seem possible to take this particular matter further at present. A model equivalent to that used here has been used by R. C. Nelson[30] to discuss the process of photoconductivity in cationic dyes. It is hoped to study the photoconductivity of the solid free radicals in the near future.

The bombardment of gelatine with H atoms gave a sevenfold increase in conductance. It is tentatively suggested that mobile positive holes are generated by a mechanism of H-atom abstraction,

$$\tfrac{1}{2}H_2 \rightarrow H \qquad\qquad \varDelta H = 51.6 \qquad kcal\ mole^{-1}$$

$$H + H{-}N{\Big\langle} \rightarrow H_2 + {\overset{\cdot}{\oplus}}N{\Big\langle} \quad \varDelta H = -18.2 \quad kcal\ mole^{-1}$$

For such a process to be of biochemical significance, it is presupposed that a supply of reactive atoms, or free radicals, are available in the cell. The initial energy requirements of 51.6 kcal $mole^{-1}$ is so high as to make this rather unlikely, the energy in a chain of oxidation reactions being generally released in a series of much smaller steps. The free radical ESR signals observed in biological systems no doubt relate to the less active resonance-stabilized radicals (if we rule out photochemical systems). The conclusion of this preliminary work is therefore that, while oxidative attack may increase conductivity in proteins, the energy requirements make the process rather unlikely.

Acknowledgement. The author's best thanks are due to British Petroleum, Ltd., for a studentship awarded to M. R. Willis and for a grant for purchase of apparatus.

References

1. D. D. Eley, G. D. Parfitt, M. J. Perry, and D. H. Taysum, *Trans. Faraday Soc.* **49**, 79 (1953).
2. D. D. Eley and G. D. Parfitt, *Trans. Faraday Soc.* **51**, 1929 (1955).
3. D. D. Eley, H. Inokuchi, and M. R. Willis, *Discussions Faraday Soc.* **28** (1959).
4. C. G. B. Garrett, in N. B. Hannay (ed.), "Semiconductors," Monograph Series No. 140, Reinhold Publishing Corporation, New York (1959).
5. D. D. Eley and H. Inokuchi, *Z. Electrochem.* **63**, 29 (1959).
6. Y. Yokozawa and I. Tatzsugaki, *J. Chem. Phys.* **22**, 2087 (1954).
7. H. Inokuchi, *Bull. Chem. Soc. Japan.* **24**, 222 (1951).
8. H. Akamatu, H. Inokuchi, and Y. Matsunaga, *Bull. Chem. Soc. Japan* **29**, 213 (1956).
9. Y. Matsunaga, *J. Chem. Phys.* **30**, 856 (1959).
10. D. Bijl, H. Kainer, and A. C. Rose-Innes, *J. Chem. Phys.* **30**, 765 (1959).
11. F. H. Winslow, W. O. Baker, and W. A. Yager, *J. Am. Chem. Soc.* **77**, 4751 (1956).
12. M. H. Cardew and D. D. Eley, *Discussions Faraday Soc.* **27**, 115 (1959).
13. D. D. Eley, *Discussions Faraday Soc.* **20**, 282 (1955).
14. G. M. Coppinger, *J. Am. Chem. Soc.* **79**, 501 (1957).
15. F. H. Banfield and J. Kenyon, *J. Chem. Soc.* **1926**, 1612.
16. M. S. Kharasch and B. S. Joshi, *J. Org. Chem.* **22**, 1435 (1957).
17. D. D. Eley, *Discussions Faraday Soc.* **27**, 237 (1959).
18. H. Inokuchi, *Bull. Chem. Soc. Japan.* **27**, 22 (1954).
19. E. A. Braude and F. C. Nachod (eds.), "Determination of Organic Structures by Physical Methods," p. 158, Academic Press, Inc., New York (1954).
20. C. A. Hutchison, R. S. Pastor, and A. G. Kowalsky, *J. Chem. Phys.* **20**, 534 (1952).
21. D. J. E. Ingram, "Free Radicals as Studied by Electron Spin Resonance," p. 127, Butterworth & Co. (Publishers), Ltd., London (1958).
22. J. J. Windle and W. H. Thurston, *J. Chem. Phys.* **27**, 1429 (1957).

23. T. L. Chu, G. E. Pake, D. E. Paul, J. Townsend, and S. I. Weissman, *J. Phys. Chem.* **57**, 504 (1953).
24. A. N. Holden, W. A. Yager, and F. R. Merritt, *J. Chem. Phys.* **19**, 1319 (1951).
25. A. Many, E. Harnik, and D. Gerlich, *J. Chem. Phys.* **23**, 1733 (1955).
26. W. Shockley, "Electrons and Holes in Semiconductors," p. 398, Van Nostrand and Company, Inc , Princeton, N.J. (1950).
27. W. Kauzmann, "Quantum Chemistry," p. 197, Academic Press, Inc., New York (1957).
28. N. F. Mott and I. N. Sneddon, "Wave Mechanics and Its Applications," p. 19, Oxford University Press, London (1948).
29. H. Inokuchi, Ph.D. thesis, University of Nottingham (1957).
30. R. C. Nelson, *J. Chem. Phys.* **30**, 406 (1959).

20

The Chemical Aspects of Semiconductive Compounds

H. Akamatu and H. Inokuchi

Introduction

A number of organic compounds that have relatively low electrical resistivity in the solid state have been found in this decade. It is believed that in those compounds the conduction is an electronic one. This has been proved from the following behaviors, which are closely related to each other.

The resistivity ρ decreases with rising temperature T, and it can be expressed as

$$\rho = \rho_0 \exp\left(\varepsilon/2kT\right)$$

where k is the Boltzmann constant, ρ_0 is a constant for each compound, and $\varepsilon/2$ is the activation energy for conductance. Conveniently, ε is called as "energy gap," since it is presumed to be the energy interval for excitation from a bound state to a free conductive state. Thus, the temperature dependence for resistivity is predominantly determined by the number of electrons that can contribute to the conductance.

The resistivity decreases with illumination of light. The photoconductivity depends on the wavelength of incident light, and it has been proved, for several compounds, to reproduce the spectral response of optical absorption in the organic solid. Furthermore, the light quanta at the threshold of the spectral response of photoconductivity are found to be nearly in agreement with the value of energy gap that is observed thermally.

Recently, the photovoltaic effect has been observed in several junctions between metals and organic compounds.

All these behaviors prove that these compounds can be adequately called "organic semiconductors." Since they are made of molecular crystals, however, in which molecular interactions is believed to be rather small, a question arises concerning the mechanism for charge transfer between molecules. This is the principal problem for the organic semiconductors.

From the chemical viewpoint, it should be also interesting to find the characteristic functions in molecular structures that can contribute to the electrical conductance. In this chapter, we shall present a survey of the chemical aspects of the organic semiconductors that have been investigated in our laboratory.

Polycyclic Aromatic Compounds

The typical examples for the compounds that possess semiconductive properties can be found in the polycyclic aromatic compounds.[1-4] The molecules of these compounds are made of a condensation of benzene rings, which consist of the conjugated double bonds; thus they are plane molecules and contain a large number of delocalized π electrons. The electrical resistivity of these compounds is dependent on the size of the molecule, and it decreases in a rather simple way as the molecular size becomes larger. Naphthalene and anthracene are electrical insulators with high values of resistivity. As the condensation of aromatic rings proceeds, the resistivity of the compound decreases. Thus, for instance, anthanthrene with six rings possesses 10^{19} ohm-cm, pyranthrene with eight rings possesses 10^{16} ohm-cm, and violanthrene with nine rings possesses 10^{14} ohm-cm. In the same way, the value of energy gap also decreases. This can be seen in Table 20.1.

It is believed that in aromatic-hydrocarbon molecules π electrons are capable of being excited readily, and their ionization potential decreases, whereas the electron affinity increases, as the molecular size becomes larger. Thus the electron transfer between molecules would be facilitated as the molecule becomes larger.

The largest aromatic molecule is the graphite molecule. The resistivity along the basal plane of graphite crystal is 10^{-5} ohm-cm, which is the same value as the resistivity of mercury. This is easily understood, since the basal plane is nothing other than the molecular plane of graphite, in which the π electrons can move freely. Whereas graphite possesses conductivity along the c axis of its crystal, the direction is perpendicular to the molecular plane. The resistivity is 10^{-1} ohm-cm in this direction. The low value of ionization potential and the high electron affinity of graphite sheet (both values are believed to be about 4.3 ev) might contribute to the conductance in this direction. The interlayer distance in graphite crystal is 3.354 A, and this value is remarkably smaller than the Van der Waals thickness of an aromatic-ring plane, which

Table 20.1. Semiconductive Date of Polycyclic Aromatic Compounds

Compound	Molecular formula	ρ_{15}, ohm-cm	ρ_0, ohm-cm	ε, ev	Threshold energy for photo-current, ev
Perylene	$C_{20}H_{12}$	4×10^{18}	10	2.0	2.3
Anthanthrene	$C_{22}H_{12}$	1.5×10^{19}	3.4×10^4	1.67	
Anthanthrone	$C_{22}H_{10}O_2$	7.7×10^{18}	9.7×10^3	1.70	
Coronene	$C_{24}H_{12}$	1.7×10^{17}	4.3×10^2	1.7	
Meso-naphthodianthrene	$C_{28}H_{14}$	4.0×10^{18}	1.8×10^8	1.2	
Meso-naphthodianthrone	$C_{28}H_{12}O_2$	1.5×10^{18}	6.0×10^6	1.30	
Pyranthrene	$C_{30}H_{16}$	4.5×10^{16}	2.0×10^7	1.07	0.85
Pyranthrone	$C_{30}H_{14}O_2$	3.9×10^{15}	3.7×10^6	1.06	1.14
Ovalene	$C_{32}H_{14}$	2.3×10^{15}	3.1×10^5	1.13	1.20
Violanthrene	$C_{34}H_{18}$	2.1×10^{14}	6.9×10^6	0.85	0.88
Violanthrone	$C_{34}H_{16}O_2$	2.3×10^{10}	2.9×10^3	0.78	0.84
Isoviolanthrene	$C_{34}H_{18}$	8.4×10^{13}	6.3×10^6	0.82	0.85
Isoviolanthrone	$C_{34}H_{16}O_2$	5.7×10^9	1.5×10^3	0.75	0.93
Indanthrazine	$C_{28}H_{16}N_2$	1.4×10^{15}	2.2×10^9	0.66	0.80
Indanthrone	$C_{28}H_{14}N_2O_4$	7.5×10^{14}	2.5×10^9	0.63	0.74
Flavanthrone	$C_{28}H_{12}N_2O_2$	1.4×10^{11}	9.5×10^4	0.70	0.76
Indanthrene black	$C_{34}H_{14}N_2O_2$	2.5×10^8	3.5×10^3	0.56	
Cyananthrone	$C_{40}H_{18}N_2O_2$	1.2×10^7	2.2×10^5	0.20	

is believed usually to be 3.7 A. R. S. Mulliken [5] suggested that the difference may be due to the effect of the charge-transfer force in addition to the Van der Waals type of force.

In crystals of polycyclic aromatic hydrocarbons, molecules are arranged so that the planes of molecules are parallel with each other. The nearest distance between molecular planes is about

3.4 A, the same value as in graphite. There is experimental evidence that leads us to believe that the resistivity of those crystals is anisotropic, and the lowest value is found in the direction of the nearest approach between planes of molecules. The π-electron orbitals of molecules, which are perpendicular to the plane of a molecule, extend in this direction. They would overlap with each other between neighboring molecules, if it is possible, in this direction. The intermolecular charge-transfer force would be anticipated to be similar to that of graphite.

In connection with this, the electronic state in the crystal, rather than in the free molecule, is especially interesting. We have tried to find the charge-transfer spectrum or exciton band for the solid, but as yet we have been unsuccessful. It has been proved, however, for several polycyclic aromatic compounds that the spectral response of photocurrent reproduces the absorption spectrum of a solid. Recently, M. Sano in our laboratory found new peaks of response in the photocurrent in the long-wavelength region outside the main response. This is illustrated in Fig. 20.1 for pyranthrene. In this figure, we can see that the light quanta at the first peak coincide with the value of the energy gap observed thermally.

In addition to the size of the molecule, some other correlations are found between resistivity and molecular structure. For instance, some quinones are more conductive than hydrocarbons. This can be seen when we compare the resistivity of violanthrone with that of violanthrene in Table 20.1. It is likely that the aza-aromatic structure can contribute to conductance more than the benzene ring does. For instance, flavanthrone has much higher conductivity than pyranthrone. Thus, the compounds with low resistivity are found in the aza-aromatic compounds. Cyananthrone, which consists of nine benzene rings and two pyridine rings has a resistivity of 10^7 ohm-cm and an energy gap of 0.20 ev. Its value is comparable to selenium, which is a typical semiconductive material.

In addition to the polycyclic aromatic compounds, much attention has been given to phthalocyanine by many investigators.[6-9] Up to the present, there are still discrepancies in the results found by different investigators. The observed values of resistivity, how-

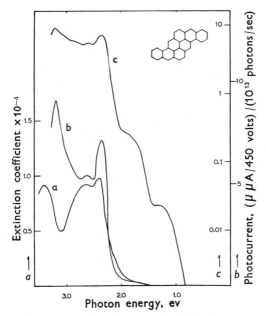

Fig. 20.1. Spectral responses of: curve a, optical absorbance; curves b and c, photocurrent in solid pyranthrene.

ever, lie between 10^{11} and 10^{15} ohm-cm, and the energy gap is about 1.5 ev.[10] Phthalocyanine forms inner complexes with metals. However, not much differences can be found in the resistivity between phthalocyanine and metal phthalocyanines.

Organic Free Radicals

It should be hoped that some special electronic state in a molecule might give the electronic conductance in solid state. Organic free radicals are such compounds. D. D. Eley assumed that the mechanism for electron transfer between molecules was due to the tunnel effect under the applied field and that the activation energy for conductance might be small in a free radical. Eley and his collaborators [10,11] observed the resistivity of diphenyl picryl hydrazyl, which is known as the only stable free radical in the solid state. It possesses 10^8 to 10^{10} ohm-cm, and the ε value is 0.26 ev. Both small values suggest that the unpaired electron in this molecule contributes to the electronic conductance.

There is an interesting compound named "violanthrone-B compound" by investigators of the indanthrene dyes. This compound is prepared, accompanied with violanthrone, in the process of alkali fusion of benzanthrone. The chemical structure of

violanthrone-B has not yet been fixed. However, T. Maki [12] has proposed a plausible formula (20.2) from the consideration of chemical synthesis. The result of chemical analysis also supports this formula. This is a paramagnetic compound with a deep violet color and exhibits a strong electron spin-resonance absorption (ESR). It has been reported in a previous paper [13] that the spin population corresponds to one-third of the molecules, and it is assumed that the origin of spin center might be due to the defect of one hydrogen atom in the proposed formula, thus leaving an unpaired electron that should be stabilized because of its delocalized nature. Recently, T. Maekawa in our laboratory has found that, after careful purification, the ESR absorption in violanthrone-B increases strongly. In addition to this, there is experimental evidence that leads us to believe that this compound is a new stable free radical with one spin center in every molecule. The observed resistivity of the purified violanthrone-B is 7×10^6 ohm-cm, with an energy gap of 0.67 ev. In connection with this, it must be mentioned that the ESR absorption in violanthrone was reported by Y. Yokozawa and I. Tatsuzaki [14] some years ago. Recently, however, M. Kinoshita in our laboratory found that after repeated purifications the ESR absorption in violanthrone was greatly reduced. Hence, the absorption previously reported for violanthrone is due to impurity, probably violanthrone-B. However, after the repeated purifications, a weak ESR absorption was still detectable; the number of spins was 10^{17} per gram of the specimen. Thus, it is still in question whether this weak absorption is due to the intrinsic property of this compound or to impurity. The resistivity of this purified specimen is 1.1×10^{11} ohm-cm with an energy gap of 0.79 ev.

The resistivity of violanthrone-B is lower than that of violanthrone by nearly 10^4 times. The difference between them should be due to the free-radical nature of violanthrone-B. There is, on the other hand, no great difference in the value of energy gap between these two compounds.

Intermolecular Addition Compounds

Electronic conduction is found in a number of intermolecular addition compounds more easily than simple compounds. Intermolecular complexes between polycyclic aromatic hydrocarbons and halogens are typical examples for such a system.[15-18] Polycyclic aromatic hydrocarbons consisting of more than four benzene rings easily form solid addition compounds with bromine or iodine. They are dark-colored substances and possess good electrical conductance. The values of resistivity lie between 10^0 and 10^1 ohm-cm, with the energy gap of smaller than 0.2 ev. The semiconductive data for typical addition compounds are shown in Table 20.2.

The bromine complexes that are formed by absorption of bromine vapor are generally not stable as the substitution reaction proceeds between bromine and hydrogen in the aromatic ring. The iodine complexes are formed as the precipitate from the iodine solution and are quite stable because of no substitution reaction.

Table 20.2. Semiconductive Data of Intermolecular Addition Compounds

Addition compound	Mole ratio	ρ_{15}, ohm-cm	ε, ev	Spin population per one hydrocarbon molecule
Perylene-bromine	1 : 2	7.8	0.13	
-iodine	1 : 1.5	10	0.06	0.06
-iodine	1 : 3	10	0.06	0.05
Pyranthrene-iodine	1 : 2	17	0.09	0.09
Violanthrene-bromine	1 : 2	66	0.20	
-iodine	1 : 2	45	0.15	0.14
Dimethyl anilin:				
chloranil	1 : 1	1.0×10^9	0.47	0.0001
bromanil	1 : 1	1.7×10^9	0.45	0.05
iodanil	1 : 1	1.9×10^8	0.43	0.17
Tetramethyl-p-phenylene diamine:				
chloranil	1 : 1	2.4×10^4	0.53	0.05
bromanil	1 : 1	1.6×10^5	0.56	0.07
iodanil	1 : 1	1.8×10^6	0.59	0.10

In violanthrene-iodine system, for instance, its resistivity depends on the iodine content, as illustrated in Fig. 20.2; the resistivity decreases as the iodine content increases, and the minimum value is attained at the composition of one molecule of violanthrene to two of iodine, the mole ratio being 2, where the resistivity is about 45 ohm-cm with an energy gap of 0.15 ev. It has been proved that the addition compound of violanthrene $\cdot 2I_2$ is formed in the solid amorphous state.

In the case of perylene-iodine system, two kinds of addition compounds with a composition of perylene $\cdot 1.5I_2$ and perylene $\cdot 3I_2$, respectively, have been found by T. Uchida in our laboratory. Both of them are in crystalline state and possess the same value of resistivity, about 10 ohm-cm with an energy gap of 0.06 ev.

All of those addition compounds might be formed with the charge-transfer interaction between molecules, where the hydrocarbon molecules act as the electron donors and the halogen molecules act as the electron acceptors. Unlike simple compounds, in addition compounds the conductance is independent of the function of molecular size but probably depends on the suitable combination between electron donor and acceptor.

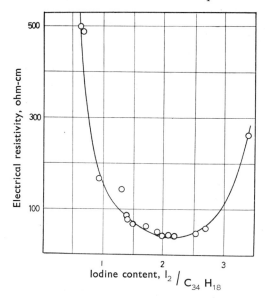

Fig. 20.2. Electrical resisitivity of violanthrene-iodine system as a function of iodine content.

Thus, the same hydrocarbons form conductive solid addition compounds with alkali metals when both of them are boiled in a suitable solvent. They are deep-green-colored substances but are unstable in the atmosphere. In this system, the hydrocarbons act as electron acceptor to the metals.

Y. Matsunaga[19] has found ESR absorption in the hydrocarbon-iodine complexes; the g values are nearly the same as those in organic free radicals and also in free electrons. The number of spin centers observed indicated that an average of about 10 per cent of the hydrocarbon molecules are in the paramagnetic state. We observed the same results. In the case of perylene-iodine system, interestingly enough, both compounds of perylene $\cdot$ 1.5I_2 and perylene $\cdot$ 3I_2 have the same population of spin centers; they possess the same value of resistivity mentioned above.

The structure of these addition compounds has not yet been clarified. However, from referring to the X-ray diffraction data and the density measurement, the most plausible structure might be similar to the one in which halogen molecules are sandwiched between every neighboring hydrocarbon molecule. Thus, the intermolecular charge-transfer effect can conjugate through the whole system.

Other examples of conductive solid addition compounds are those formed between dimethylaniline or tetramethyl-p-phenylene diamine (donors) and chloranil, bromanil, or iodanil (acceptors). [20,21] In these compounds, the resistivity possesses a much higher value than that of the aromatic hydrocarbon-halogen compounds (see Table 20.2). ESR absorption has been observed also in these addition compounds.

Thus, the paramagnetism is a common property of these solid donor-acceptor systems. This might be due, at least in part, to the transferred electrons between donors and acceptors; their spins are not in the coupled state. Therefore, the situation is something like that found in free electrons. The mechanism for the charge carriers should be in close connection with such an electronic state.

Sulfur Compounds of Aromatic Hydrocarbons

Recently, we found another series of compounds that have low resistivity. When aromatic hydrocarbons are heated with an excess amount of sulfur in evacuated closed tubing up to 450°C, they react with sulfur liberating hydrogen sulfide. After removing unreacted sulfur, dark-colored compounds in an amorphous solid are obtained. These compounds possess semiconductive properties. The values of resistivity lie between 10^2 and 10^4 ohm-cm, with an energy gap of about 0.2 ev. Thus the resistivity is greatly reduced in those compounds from that of the original hydrocarbons. The X-ray-diffraction pattern of those compounds is an amorphous one, consisting of a halo with a spacing of about 3.5 A. Thus, it is like the diffraction pattern of amorphous carbon. However, those compounds are not carbonized material, because violanthrene, for instance, is quite stable up to 450°C. The chemical analysis indicates that all hydrogens in aromatic rings are replaced

by sulfur. Therefore, they are sulfur compounds of aromatic hydrocarbons. The semiconductive data of these compounds with the
chemical composition are illustrated in Table 20.3.

Table 20.3. Semiconductive Data and Sulfur Content of Sulfur Compounds
of Aromatic Hydrocarbons

Hydrocarbon	ρ_{15}, ohm-cm	ρ_0, ohm-cm	ε, ev	Sulfur content, number of sulfur atoms per hydro-carbon molecule
Anthracene	1.0×10^4	2.7×10^2	0.18	5.8
Tetracene	1.4×10^4	1.9×10^2	0.15	7.1
Perylene	2.0×10^9	5.1×10	0.57	8.6
Pyranthrene	5.0×10^3	7.9×10	0.22	11.5
Violanthrene	1.1×10^4	2.0×10^2	0.19	9.7
Violanthrone	4.0×10^2	3.2×10	0.16	9.5

The chemical structure of these compounds has not yet been
discovered. However, from the amount of sulfur combined with
the hydrocarbon molecule, it is likely that aromatic molecular
sheets are conjugated with each other by a sulfur bridge. As an
example, the following structure is presumed for sulfur compound
of anthracene:

It would be interesting to speculate on the reason for the increased conductance by the sulfur bridge. In Table 20.3, it can be
seen that the molecular *size* of the hydrocarbon is not very important, but the molecular *shape* appears to be important. For

instance, a sulfur compound of perylene possesses remarkably higher resistivity than that of anthracene.

In connection with this, an interesting type of condensed-ring system including the sulfur atoms, thio-thiophthen, has been proposed by S. Bezzi, M. Mammi, and C. Garbuglio.[22] This Italian group has found from X-ray-diffraction analysis that the thio-thiophthen molecule is likely to be planar, and they assumed the following resonance structures, which gives the aromaticity of this compound:

By analogy with thio-thiophthen, the molecule of the sulfur compounds of aromatic hydrocarbons might have a planar structure. This would be expected if the trivalent bonding of S^+ could occur in possible resonance structures for the sulfur compounds in the same way it occurs in the resonance structures of thiophene molecule. Thus, we can expect the aromaticity for such a ring system consisting of sulfur bridge between the network plane of carbon atoms; it might be called a "thia-polycyclic aromatic structure."

Furthermore, the ESR absorption has been observed in these sulfur compounds. The population of spin centers possesses nearly the same value as that found in the halogen complexes. Thus, the structure of those compounds is interesting in association with their semiconductive property.

Appendix
Molecular Structures of Semiconductive Compounds

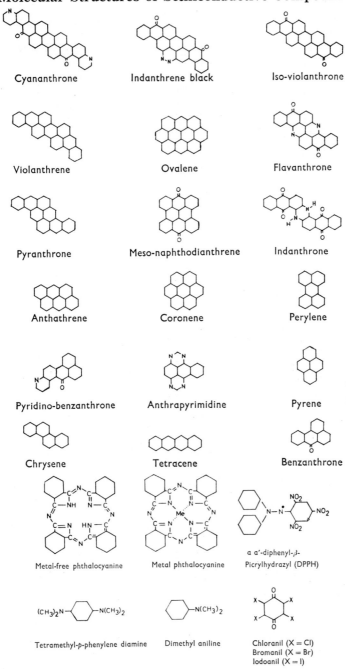

Cyananthrone

Indanthrene black

Iso-violanthrone

Violanthrene

Ovalene

Flavanthrone

Pyranthrone

Meso-naphthodianthrene

Indanthrone

Anthathrene

Coronene

Perylene

Pyridino-benzanthrone

Anthrapyrimidine

Pyrene

Chrysene

Tetracene

Benzanthrone

Metal-free phthalocyanine

Metal phthalocyanine

a a'-diphenyl-β-
Picrylhydrazyl (DPPH)

Tetramethyl-p-phenylene diamine

Dimethyl aniline

Chloranil (X = Cl)
Bromanil (X = Br)
Iodoanil (X = I)

290 H. AKAMATU AND H. INOKUCHI

References

1. H. Akamatu and H. Inokuchi, *J. Chem. Phys.* **18**, 810 (1950); **20**, 1481 (1952).
2. H. Inokuchi, *Bull. Chem. Soc. Japan* **24**, 222 (1951); **25**, 28 (1952); **27**, 22 (1954); **28**, 570 (1955); **29**, 131 (1956).
3. H. Akamatu, H. Inokuchi, and T. Handa, *Nature* **168**, 520 (1951).
4. H. Akamatu and H. Inokuchi, "Proceedings of the Third Conference on Carbon," p. 51, Pergamon Press, Ltd., London (1959).
5. R. S. Mulliken, "Conference on Quantum-mechanical Methods in Valence Theory," p. 108, Office of Naval Research, Washington (1951); *J. Phys. Chem.* **56**, 801 (1952).
6. A. T. Vartanyan, *Zhur. Fiz. Khim.* **22**, 769 (1948).
7. D. D. Eley, *Nature* **162**, 819 (1948).
8. P. E. Fielding and F. Gutman, *J. Chem. Phys.* **26**, 411 (1957).
9. W. Felmayer and I. Wolf, *J. Electrochem. Soc.* **105**, 141 (1958).
10. D. D. Eley and G. D. Parfitt, *Trans. Faraday Soc.* **51**, 1529 (1955).
11. D. D. Eley and H. Inokuchi, *Z. Elektrochem.* **63**, 29 (1959).
12. T. Maki, *J. Ind. Chem. Soc. Japan* **35**, 1437 (1932).
13. H. Akamatu, S. Mrozowski, and D. Wobschall, "Proceeding of the Third Conference on Carbon," p. 135, Pergamon Press, Ltd., London (1959).
14. Y. Yokozawa and I. Tatsuzaki, *J. Chem. Phys.* **22**, 2087 (1954).
15. H. Akamatu, H. Inokuchi, and Y. Matsunaga, *Nature* **173**, 168 (1954).
16. H. Akamatu, H. Inokuchi, and Y. Matsunaga, *Bull. Chem. Soc. Japan* **29**, 213 (1956).
17. Y. Matsunaga, *Bull. Chem. Soc. Japan* **28**, 475 (1955).
18. H. Akamatu, Y. Matsunaga, and H. Kuroda, *Bull. Chem. Soc. Japan* **30**, 618 (1957).
19. Y. Matsunaga, *J. Chem. Phys.* **30**, 855 (1955).
20. D. D. Eley and H. Inokuchi, "Proceedings of the Fhird Conference on Carbon," p. 91, Pergamon Press, Ltd., London (1959).
21. D. D. Eley, H. Inokuchi, and M. Willis, *Discussions Faraday Soc.* (in press).
22. S. Beizzi, M. Mammi, and C. Garbuglio, *Nature* **182**, 247 (1958).

Photoconduction and Photovoltaic Effects in Carotenoid Pigments

Barnett Rosenberg

I. Introduction

β-carotene is a typical hydrocarbon member of the C_{40} carotenoid pigments. It is a biologically interesting material that occurs in both plants and animals. It has been implicated in the processes of photosynthesis and phototropism and can be considered a pre-

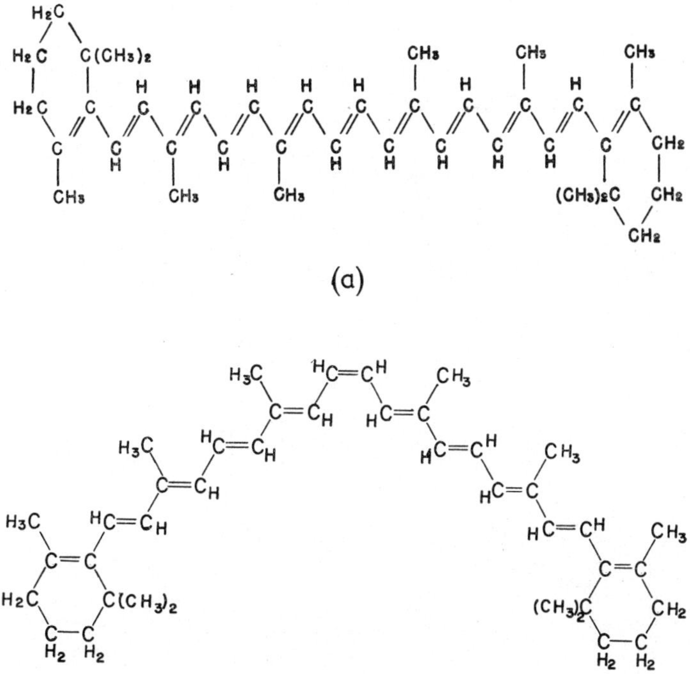

(a)

(b)

Fig. 21.1. Molecular structure of β-carotene: (a) all *trans* form; (b) 15–15′ *cis*.

[291]

cursor of retinene, the C_{20} carotenoid involved in all visual receptors. The interesting portion of the molecule for our purposes is the linear chain of 11 conjugated bonds. These determine the optical spectrum and the photoconductive and photovoltaic excitation

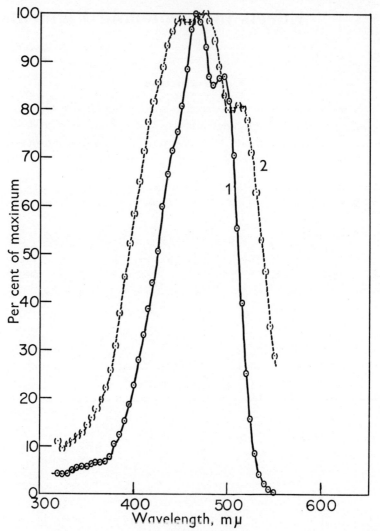

Fig. 21.2. Absorption spectrum of all *trans* β-carotene: curve 1, solution; curve 2, glass film.

spectra. The molecule may exist as a number of geometrical isomers. The straight linear chain is the all trans form. With rotation about a number of possible double bonds, various monocis and dicis forms occur and are stable, including one hindered *cis* modification.

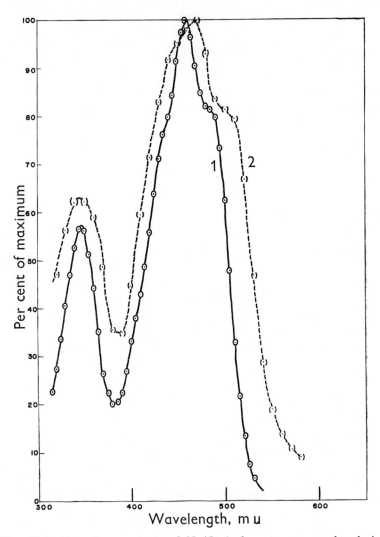

Fig. 21.3. Absorption spectrum of 15–15′-*cis* β-carotene: curve 1, solution; curve 2, glass film.

Two forms are shown in Fig. 21.1, which we have worked with extensively, the all *trans* and the 15–15′ *cis*. The visible-region absorption spectrum of a solution of all *trans* β-carotene consists of a single electronic band, a singlet-singlet π-electron transition,

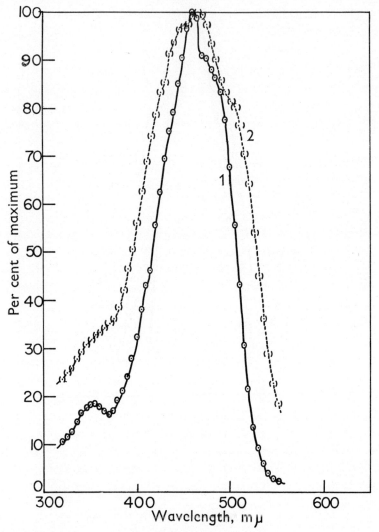

Fig. 21.4. Absorption spectrum of isomerized β-carotene: curve 1, solution; curve 2, glass film.

covering the region from about 4,000 to 5,000 A, with vibrational peaks. The spacing of the vibrational energy levels is 0.177 ev. The spectrum of the various *cis* forms is almost identical in this region. However, a new peak occurs at 3,500 A (in benzene) called the "*cis* peak." This too is a singlet-singlet π-electron transition that arises presumably from a dipole moment perpendicular to the straight linear chain when the molecule is bent. The largest *cis* peak occurs in the isomer with the largest perpendicular dipole, namely, the 15–15′ *cis*. The optical absorption curves of these two isomers in solutions of chloroform are shown in Figs. 21.2 and 21.3.

It has been shown by a number of investigators, notably Zechmeister,[1] that a solution of all *trans* β-carotene can be isomer-

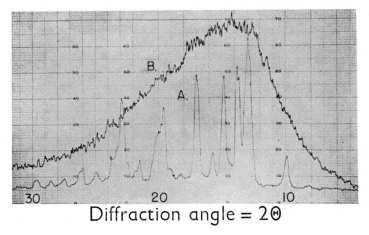

Diffraction angle = 2θ

Fig. 21.5. X-ray diffraction of β-carotene: curve A, crystals; curve B, glass.

ized to an equilibrium mixture of *cis-trans* forms by the action of light in the presence of iodine, or by melting the pure crystals. The absorption spectrum of a solution of such isomerized material in chloroform is shown in Fig. 21.4. When such a melt of crytstal is cooled, the presence of the mixture of geometric isomers prevents recrystallization, and a glass is formed instead. This glass is optically isotropic, and as shown in Fig. 21.5, shows an X-ray-diffraction pattern typical of amorphous substances. It has been previously reported by Rosenberg [2,3] that both the powder and glass forms are photoconductive and semiconductive, and in this paper we shall report on some photovoltaic properties as well. Glass films of the isomerized β-carotene can be prepared by evaporating the solvent of a solution. This exhibits the same electrical characteristics as the melt. Evaporated glass films can also be prepared of the pure isomers if the solution is dilute enough and the rate of evaporation is very rapid. The absorption spectra of such films with an areal density of about 5 to 10 μg cm^{-2} has been shown with the corresponding solution spectra. It will be noted that the absorption spectra of the glass films are broadened over the corresponding dilute-solution curves. In addition, there is some evidence of a small red shift of the longest wavelength band, although this is not the invariable case. The broadening is particularly obvious in the *cis*-peak region.

2. Photoconductive and Photovoltaic Excitation Spectra

The photocurrent for equal quantum numbers of light incident on the sample in melted-glass and evaporated-glass cells yields an excitation spectrum consisting of a broad band peaking at 3,500 A, the *cis*-peak absorption region. This is shown as curve 1 in Fig. 21.6. As can be anticipated, the photovoltaic excitation spectrum is quite similar, although usually narrower. This is curve 2.

The photocurrent spectrum is obtained by irradiating the positive electrode of the sandwich cell. If this side is negative, the light that is strongly absorbed causes a photocurrent smaller by a factor of 10^5. Light that is weakly absorbed can penetrate to the opposite positive electrode and thereby give rise to a photocurrent. This is proved in the data shown in Fig. 21.7. Here curve 1 is the photocurrent excitation spectrum in the back rectifying direction, curve 2 is the optical transmission of the β-carotene glass, and curve 3 is obtained by irradiating the sample in the forward rectifying direction with light passed through an identical sample as a filter. The obvious identity of 1 and 3 proves the above contention. Thus we may interpret these results as implying that the predominant current carrier in β-carotene is the positive hole, which is consistent with what we know for the case of aromatic hydrocarbons. The sign of the photovoltaic effect corroborates this. In all cases, the back electrode becomes positive with respect to the irradiated electrode in sandwich cells. It should be pointed out here that β-carotene glass exhibits no detectable fluoresence, although in

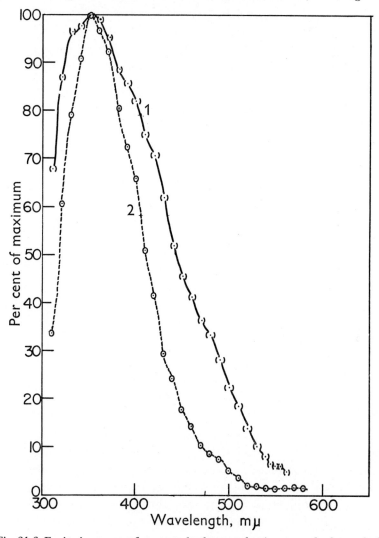

Fig. 21.6. Excitation spectra for: curve 1, photoconductive; curve 2, photovoltaic effects in β-carotene isomerized glass cells.

dilute solutions it is weakly fluorescent and at liquid nitrogen temperature it is weakly phosphorescent.

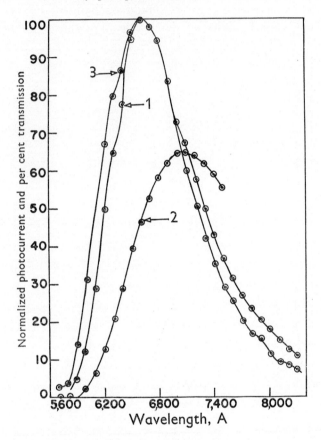

Fig. 21.7. Excitation spectra of reverse rectifying direction in β-carotene glass.

3. Semiconductivity

The dark conductivity of β-carotene glass cells (melted and
evaporated) as a function of temperature has been determined.
The results follow the usual form for semiconduction of $i =
i_0 \exp (\ E/2KT)$, with the value of the activation energy of about
$E = 3$ ev. This is shown in Fig. 21.8 curve 1. It was previously
reported to be the same value for powdered all *trans* β-carotene.

We have since found, however, in repeating the experiment, that during the temperature-cycling process before data were taken,

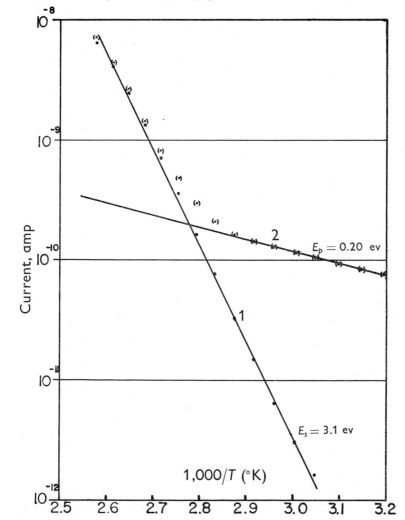

Fig. 21.8. Semiconduction and photoconduction in β-carotene isomerized glass cells: curve 1, semiconduction; curve 2, photoconduction and semiconduction.

the powder had sintered, giving rise to the intrinsic-body semi-conduction activation energy of 3.0 ev. With lowered temperatures of cycling, the present results indicate activation energies for powdered all *trans* and powdered 15–15′ *cis* of about 1.5 to 1.6 ev.

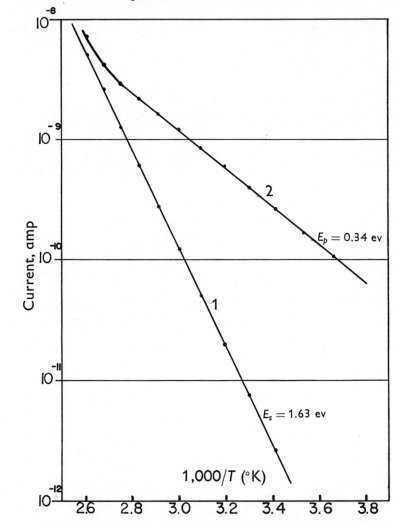

Fig. 21.9. Semiconduction and photoconduction in β-carotene; all *trans* powder. Curve 1, semiconduction; curve 2, photoconduction.

These are shown in Figs. 21.9 and 21.10, curve 1. It is felt at present that these values represent surface conduction phenomena.

This belief is strengthened by the fact that the currents in powders are enormously sensitive to the presence of weakly adsorbed oxygen

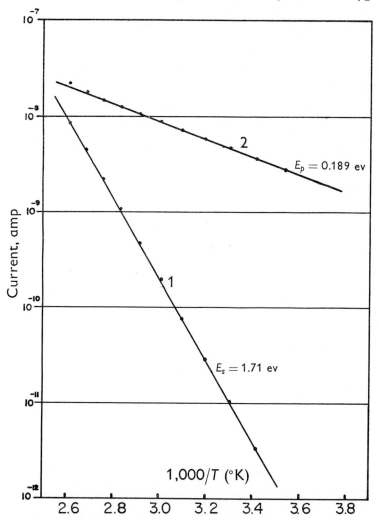

Fig. 21.10. Semiconduction and photoconduction in β-carotene 15–15'-*cis* powder. Curve 1, semiconduction; curve 2, photoconduction.

gas. This has been reported elsewhere.[4] All measurements were made in an atmosphere of dry nitrogen or dry argon.

4. Interpretation of Results in Terms of Triplet–State Theory

In a previous paper [5] the writer suggested that the formation of a triplet state in organic molecules is an essential step leading to the creation of mobile charges after singlet-singlet excitation by photons. The position of the lowest triplet-state level has not yet been determined for β-carotene. However, the phosphorescence emission of lycopene, a similar C_{40} carotenoid with the identical conjugated chain, has been measured by Lewis and Kasha.[6] The highest energy band occurs at 3.1 ev. As has occurred in other substances, the agreement of the phosphorescence value with the activation energy for semiconduction is very good (assuming $E/2KT$ as the exponential factor). Rosenberg [3] applied the triplet-state theory to the β-carotene photoconduction and semiconduction processes. Here, the semiconduction was assumed to arise from the radiationless transition from a high vibrational level of the singlet ground state to the triplet state. We can now draw the pertinent π-electron energy levels for the β-carotene molecule, as shown in Fig. 21.11. The triplet level falls above the lowest excited singlet level and below the second excited singlet level, the *cis*-peak state that occurs only in *cis* modifications of the molecule. Since the photoconduction excitation spectrum shows only the peak at 3,500 A in the *cis*-peak region, it follows that transitions from the lowest excited singlet state to the triplet state have a lower probability than transitions from the *cis*-peak state to the triplet state. One fairly obvious reason for this is explained by the Boltzmann factor determining the steady-state triplet-state density N_T:[4]

$$N_T = \alpha I \tau_T (P/A) \exp\left(-E_1/KT\right) \qquad (21.1)$$

where E_1 is the energy between the lowest vibrational level of the excited singlet state and the vibrational level nearest the crossover point of the singlet potential-energy curve with the triplet-state potential-energy curve. In the all *trans* molecules, the absorption-transition probability to the *cis*-peak state must be very small, and the only way to populate the triplet state will be by thermal excitation from the lowest excited state. Since the relative spacing of the singlet and triplet levels is not known with sufficient accuracy, it is possible that either two or three vibrational quanta are required to effect a radiationless intersystem crossing. This would mean that the photoconduction activation energy E_1 in Eq. (21.1) should be either 0.35 or 0.53 ev. If now in *cis* isomers the photoconduction activation energy for the *cis*-peak state is significantly less, say one vibrational quantum or $E_1 = 0.18$ ev., then the intersystem crossing to the triplet state from this level will preponderate over that

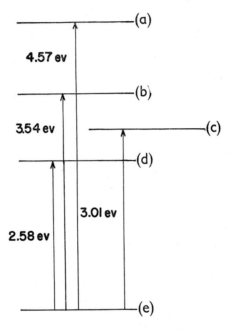

Fig. 21.11. β-carotene π-electron energy levels. (a) Third excited singlet state S_3; (b) second excited singlet state S_2 (*cis* peak); (c) triplet state T; (d) first excited singlet state S_1; (e) single ground state S_0.

from the lower singlet, and the photoconduction excitation spectrum will follow the absorption in the *cis*-peak region. It was reported by Lewis and Kasha [6] that at liquid-nitrogen temperatures they were not able to detect any phosphorescence in all *trans* lycopene but were able to measure it when the material was isomerized to a *cis-trans* mixture. This is consistent with the above picture.

The triplet-state model has therefore predicted that the photoconduction activation energies of the *cis* molecules should have a significantly lower value (by a factor of 2 or 3) than the all *trans* activation energy.

5. Experimental Determination of Photoconduction Activation Energies

Since it is almost impossible to make glass films of all *trans* β-carotene thick enough to sustain a significant electric field over the necessary temperature range without breakdown, it was decided to make the measurements on all *trans* powder in sandwich cells and to compare this to a similar cell of 15–15′-*cis* powder and glass films, both melted and evaporated, of isomerized β-carotene. It is unfortunate, however, that owing to some as yet uncontrolled factor there is an irritating lack of reproducibility from sample to sample, though the measurements on any single sample can be repeated with only a few per cent variation in the data.

Selected activation-energy curves for photoconduction are shown in Figs. 21.8, 21.9, and 21.10, curves labeled 2, for the cases of melted isomerized glass, all *trans* powder, and 15–15′-*cis* powder, respectively. In the case of the glass the exciting-light intensity was considerably lower than the other cases. The radiation was in all cases white light filtered with a Corning 1−56 filter, which passes light in the main absorption region of the β-carotene. In all samples the radiation was incident through the positive conductive glass electrode. Changes in pressure in the powder cells did not produce any significant change in the currents. As rear electrodes the following materials were tested: conductive glass, brass, aluminium, mercury, stainless steel, and monel metal. The same results were obtained with each. Thus the nature of the rear electrode is not significant. For evaporated thin films, mercury was used for the rear electrode.

Because of the lack of sufficient reproducibility, all measurements on a given type of sample were averaged without weighting factors. In general the data clustered well around the means, and the simple average-deviation measure is given. The results are shown in Table 21.1. Here it can be seen that the semiconduction activation energies for the all *trans* powder and the

Table 21.1. Semiconduction and Photoconduction Activation Energies of β-Carotene

Form	Semi-conduction, ev	No. of measurements averaged	Value suggested by triplet-state theory, ev	Photo-conduction, ev	No. of measurements averaged	Value suggested by triplet-state theory, ev
All-trans powder	1.47±0.11	26	—	0.374±0.041	20	0.354 or 0.531
15′15′-cis powder	1.59±0.15	6	—	0.199±0.02	5	0.177[a]
Melted glass.	3.07±0.26	24	3.1[b]	0.195±0.02	7	0.177
Evaporated glass	3.01±0.05[c]	6				

[a] Energy of dominant vibrational quanta in absorption spectra.
[b] From phosphorescence measurement on lycopene.
[c] Results of prior work.

15–15'-*cis* powder are the same, with the value of one overlapping those of the other. None of these 32 sets of values overlapped the 30 sets of values obtained for the melted or evaporated glass (averaged together). In the case of the glass cells, the average of 24 values agrees well with the previously reported average value for 6 measurements, but the dispersion is larger. Both of these average values are in good agreement with the value obtained from the phosphorescence measurements on lycopene.

In the case of the photoconduction activation energy, the excellent agreement of the 15–15'-*cis* powder and the glass cells strongly indicates that the surface-conduction effects are not involved in photoconduction in powders, and these values are intrinsic to the molecules. The photoconduction activation energy for the all *trans* powder is given as 0.374 ev. Out of the 20 sets of data, 8 fell within 5 per cent of 0.354 ev and 3 within 5 per cent of 0.53 ev, leaving the problem of two or three quanta incompletely resolved. In any case, no one of the 20 values overlapped any of the 5 values for the 15–15' *cis* or the 7 values of the glass. This enables us to draw the safe conclusion that the photoconduction activation energies for the all *trans* are at least twice the value of the activation energy in *cis* isomers and that both are very close to the values predicted by the triplet-state theory. The difference of a factor of 2 in the exponential term produces an increase in the density of triplet states owing to the probability of inter-system crossing from the *cis*-peak state of 10^3 over that from the lowest singlet state, assuming all other factors in Eq. (21.1) are the same for both states.

These conclusions lead to a further prediction from the triplet-state theory. That is, that the photoconduction excitation spectrum of all *trans* β-carotene should not agree with the *cis*-peak absorption region but should follow the absorption curve into the first excited state, the region from 4,000 to 5,000 A, and should be much smaller in magnitude than a corresponding *cis* isomer. This cannot be tested in powder samples and, as previously mentioned, cannot be measured in the very thin glass evaporated films we can make with the pure all *trans* isomer due to electrical breakdown. The situation can be saved however if we make use of the fact that in isomerized glass cells the photoconduction and photovoltaic spectra are almost identical, and indeed both

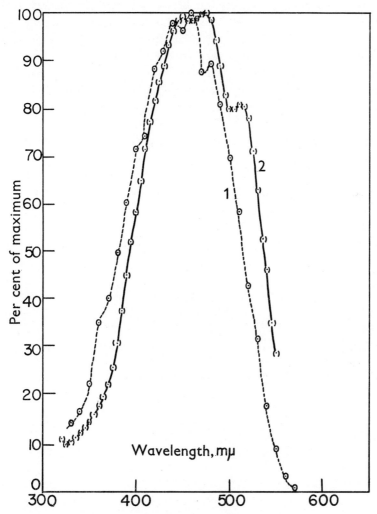

Fig. 21.12. (1) Photovoltaic spectrum; (2) film absorption spectrum of all *trans* β-carotene.

peak at 3,500 A. We assume that the same should be true for the all *trans* isomer and measure the photovoltaic spectrum, which we can barely do. The results are shown in Fig. 21.12. Here the photovoltaic spectrum is superimposed on the absorption spectrum of the thin glass film prepared by evaporating the solvent. The identity is obvious. In addition, the peak voltage measured was 1.9 mv, whereas in isomerized glass films the peak voltages were about 60 to 70 mv (these are with fairly weak monochromatic light; with high-intensity blue light the measured photovoltages in isomerized glass films were about 200 mv). Thus a further prediction of the triplet-state theory has been well verified.

Acknowledgements. It is a pleasure to thank Dr. R. H. Bunnel of Hoffmann-LaRoche, Inc., for the gift of the synthesized 15–15′ *cis* β-Carotene, as well as Mr. R. A. Orlando and Miss M. Walker for their invaluable assistance in the experimental work. This work was supported by Research Grant B-1936 from the National Institute of Neurological Diseases and Blindness, United States Public Health Service, and in part by a grant from the Research Corporation.

References

1. L. Zechmeister and A. Polgar, *J. Am. Chem. Soc.* **65**, 1522 (1943).
2. B. Rosenberg, *J. Opt. Soc. Am.* **48** 581 (1958).
3. B. Rosenberg, *J. Chem. Phys.* **31**, 238 (1959).
4. B. Rosenberg, *J. Chem. Phys.* **34**, 812 (1961).
5. B. Rosenberg, *J. Chem. Phys.* **29**, 812 (1961).
6. G. N. Lewis and M. Kasha, *J. Am. Chem. Soc.* **66**, 2100 (1944).

22

Semiconductive Properties of Molecular Complexes

Robert Sehr, Mortimer M. Labes, Monisha Bose,
Hana Ur, and Franz Wilhelm

1. Introduction

In our earlier work,[1] we prepared 30 molecular complexes involving quinones, halogens, polynitroaromatics, or tetracyanoethylene as electron acceptors and aromatic hydrocarbons or substituted aromatics as electron donors, measured their room-temperature electrical resistivities, and discussed these results in terms of available crystal-structure data and charge-transfer-complex theory. For comparative measurements, we have selected nine materials, which can be divided into three groups: (a) the complexes of p-phenylenediamine with chloranil, bromanil, and iodanil; (b) the complexes of 3,8- and 3,10-diaminopyrene with the above-mentioned tetrahalogen-p-benzoquinones; (c) the complexes of aromatic hydrocarbons with iodine. We have measured the activation energy of electrical conduction, the Seebeck coefficient as a function of temperature, and the spin density at room temperature. Since these measurements were made on microcrystalline material compounded into pellets, we have also studied the effect of compounding pressure on conductivity.

2. Experimental

a. Materials. p-Phenylenediamine and chloranil (Eastman) were purified by simple recrystallization to constant melting point. Iodine was Merck reagent grade.

3,8- and 3,10-Diaminopyrene were prepared by the procedure of Vollman et al.[2] The 3,8 isomer was crystallized three times from xylene (melting point 226 to 227°); the 3,10 isomer was

Table 22.1. Microanalytical Data on Amine-Quinone Complexes

Sample no.	Name A—B	Calc'd for Ratio A:B	Percent C Calc'd	Percent C Found	Percent H Calc'd	Percent H Found	Percent N Calc'd	Percent N Found
73	3,8-Diaminopyrene -chloranil	1:1	55.3	55.3	2.5	2.6	5.9	5.3, 5.2
108	3,8-Diaminopyrene -chloranil	1:1	55.3	55.4	2.5	2.7	5.9	5.7
88	3,8-Diaminopyrene -bromanil	1:1	40.2	42.1	1.8	2.1	4.3	4.6
97	3,8-Diaminopyrene -bromanil	1:1	40.2	43.3	1.8	1.9	4.3	3.8
96	3,8-Diaminopyrene -iodanil	1:1	31.3	32.6	1.4	1.4	8.9	8.9
92	3,8-Diaminopyrene -iodanil	1:1	31.3	33.3	1.4	1.5	3.3	2.8
77	3,10-Diaminopyrene -chloranil	3:1	68.8	68.6	3.9	4.0	8.9	8.9
86	3,10-Diaminopyrene -chloranil	3:1	68.8	69.7	3.9	4.3	8.9	8.4
1	p-Phenylenediamine -chloranil	3:2	44.1	44.2	2.9	3.1	10.3	7.8, 7.9
1A	p-Phenylenediamine -chloranil			45.4		3.3		9.5
95	p-Phenylenediamine -chloranil			47.3		3.4		9.7
101	p-Phenylenediamine -chloranil			46.4		2.6		7.5
46	p-Phenylenediamine -bromanil	3:1	38.5	39.5	3.2	3.2	11.2	10.4
55	p-Phenylenediamine -iodanil	3:2	23.2	24.9	1.5	1.5	1.4	5.7

crystallized three times from xylene and twice from toluene, (melting point, 160 to 162°).

Bromanil and iodanil were prepared according to the procedure of Jackson and Bolton.[3] Bromanil was crystallized twice from benzene (melting point, 299 to 299.5°). Iodanil was crystallized twice from ethyl acetate (melting point, 265 to 268°).

Coronene and perylene were purified by the continuous-adsorption purification technique described by Sangster and Irvine.[4]

The amine-quinone complexes were generally made by mixing the ingredients separately dissolved in benzene or xylene. s-Tetrachloroethane was a convenient solvent for the iodine complexes of coronene and perylene. The complexes were formed gradually upon cooling in the cases where hot solvents were employed and instantaneously when mixed with cold saturated solutions.

Table 22.1 summarizes analytical data on the amine-quinone complexes. The correspondence of these data to simple stoichiometry is far from satisfactory, and multicomplexing can and

Table 22.2. Analysis of Iodine Complexes

Sample no.	Hydrocarbon	Per cent I[a]	Method of preparation moles hydrocarbon: moles I_2
70	Coronene	45.9, 44.8	1 : 5 [b]
74	Coronene	47.2, 47.5	1 : 10 [b]
75	Coronene	47.3, 47.7	1 : 30 [b]
76	Coronene	45.5	1 : 10 [c]
77	Coronene	46.3	1 : 10 [d]
105	Coronene	44.2	1 : 5 [b]
107	Coronene	45.2	1 : 5 [b]
106	Perylene	75.5	1 : 5 [b]
109	Perylene	74.6	1 : 5 [b]

[a] Theoretical per cent I: Coronene-iodine 1 : 1 = 45.8; perylene-iodine 1 : 3 = 75.1.

[b] Individual compounds dissolved in hot -s-tetrachloroethane, mixed and allowed to cool.

[c] Combined compounds boiled in stream of air for 2 hr.

[d] Combined compounds boiled in stream of nitrogen for 2 hr.

does occur. Furthermore, the amine-quinone complexes are not stable in solution; the intensity of their visible absorption changes markedly with time. However, the complexes seem to be stable in the solid state. This is indicated by the fact that (a) resistivity does not change upon storage and (b) the visible-absorption spectra of two redissolved solid samples of 3,8-diaminopyrene-chloranil stored for 1 and 8 months, respectively, were almost identical.

Table 22.2 gives the composition of samples of coronene-iodine and perylene-iodine complexes. We have only been able to obtain a 1 : 1 complex of coronene and iodine, regardless of the excess of iodine present during preparation. Coronene absorbs 1 and only 1 mole of iodine when stored over iodine *in vacuo*. Perylene, on the other hand, forms several complexes. We report results

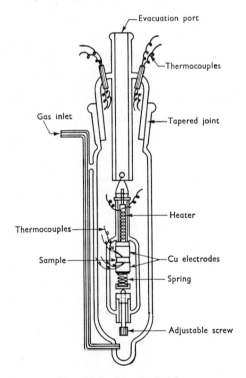

Fig. 22.1. Sample holder.

on only the 1 : 3 complex. Perylene absorbs 3 moles of iodine when stored over iodine *in vacuo.*

b. Measurements. The sample holder in which the conductivity and Seebeck coefficient were measured is shown in Fig. 22.1. The sample is held between spring-loaded copper disks, one of which can be heated. A thermocouple is soldered into each disk, measuring the temperature on the surface of the sample. After experimenting with various foil and paint electrodes, metal-powder electrodes were found to give the best electrical and mechanical contact. These electrodes are made by sandwiching the powder of complex between small quantities of metal powder and compressing in a 1/2-in.-diameter die. In this fashion a one-piece sandwich, about 2 mm thick, is produced in which the sample material is embedded between two metal layers approximately 0.05 mm thick. Immediately before pressing the pellet, the powder was degassed by evacuating the die for 15 min.

Either one of two Keithley voltmeters, model 610 or 150, were used for the electrical measurements, depending upon the sample resistance. All apparatus was contained in a steel enclosure to provide shielding against pickup noise, especially at higher resistances.

The electron-spin-resonance experiments were carried out around 9.5 kmc, with a Varian model V4500 EPR spectrometer. All measurements were made with microcrystalline samples at room temperature, and spin densities were estimated by comparison against α, α-diphenyl-β-picrylhydrazl as a standard, prepared by heating its benzene complex *in vacuo.*[5]

3. Results

The effect of compacting pressure on the resistivity was studied on two different complexes. The results are shown in Fig. 22.2 for *p*-phenylenediamine-chloranil (upper two curves) and for 3,8-diaminopyrene-chloranil (lower 3 curves). X-ray patterns taken on pellets made of unground powder showed no line broadening but a continuous decrease of line intensity with increasing pressure, indicating increasing orientation of the microcrystals. This interpretation is further substantiated by the fact

that at higher pressures many pills split into several layers. Upon
grinding and repressing, the X-ray lines become much broader
and less intense, indicating a smaller average particle size in the

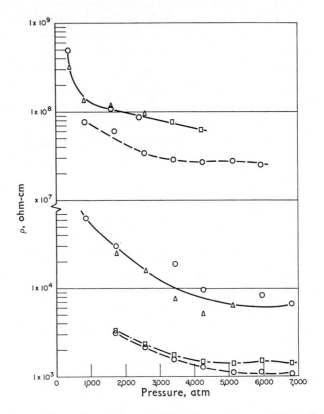

Fig. 22.2. Effect of pressure on room-temperature resistivity. Upper two
curves: *p*-phenylenediamine-chloranil. Lower three curves: 3,8-diaminopyrene-
chloranil. (—, pressed once at indicated pressure; — —, pressed once at 1,800
atm, ground, and then pressed at indicated pressure; . —, pressed twice at
1,800 atm, grinding between pressings, and then pressed at indicated pressure.

pellet. The lower resistivity on twice- and three-times ground and
repressed samples can be attributed to dense packing and less
tendency to orientation. Density measurements on the pills confirm the first of these points.

Figure 22.3 presents experimental data on the temperature dependence of the resistivity for six complexes, from which the activation energies have been determined. The reproducibility

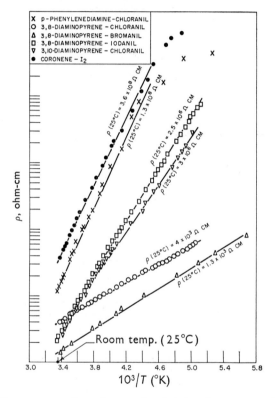

Fig. 22.3. Temperature dependence of resistivity: $\log \rho$ versus $10^3/T$ (°K).

of these data is indicated in Fig. 22.4 for the case of p-phenylenediamine-chloranil at two different compounding pressures.

Although the resistivity for a particular complex may vary by an order of magnitude depending on the compounding pressure, the activation energy determined from these curves does not. For the material of lowest resistivity, the perylene-iodine 1 : 3 complex, the reproducibility is not as satisfactory, as may be seen from Fig. 22.5. The activation energies derived from measurements on several samples of each of the molecular complexes studied, are listed in Table 22.3, together with the compounding condition. Due to the high resistivity of p-phenylenediamine-bromanil and iodanil the temperature dependence could not be studied with the present instrumentation.

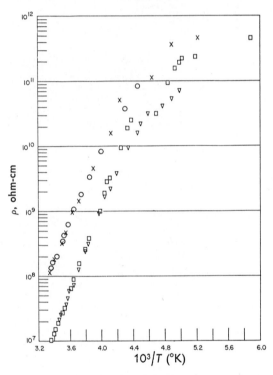

Fig. 22.4. log ρ versus $1/T$ for four samples of p-phenylenediamine-chloronil. X, 0, measured on pellets (samples 95), pressed once at 900 atm; □ , △ measured on pellets (sample 101), pressed twice at 2,600 atm.

Seebeck coefficients S as functions of temperature are given in Fig. 22.6. Relative S values measured against copper, except in the case of perylene- and coronene-iodine, which were measured against platinum, are reported. Reproducibility is generally within 15 per cent, as shown in Fig. 22.7, for the 3,8-diamino-pyrene-chloranil complex. For this complex the steep rise in S

Table 22.3. Activation Energies of Seven Molecular Complexes

Sample no.[a]	Name of complex	Resistivity[b] ohm-cm at 25°C	Temperature range, °C	E_a, ev
95[e]	p-Phenylenediamine chloranil	1×10^8	25–70	0.57
101[c]		6×10^6	25–70	0.67
101[c]		6×10^6	25–70	0.65
73[d]	3,8-Diaminopyrene-chloranil	4×10^3	25–70	0.15
77[d]	3,10-Diaminopyrene-chloranil	1×10^7	25–70	0.39
86[d]		3×10^6	25–70	0.41
88[d]	3,8-Diaminopyrene-bromanil	1×10^3	25–70	0.15
88[d]		1×10^3	-70–180	0.12
96[d]	3,8-Diaminopyrene-iodanil	2×10^6	25–70	0.43
96[d]		2×10^6	25–70	0.38
106[d]	Perylene-iodine	2	25–70	0.011
109[d]		3	25–70	0.019
105[d]	Coronene-iodine	2×10^8	25–70	0.50
107[d]		2×10^8	25–70	0.50

[a] Measurements made *in vacuo* except for iodine complexes, where they were made in N_2.

[b] All electrodes made of Cu powder except for iodine complexes, where Pt powder was used.

[c] Pressed twice at 2,600 atm.

[d] Pressed twice at 1,700 atm.

[e] Pressed once at 900 atm.

at low temperatures may be due to contact problems, and requires substantiation. Perylene-iodine, the only complex with a negative S, is an exception to this reproducibility; the two curves shown represent the limits we have encountered.

Initial measurements of the spin densities and line widths at room temperature on the nine selected complexes have been made. The results are presented in Table 22.4, together with the number of unpaired electrons per molecule and the average room-temperature conductivity.

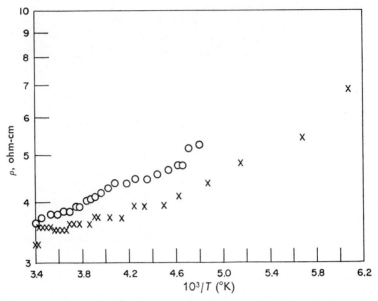

Fig. 22.5. log resistivity versus $1/T$ for the perylene-iodine $1:3$ complex.

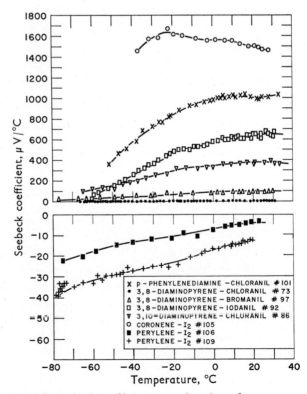

Fig. 22.6. Seebeck coefficient as a function of temperature.

Table 22.4. Comparison of Room-temperature Spin Density and Conductivity

Number	Compound A-B	Composition A-B	Line width, gauss	Spin/mole x 10^{-21}	No. of unpaired spins per molecule	Conductivity at 300° K	Carrier density (cm^{-3})
101	p-Phenylenediamine -chloranil	3:2	5 (structure)	7	0.01	1.7×10^{-7}	10^{15}
46	p-Phenylenediamine -bromanil	3:1	12	21	0.03	5×10^{-11}	3×10^{11}
55	p-Phenylenediamine -iodanil	3:2	20	17	0.02	7×10^{-11}	5×10^{11}
73	3,8-Diaminopyrene -chloranil	1:1	4	3	0.004	2×10^{-4}	2×10^{18}
88	3,8-Diaminopyrene -bromanil	1:1	3	9	0.01	1×10^{-3}	6×10^{18}
96	3,8-Diaminopyrene -iodanil	1:1		0	0	5×10^{-7}	3×10^{15}
77	3,10-Diaminopyrene -chloranil	3:1	7	112	0.20	2×10^{-7}	10^{15}
98	Perylene-I_2	1:3	6	17	0.03	3×10^{-1}	2×10^{21}
76	Coronene-I_2	1:1		0	0	5×10^{-9}	3×10^{13}

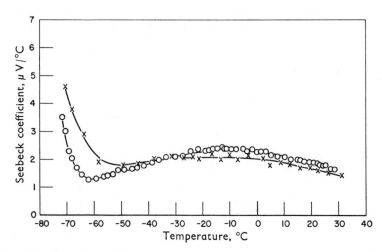

Fig. 22.7. Seebeck coefficient as a function of temperature for two samples of 3,8-diaminopyrene-chloranil.

4. Discussion

The validity of our results for the respective complexes depends, of course, on how closely they are reproducible on single crystals. There is some indication[1,6] that electrical measurements on single crystals and those on compressed powders for molecular complexes are comparable. We are now able to grow crystals of some of the complexes in experimentally useful size and hope to report comparative measurements at a later date.[15] The gravest objection to powder measurements on low-carrier-density semiconductors is the possible development of space-charge layers in the grains due to adsorbed surface charges or slow diffusion of surface impurities. We have checked this possibility by precipitating molecular complexes in solvents through which different gases were bubbled and also by changing the ambient during measurements. In all cases we found the same activation energy of conduction within the experimental error.[1]

Due to the marked anisotropy in these crystals we can measure only some kind of average on powders. Assuming a completely random distribution of crystal axes in finely ground powders, the measured resistivity should be a linear average of the single-crystal values parallel and perpendicular to the molecular plane. On the other hand, our values obtained on highly compressed, unground microcrystals, which tend to align themselves perpendicular to the subsequently applied electrical field, should be close to the resistivity perpendicular to the molecular plane.

The problem of crystal growth and the problem of purity are intimately associated, much more so than in inorganic semiconductors, because of the higher complexity of the lattice constituents. Starting with "very pure" components (in the organic chemist's sense) we may encounter chemical changes during preparation and may then be unable to recrystallize the resulting complex. These factors are reflected in the generally poor character of the analytical data. Yet our electrical measurements indicate an insensitivity to impurities as compared to inorganic semiconductors.

Very few measurements of Seebeck coefficients on organic materials have been reported.[7-9] The Seebeck coefficients measured here, as shown in Fig. 22.5, increase continuously with temperature between −80 and −10°C and level out at higher temperatures. This is in agreement with Joffe's empirical rule[14] that starting with $S = 0$ at $T = 0$, S is at first proportional to T, then rises less steeply or remains constant with T, and then begins to decrease approaching the theoretical expression. See Eq. (22.3), below. This same kind of behavior is also found in "narrow-band" semiconductors, such as the 3 d-oxides, where there is relatively little overlap of the atomic wave functions.

S is related to the average charge carrier energy $\bar{\varepsilon}$ and the chemical potential μ by

$$S = (k/e)[(\bar{\varepsilon}-\mu)/T] \qquad (22.1)$$

where e is the unit charge and T is the absolute temperature. This relation holds regardless of conduction mechanism assumed. Now, if E_c denotes the energy of the "conductive state," we can write for $\bar{\varepsilon}$,

$$\bar{\varepsilon} = E_c + AkT \qquad (22.2)$$

Introducing this into Eq. (22.1) yields

$$S = k/e\{[(E_c - \mu)/kT] + A\} = (k/e)[(E_a/kT) + A] \quad (22.3)$$

where E_a is the measured activation energy.

Since S and E_a are measured, we can calculate A. The resulting values are listed in Table 22.5. Comparing these values with those for inorganic semiconductors, we find they are extremely high.

Table 22.5. Comparison of A with Ea/kT at 300 °K

Compound	S, volts deg^{-1}	$S/(k/e)$	Ea/kT	A
Coronene-I_2	1.5×10^{-3}	17.3	24.0	6.7
p-Phenylenediamine -chloranil	1.0×10^{-3}	11.5	22.0	10.5
3,8-Diaminopyrene -iodanil	7×10^{-4}	8.1	15.5	7.4
3,10-Diaminopyrene -chloranil	4×10^{-4}	4.6	15.4	10.8
3,8-Diaminopyrene -bromanil	1×10^{-4}	1.15	5.8	4.6
3,8-Diaminopyrene -chloranil	5×10^{-6}	0.06	5.6	5.5
Perylene-I_2	-1×10^{-5}	0.12	0.6	0.7

Scattering theory accounts quite well for the A values found in inorganic semiconductors. They range from $A = 2$, for neutral scattering centers in covalent crystals, to $A = 4$, for ionic scattering centers in ionic crystals. Scattering theory cannot account for A values above 4; we must consider other charge-transport mechanisms. One such possibility would be discrete conductive states, localized at a lattice site, which charges carriers can occupy by means of a hopping process.

There is another conclusion to be drawn from Eq. (22.3). Since the left-hand side is experimentally found to be proportional to T while the first term on the right is inversely proportional to T (because E_a is constant), we require

$$A > E_a/kT \quad (22.4)$$

However, this condition is not fulfilled, as seen from Table 22.5. Therefore, we suspect that the activation energy for bringing carriers into a conductive state is actually much smaller than the experimental activation energy of conduction; the increase of conductivity with temperature may be due to an increase of mobility with temperature, which would bring about a temperature dependence of A of the necessary form.

We have tried to measure the mobility in a Hall experiment on 3,8-diaminopyrene-chloranil and bromanil and also on perylene-iodine. In no case did we detect a Hall voltage. The sensitivity of our apparatus was such that we could have measured a mobility of not less than 10^{-2} cm²/volt-sec for the first two mentioned complexes and 8×10^{-3} cm²/volt-sec for perylene-I_2. Since these three complexes are those with the highest conductivity, it is probable that the complexes in general have very low mobilities. Such low mobilities again cannot be explained by scattering theory, because they would imply a mean free path of less than the interatomic distance.

The preliminary results of our electron-spin-resonance study confirms the existence of unpaired spins in aromatic amine-tetrahalogen-p-benzoquinone[10,11] and aromatic hydrocarbon-iodine[6,12,13] complexes, with two exceptions (coronene-iodine and 3,8-diaminopyrene-iodanil). Our spin densities and line widths for p-phenylenediamine complexes with the quinones are not in agreement with those reported by Bijl, Kainer, and Rose-Innes,[10] but the composition of their material is not given, and the measurements were performed at different temperatures.

It is of interest to obtain an estimate for the charge carrier density of the various complexes. Using the room-temperature conductivity given in column 7 of Table 22.4 and an order of magnitude mobility of 10^{-3}, we find the charge-carrier densities N listed in column 8. It is clear from comparison of columns 5 and 8 that there is no correlation between the spin density and the carrier density. This lack of simple correlation of spin densities and conductivities might be expected from the fact that $\alpha,\alpha,$-diphenyl-β-picrylhydrazyl, having one unpaired electron per molecule, has a relatively low conductivity. As suggested in our earlier work,[1] crystal structure and packing conditions are probably more important in obtaining high conductivity, but the existence of unpaired electrons in complexes is indicative of ground-state bonding with a large ionic component. Narrow line widths are also indicative of this strong exchange interaction.

In summarizing our results we may say that the investigated molecular complexes represent semiconductors (by virtue of their *activated* charge transport) with the following peculiarities:

1. They are very insensitive to impurities.
2. They have extremely low mobilities.
3. They exhibit a proportional increase in thermopower with temperature up to a saturation value.

Acknowledgements. We wish to gratefully acknowledge helpful discussions with Dr. David Fox of the State University of New York, College on Long Island, and Dr. Frank Donahoe, Jr., of The Franklin Institute.

References

1. M. M. Labes, R. Sehr, and M. Bose, Paper presented at the Princeton University Conference on Semiconduction in Molecular Solids, (Feb. 16–17, 1960); *J. Chem. Phys.* **33**, 868 (1960).
2. H. Vollman, H. Becker, M. Correll, H. Streeck, and G. Langbein, *Ann.* **531**, 1 (1937).
3. C. L. Jackson and E. K. Bolton, *J. Am. Chem. Soc.* **36**, 301 (1914).
4. R. C. Sangster and J. W. Irvine, Jr., *J. Chem. Phys.* **24**, 670 (1956).
5. J. A. Lyons and W. F. Watson, *J. Polymer Sci.* **18**, 141 (1955).
6. L. S. Singer and J. Kommandeur, *Bull. Am. Phys. Soc.* (II) **4**, 421 (1959); J. Kommandeur and F. R. Hall, *Bull. Am. Phys. Soc.* (II) **4**, 421 (1959).
7. P. E. Fielding and F. Gutman, *J. Chem. Phys.* **26**, 411 (1957).
8. C. Schroeder, M.Sc. thesis, Ohio State University (1952).
9. M. M. Labes, R. Sehr, and M. Bose, *J. Chem. Phys.* **32**, 1570 (1960).
10. D. Bijl, H. Kainer, and A. C. Rose-Innes, *J. Chem. Phys.* **30**, 765 (1959).
11. H. Kainer and A. Überle, *Chem. Ber.* **88**, 1147 (1955).
12. Y. Matsunaga, *Bull. Chem. Soc. Japan* **28**, 475 (1955).
13. Y. Matsunaga, *J. Chem. Phys.* **30**, 855 (1959).
14. A. F. Joffe, "Semiconductor Thermoelements and Thermoelectric Cooling," Infosearch, London (1957), p. 35.
15. Two papers are in press which present single crystal measurements on some of these complexes. See M. M. Labes, R. Sehr, and M. Bose, Proc. International Conference on Semiconductor Physics, Prague, Aug. 29—Sept 2, 1960; P. L. Kronick and M. M. Labes, *J. Chem. Phys.* **35** (1961).

23

Electric and Magnetic Properties of Some Low-Resistance Organic Semiconductors

J. Kommandeur and L. S. Singer

Introduction

Some years ago Akamatu et al.[1] reported high electronic conductivities in violanthrene and perylene treated with bromine and iodine. The lack of stoichiometry and the time dependence of the currents, however, make their work subject to serious criticism. It was, therefore, of interest to see whether such phenomena could also be found in similar materials of a more clearly defined nature. This paper reports on the preparation, the electronic conductivity, and the electron-spin-resonance of the iodine complexes of pyrene and perylene. A summary of the results of our studies is given here; a more detailed description of results and experimental procedures will be published elsewhere.

Composition and Preparation of the Complexes

The composition of the pyrene-iodine complex was determined by a phase study and an analysis of the change of density with the iodine concentration in the pyrene-iodine system. The results are given in Fig. 23.1 and 23.2, respectively. It is clear that a stable complex pyrene $\cdot 2I_2$ occurs, as well as a metastable complex 2pyrene $\cdot I_2$. The pyrene-iodine complex used for the electrical and magnetic measurements was the stable one, prepared by cooling a CCl_4 solution of pyrene and iodine to $-20°C$.

The perylene complex, 2perylene $\cdot 3I_2$, has been prepared before.[2] Although there has been some argument about its composition,[3] the fact that single crystals always contained 60 mole per cent iodine settles the argument in favor of the earlier work.

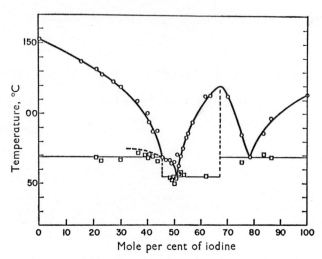

Fig. 23.1. Phase diagram of the pyrene-iodine system.

These single crystals were grown by cooling a benzene solution of perylene and iodine from 65 to 25°C. over periods varying from 1 to 2 weeks. The polycrystalline precipitate was then scanned for single crystals. The crystals were small (length about 2 mm,

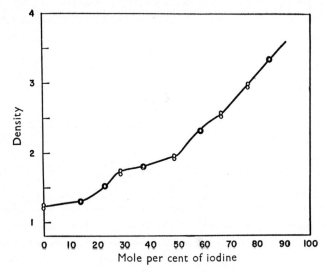

Fig. 23.2. The change of density in the pyrene-iodine system.

width 3 mm, and thickness of a few microns), fragile, and quite volatile. In open air, iodine evaporates slowly and leaves yellow spots of perylene on the exposed surface. In closed vials, however, the crystals are stable indefinitely.

The Electrical Conductivity

The electrical measurements were made with a four-probe arrangement. Two-probe determinations led to difficulties because of the high contact resistances involved. The specific resistivities of pressed pellets of pyrene-iodine and perylene-iodine were 75 and 8 ohm-cm, respectively.

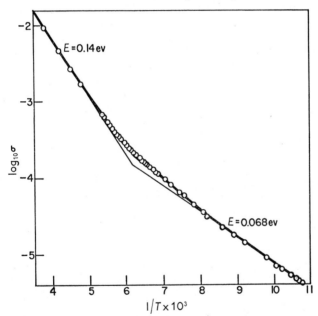

Fig. 23.3. The variation of the logarithm of the conductivity with the reciprocal temperature for pyrene $\cdot 2I_2$.

Some measurements were carried out on single crystals of perylene-iodine, and at room temperature the specific resistivity of these was, within the experimental error, equal to that measured on pressed pellets. Unfortunately, the single crystals always sheared at the contact points when the temperature was changed.

Therefore, measurements of the conductivity versus temperature had to be made on pressed pellets.

Figure 23.3 gives a plot of log σ versus $1/T$ for pyrene-iodine. A curve, consisting of two straight lines with activation energies of 0.14 and 0.07 ev, respectively, was obtained. Figure 23.4 gives a similar plot for perylene-iodine. Only one line with an activation energy of 0.019 ev is found in this case. Since this energy is of

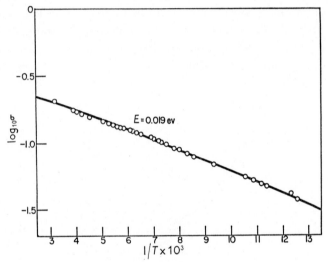

Fig. 23.4. The variation of the logarithm of the conductivity with the reciprocal temperature for 2perylene·$3I_2$.

the order of kT at room temperature and the number of excited species becomes an appreciable fraction of the total number of molecules, a slight curvature in this line is expected, and this is indeed observed.

Attempts were made to measure the Hall effect on these samples. These attempts were unsuccessful, but an upper limit for the mobility of $\mu \leq 0.01$ cm^2 volt^{-1} sec^{-1} could be set, if the case of an equal number of carriers with exactly equal mobilities can be excluded. With this upper limit for the mobility and the value for the specific conductivity, lower limits for the number of charge carriers can be given. They are for pyrene-iodine and perylene-iodine $N \geqq 3 \times 10^{18}$ carriers per gram and $N \geqq 3 \times 10^{19}$ carriers per gram, respectively.

Both materials are shiny black in appearance. An effort was made to obtain optical spectra in the near infrared, the visible, and the ultraviolet. The absorption intensity, however, appeared to be extremely high. Even layers having a thickness of 0.1 micron were not thin enough to obtain an absorption spectrum. The extinction coefficients, therefore, must be at least 5×10^5.

Electron-Spin-Resonance Measurements

All the ESR experiments were performed at 9,500 mc/sec, using a magnetic-field modulation scheme of the conventional type. The g-factor measurements, accurate to 1 part in 20,000, were made by comparing the microwave and proton resonance frequencies with the 10 mc sec^{-1} frequency standard of WWV.

A Varian sample cavity was slightly modified to accept a thin-walled pyrex dewar tube for use in a blower arrangement. A small quartz dewar of approximately 200 ml capacity was used for measurements at 77 and 4.2°K., one liquid-helium filling lasting approximately 20 min. For measurements between 90°C. and room temperature, cold N_2 gas was blown through a pyrex dewar tube, the desired temperature being attained by controlling the flow rate.

Approximate spin concentrations are usually determined by a simple comparison of the integrated ESR absorption with that of a standard sample.[4] However, the ESR measurement of spin concentrations over a wide temperature range with an accuracy of better than 10 per cent requires considerable attention to a number of experimental and theoretical details not usually considered. A more elaborate description of these details is given elsewhere; suffice it to state here that the basis for the measurements of integrated absorption, line shape, radio-frequency field intensity, and relaxation times was carefully considered. The actual determination of spin concentration was made by comparing the sample signal with that from a single crystal of ruby at a fixed position in the cavity.[5] Measurements of spin concentration for the pyrene and perylene complexes were made over the temperature range from 100 to 300° K. A few measurements were also carried out on powders and single crystals at 77 and 4.2°K.

Figure 23.5 shows the results for powdered $2perylene \cdot 3I_2$. The solid curve was calculated from the activation energy

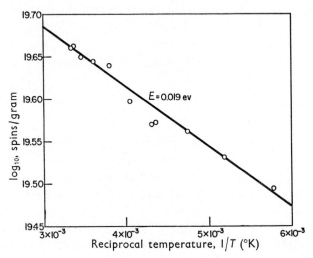

Fig. 23.5. The variation of the logarithm of the spin concentration with the reciprocal temperature for $2perylene \cdot 3I^2$. (The solid line represents the conductivity data.)

$E = 0.019$ ev, which was obtained from the electrical conductivity measurements. The maximum deviation of the experimental points (circles) from the calculated solid curve corresponds to 5 per cent of the spin concentration.

The results for the $pyrene \cdot 2I_2$ powder are shown in Fig. 23.6. It is evident that there are two contributions to the spin concentration: a thermally activated species and a constant number of spins at low temperatures. The solid line was calculated as the sum of this constant (1.4×10^{18} spins per gram,) and the energy of 0.14 ev was determined from the electrical conductivity measurements. It is again seen that the activation energies for the conduction and the spin resonance are in excellent agreement, at least at temperatures above 200°K.

The room-temperature (300°K) spin concentrations, 1.7×10^{19} g^{-1} and 4.6×10^{19} g^{-1} for pyrene $2I_2$ and 2 perylene $3I_2$, respectively, are in agreement with the estimates provided by the maximum-mobility arguments. However, out value for 2 perylene · $3I_2$ is about 30 per cent lower than that reported recently by Matsunaga.[1] In the case of pyrene $2I_2$, the spin concentration results are consistent with a model that depicts every I_2 molecule as a potential paramagnetic site. For 2 perylene $3I_2$, the results indicate a concentration of potential paramagnetic sites about ten times less than the I_2-molecule concentration.

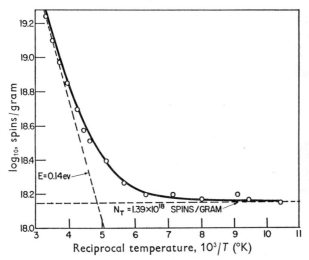

Fig. 23.6. The variation of the logarithm of the spin concentration with the reciprocal temperature for pyrene·$2I_2$. The solid line represents log $[N_T + N \exp{(-E/kT)}]$, where $NT = 1.39 \times 10^{18}$ spins per gram, and $E = 0.14$ ev, as found from the conductivity data.

Measurements of the spin concentration of pyrene·$2I_2$ powder at 4.2°K indicated no apparent change from the 1.4×10^{18} g^{-1} shown in Fig. 23.4. On the other hand, a 2perylene·$3I_2$ single crystal showed a decrease in spin concentration by a factor of 10 in going from 77 to 4.2°K. This decrease is much less than would be expected for a 0.019-ev activation energy. It is, there-fore, probable that a different paramagnetic species with a temperature-independent spin concentration also occurs in the perylene complex. This would result in a curve similar to Fig. 23.6, except that the break would occur somewhere between 77 and 4.2°K.

A number of other ESR properties were determined for these complexes. For example, the line width as a function of temperature for pyrene-iodine is shown in Fig. 23.7. Note that the line-width minimum occurs roughly at the same temperature at which the break in spin concentration occurs in Fig. 23.6.

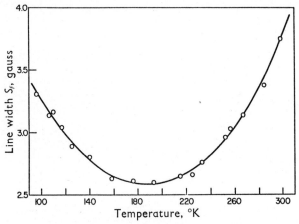

Fig. 23.7. Line width of the ESR signal versus temperature for powdered pyrene·2I₂.

The g-factors for powdered pyrene·2I$_2$ and 2perylene·3I$_2$ at room temperature were 2.0029 ± 0.0001 and 2.0033 ± 0.0001, respectively. The deviations from the Lorentz shape for ESR curves of powdered 2perylene·3I$_2$ below 100°K strongly suggested anisotropy broadening at lower temperatures. Measurements of the g-factor anisotropy of single crystals of 2 perylene·3I$_2$ at 77°K showed this to be the case. Figure 23.8 compares the experimental results with those alclulated from the expression

$$g = g_\perp + \Delta g \cos^2 \theta$$

where $g_\perp = 2.00238$, $\Delta g = g_\parallel - g_\perp = 0.00110$, and θ is the angle between the static magnetic field and the normal to the broad face of the thin crystal prisms. No attempt was made to

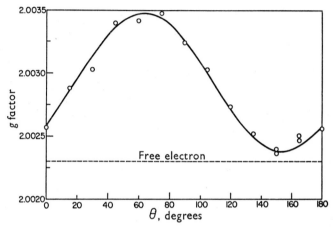

Fig. 23.8. The variation of the g factor of the ESR signal with orientation for a single crystal of 2perylene·$3I^2$ at 77°K. The solid line represents the function $g = g_\perp + \Delta g \cos^2 \theta$.

relate θ, $g_\parallel$, or $g_\perp$ to any molecular directions, since the crystal structure of this material is at present unknown.

Discussion

The energy required for charge separation in a molecular solid can be approximated qualitatively with the following thought experiment.[7]

Two molecules are taken out of the solid. This requires an energy $2E_s$. Then one molecule is ionized (I), and the electron is attached to the other molecule ($-E$). Then both ions are brought back into the solid without letting the electronic system of either or the lattice relax. The energy required for this process will, to a high degree of accuracy, be equal and opposite to the energy of taking them out ($-2E_s$). If now the electronic system of ions and lattice if left to relax, the contributions P_- and P_+ from the polarization energy around the negative and positive ion will be

gained, i.e., the total energy required for charge separation
will be

$$E_{cs} = I - E - P_- - P_+$$

This will be the energy required for charge separation to a
distance where no coulombic interaction of the ions takes place.
It therefore gives an upper limit. If coulombic interaction still
operates, that energy has to be subtracted also. At the present
time, without knowledge of the crystal structure and the anisotropic polarizabilities of the molecules involved, a more than
qualitative approach to E_{cs} is certainly not warranted. However,
it is clear that when I is small and E, P_-, and P_+ are large, E_{cs}
will be small. These conditions seem to be fulfilled in the hydrocarbon iodine complexes. For the bigger aromatics, like pyrene
and perylene, I is relatively small,[8] and both iodine and the
hydrocarbons have high dielectric constants, which will allow a
high value for the energies of polarization. Then it is conceivable
that E_{cs} becomes of the order of 0.1 ev or less, as was observed in
this case.

An alternative way of describing conduction in molecular solids
is by means of a charge-transfer interaction. In his treatment of
the spectra of hydrocarbon-iodine complexes in solution, Mulliken[9] considers an excited state in which an almost complete
transfer of electronic charge from the hydrocarbon to the iodine
has occurred. It is possible that in a solid, where one hydrocarbon
molecule can interact at the same time with many iodine molecules,
the excited charge-transfer states occur at much lower energies.
By extension this could also provide a mechanism for the transfer
over more than one lattice parameter and therefore lead to conduction. In this context it is interesting to note that the red
shift of the fluorescence spectrum of crystalline pyrene and of
concentrated pyrene solutions[10] is also explained with a charge-
transfer interaction.[11] The perylene fluorescence spectrum shows
essentially the same behavior. Pyrene and perylene, therefore,
appear to be particularly susceptible to charge-transfer interaction.
The extreme opacity of these solids also indicates a number of
low-lying excited states.

The close agreement between the activation energies for conduction and spin concentration for the pyrene $\cdot 2I_2$ and 2perylene $\cdot 3I_2$ complexes above 200°K is strong evidence that the observed unpaired spins are charge carriers. The agreement of the magnitude of the spin concentrations with the estimates obtained from the electrical properties further confirms this identification. There are, however, several aspects of the experimental results that require additional explanation.

The source of the constant number of spins that dominate the ESR of the pyrene complex at low temperatures is not understood. We might attempt to associate the spins with shallow traps, but this can be ruled out in the following way: if a constant number of spins, denoted N_T in Fig. 23.6, exists in shallow traps and thus can take part in the conduction, the 0.07-ev activation energy for the conductivity below 200°K must be due to an activated mobility. Then we should not expect the activation energies for conduction and spin concentration to agree at the higher temperatures. A more likely possibility is that the pyrene contains as an impurity about 0.1 mole per cent of a compound that forms another complex with I_2. The electrical measurements indicate, then, that a 0.07-ev activation energy would be required to promote the carriers from these impurity sites to the conducting state. Since the spin concentration is independent of temperature below 200°K, this impurity would have to be a molecular complex with an almost completely ionic ground state. These complexes might be similar to those studied by Bijl, Kainer, and Rose-Innes.[12] Impurities are probably also involved in the perylene case. However, due to the small activation energy and the high concentration of the carriers in 2perylene $\cdot 3I_2$, the temperature-independent spin concentration becomes evident only at temperatures below 77°K. The possible role of impurities in the conduction phenomena is still under investigation in this laboratory

Another problem arises when we attempt to relate the total number of complex molecules N to the number of spins N_1, and the activation energy E. In the case of perylene-iodine, since the activation energy is of the order of kT, we expects to find a spin on every third 2perylene $\cdot 3I_2$ molecule at room temperature. However, it is found that only 1 in 10 complex molecules has an unpaired spin. It therefore seems probable that a number of molecules are engaged in stabilizing each charge carrier. If the production of charge carriers is discussed in terms of a localized process, it is reasonable to assume that the energy of excitation will be increased by the fields of the charge carriers already present. Thus charge-carrier formation involves excitation of a small domain in which a number of molecules are cooperating. Then, instead of using the normal exponential relation $N_1/(N - N_1) = \exp(-E/kT)$, we must use $N_1/(N-N_1-nN_1) = \exp(-E/kT)$, where n is the number of complex molecules engaged in stabilizing the spin. In the case of perylene-iodine this "cooperation factor" n is found to be approximately 3.

A similar mechanism should be operative in pyrene-iodine. However, $(n + 1)N_1$ is so small compared to N in this case that any such cooperative effect is not observable within the temperature range studied.

The other properties of the spin-resonance signal are consistent with the model of charge carriers. However, the lack of structural information on the complexes precludes further speculation as to the origin of the line widths, the anisotropy, and the saturation behavior.

References

1. H. Akamatu, H. Inokuchi, and Y. Matsunaga, *Bull. Chem. Soc. Japan* **29**, 213 (1956).
2. K. Brass and E. Clar, *Chem. Ber.* **65**, 1660 (1932).
3. M. Pestemer and E. Treiber, *Chem. Ber.* **74**, 964 (1941).
4. D. J. E. Ingram, "Free Radicals," p. 98, Academic Press, Inc., New York (1958).
5. L. S. Singer, *J. Appl. Phys.* **30**, 1463 (1959).
6. Y. Matsunaga, *J. Chem. Phys.* **30**, 855 (1959).
7. L. E. Lyons, *J. Chem. Soc.* **1957**, 5001.
8. F. A. Matsen in "Proceedings of the Third Conference or Carbon," p. 21, Pergamon Press, Ltd., London 1959.
9. R. S. Mulliken, *Am. Chem. Soc.* **74**, 811 (1952).
10. T. Forster and K. Kasper, *Z. Elektrochem.* **59**, 976 (1955).
11. J. Ferguson, *J. Chem. Phys.* **28**, 765 (1958).
12. D. Bijl, H. Kainer, and A. C. Rose-Innes, *J. Chem. Phys.* **30**, 765 (1959).

24

Electrical and Thermal Properties of Poly-Copper Phthalocyanine

Arnold Epstein and Bernard Wildi

Introduction

To place the study of electrical properties of organic semi-conductors on a more familiar footing and perhaps open the way to an understanding of the conduction mechanism in organic compounds, efforts have been devoted to preparing and studying compounds having resistivities of suitable magnitude for Hall-effect measurements. A satisfactory compound for this purpose, chosen because of its chemical stability and relative ease of physical preparation, is a polymeric form of copper phthalocyanine prepared by heating pyromellitonitrile with cuprous chloride and urea.

[337]

This paper considers the chemical preparation of the compound and some electrical and thermal measurements that have been carried out.

Chemical Preparation of Material (Synthesis)

Monomeric phthalocyanines can be prepared by heating phthalonitrile with the appropriate metal and a trace of urea serving as a source of hydrogen.[1] Poly-copper phthalocyanine was prepared by heating pyromellitonitrile (1,2,4,5-tetracyanobenzene) with cuprous chloride. A purplish black material was obtained, which was purified by exhaustive extraction and sublimation procedures. The material was difficult to analyze, giving consistently low values for carbon. (Pyrolysis of the polymer at 410°C showed a marked change in the nitrogen content. The nature of the change is being investigated in more detail.)

Pyromellitamide. A mixture consisting of 109 g (0.5 mole) of pyromellitic dianhydride (melting point 285 to 287°C), 100 g (1.65 mole) of urea, and 740 g of trichlorobenzene was heated at 130°C for several hours, then at 150 to 160°C for 2 hr. The crude, pink-colored pyromellitimide did not melt below 310°C. Treatment of the crude imide with 750 ml of aqueous ammonia at room temperature gave 83 g of nearly colorless pyromellitamide. The amide decomposed at 285°C.

Pyromellitonitrile. A suspension of 50.0 g of crude pyromellitamide in 750 ml of dimethyl formamide was treated with phosgene for 4 hr, during which the temperature rose from 10 to 30°C. After the addition was completed, the mixture was stirred at 30°C for 18.5 hr, then centrifuged to remove 3.6 g of the starting amide. The supernatant liquid was poured into 2 liters of ice and water and filtered to yield 29 g of tan solid. Recrystallization of the product from a solution of 400 ml of dioxane and 150 ml of water yielded 23.4 g (66 per cent yield; 71 per cent conversion) of pyromellitonitrile, melting point, 264 to 267°C. A sample was prepared for analysis by a recrystallization from dioxane and sublimation at 0.05 mm.

Analysis (calculated for $C_1°H_2N_4$): C, 67.41; H, 1.13; N, 31.45. Found: C, 67.36, 67.36; H, 1.33, 1.44; N, 31.33.

Poly-Copper Phthalocyanine. A mixture of 16 g of pyromellitonitrile, 5.3 g Cu_2Cl_2, and 1.0 g urea was ground in a mortar then heated at 300°C under 1,000 psi of nitrogen in a glass-lined bomb for 18 hr. The temperature was raised to 350°C, and the mixture was heated for 2 additional hours. The solid was ground in a mortar then triturated with boiling pyridine until the triturates were colorless. The product was dried and heated at 350°C/0.05 mm for 72 hr. During the sublimation a trace of white material was removed. The residue was again extracted for 48 hr with boiling pyridine in a soxhlet to remove traces of copper salts. The material was dried and again heated at 340°C/0.05 mm for 6 hr.

Analysis of the polymer gave the following results:

Analysis (calculated for $C_{20}H_4N_8Cu$): C, 57.20; H, 0.960; N, 26.68; Cu, 15.14.

Found: C, 52.91, 52.93; H, 1.25, 1.21; N, 27.06, 27.24; Cu, 15.93, 15.90.

The polymer was a black-purple solid, only slightly soluble in cold sulfuric acid.

Electrical Properties

Preparation of Samples for Electrical Measurements. The polymer of copper phthalocyanine as made is in the form of a powder. To prepare samples for Hall effect and electrical measurements the material was pressed in the shape of rectangular parallelopipeds. Samples having dimensions $0.9 \times 0.3 \times 0.8$ cm were used. Samples were compacted using pressures from 20, 000 lb in.$^{-2}$ to 200,000 lb in.$^{-2}$. Sample resistances were of the order of 5,000 ohms or less.

For electrical contacts, pressure-type contacts, evaporated silver, or silver paint were used. Reproducible results were obtained with each type of contact, and linearity of the current and voltage was found in the range of currents used. Current densities to 8×10^{-2} amp cm^{-2} were used. Temperature was measured by means of an iron-constantan thermocouple (B. and S. gauge 30). The sample was placed on a lavite sample holder, and electrical connections to external circuits were arranged through glass-metal seals. The sample holder was placed in a vycor tube and so arranged that it was possible to either evacuate the system or expose the sample to any desired atmosphere. In this way

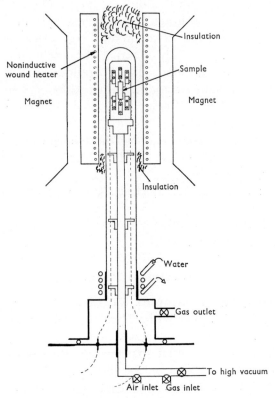

Fig. 24.1. Experimental arrangement for measurement of electrical resistivity and Hall effect.

experiments were carried out *in vacuo* at pressures from 10^{-2} to 10^{-5} mm Hg. A heater was placed around the vycor tube to provide the desired temperature. The experimental arrangement is shown in Fig. 24.1.

Effect of Grain Boundaries and Contact Resistance. To investigate the effect of grain-boundary contributions, contact resistance, and pressure on the results obtained below, both d-c and a-c measurements of resistivity were carried out. The a-c measurements were carried out on a Q meter type 260-A (Boonton Radio Corp.) to 5 Mc; d-c measurements were made using the Kelvin method. Within the accuracy of our experiment (20 per cent), bot d-c and a-c measurements were found to give the same results within the range of pressures used (20,000 to 200,000 lb in.$^{-2}$) and within the range of frequencies from d-c to 5 Mc.

It was therefore possible to conclude that the measurements reported below were not primarily due to contact effects or to grain-boundary contributions.

Electrical Measurements

To provide comprehensive electrical data on the polymer of copper phthalocyanine, d-c electrical resistivity and Hall-effect measurements were carried out as a function of temperature in the range of temperatures from 25 to 450°C. To check the validity of the Hall coefficient measurements, determination of the linearity of Hall voltages with magnetic field and electrical current were carried out at various temperatures. In all cases the Hall voltage was found to be linear with both the magnetic field in the range of fields used, which was to 4,000 gauss, and the current. Similar linearity was found between the current and voltage drop used in measuring the resistivity. Current densities to 8×10^{-2} amp cm^{-2} were used. The d-c measurements were obtained using a Leeds and Northrup type K-3 potentiometer and a Kintel electronic galvanometer, model 204A. A Varian 4 in. magnet with regulated supply was used to obtain the d-c magnetic field.

The measurements were carried out in the following manner: After the sample was placed in the vycor tube, the system was evacuated and measurements of the d-c Hall effect and resistivity were obtained from 25 to 250°C. The system was then permitted to cool down to room temperature (25°C.), and the procedure was repeated twice. The results are shown in Figs. 24.2 and 24.3 where the measurements are denoted by symbols *A*, *B*, and *C*. Following this, the sample was sufficiently outgassed so that reproducibility was noted, and the runs believed characteristic of the materials are shown in Figs. 24.4 and 24.5.

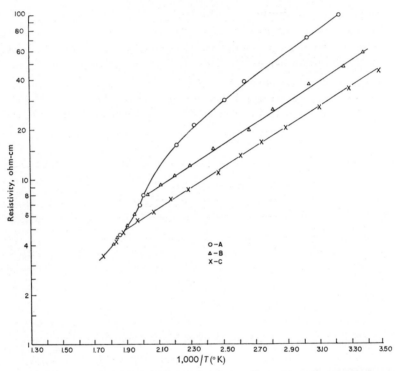

Fig. 24.2. Electrical resistivity versus inverse absolute temperature [$1,000/T(°K)$] of poly-copper phthalocyanine, sample 30, as a function of outgassing.

In Figs. 24.2 and 24.3 there are several effects to be noted. The Hall coefficient is negative for curves *A* and *B* at room temperature, undergoing a reversal just above this temperature and becoming *p* type. There is a decrease in the magnitude of the Hall coefficient with outgassing. Similarly, the resistivity decreases with the outgassing. It is noted that in general the

R/ρ ratio is lower for curve B than for curve A. With increased outgassing the reversal in Hall coefficient can be removed, and the type remains p type (curve C, Figs. 24.2 and 24.3) throughout the range of measurements and thereafter. The apparent irreversibility in the resistivity curve disappears on repeated

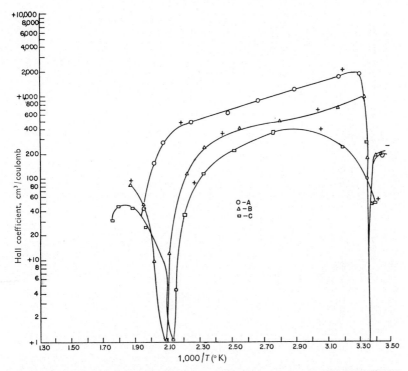

Fig. 24.3. Hall coefficient versus inverse absolute temperature $[1,000/T(^\circ K)]$ of polycopper phthalocyanine, sample 30 as a function of outgassing.

heating and is believed related to outgassing of the material. Similar effects, as noted by resistivity versus temperature measurements, have been found on other organic compounds.[2, 3]

Characteristic resistivity and Hall effect versus temperature runs are shown in Figs. 24.4 and 24.5 for poly-copper phthalocyanine. The resistivity curve is reproducible with a room-temperature resistivity for the material of 40 ohm-cm. This is a decrease by factor of 3 in the material over that which has not been outgassed. The Hall coefficient is similarly decreased, which suggests that the number density of effective carriers may be increasing. As temperatures increase up to $\sim 250°C$ we can associate an activation energy with the resistivity versus tempera-

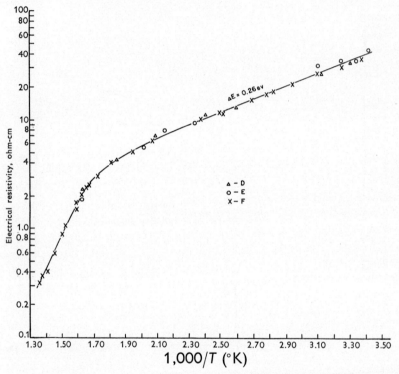

Fig. 24.4. Characteristic curve of electrical resistivity versus inverse absolute temperature [$1,000/T(°K)$] of polycopper phthalocyanine, sample 30.

ture curve of 0.26 ev, *assuming* an expression for the resistivity of $\rho = \rho_0 \exp (\Delta E/2kT)$. No such slope is evident on the Hall curve, but it will be noted that the Hall curve, though remaining p type, shows a minimum at $\sim 250°C$ and a steep decrease before that; the minimum shifts in temperature and changes in magnitude depending on the highest temperature to which the sample is heated. Following the minimum, the Hall coefficient increases until a value of ∼ +60 cm³/coulomb is reached, whereupon it decreases in magnitude to a value of +5 at a temperature of 450°C. The transition is also reflected in the resistivity versus temperature curve, which indicates a much more rapid decrease in resistivity. At the temperature of 450°C the resistivity has decreased to a

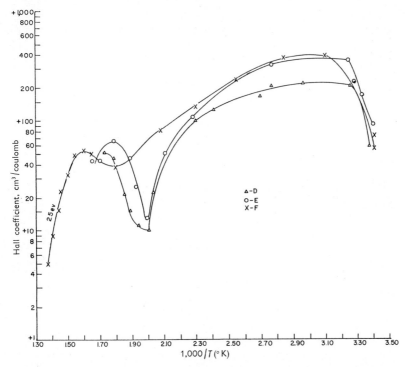

Fig. 24.5. Characteristic curves of Hall coefficient versus inverse absolute temperature [1,000/T(°K)] of poly-copper phthalocyanine, sample 30.

value of ∼ 0.4 ohm-cm. Provided we do not heat the material above 350° C, it is possible to reproduce the resistivity curve and the general shape of the Hall curve. On heating above 350°C, however, and especially above 400°C, there is a pronounced ir-reversibility in both the Hall effect and the electrical resistivity. The effects of this irreversibility are shown in Fig. 24.6, where a sample previously heated to 450°C, on reheating, exhibits entirely

new Hall-effect and electrical-resistivity characteristics. It will
be noted that the Hall coefficient, while still positive (p type),
has dropped by almost an order of magnitude in value and becomes
constant with a value of $+10$ cm³ coulomb⁻¹. The resistivity
also shows a tenfold decrease from ~ 40 ohm-cm to ~ 4 ohm-cm
at room temperature ($25°C$) with an activation energy of 0.12 ev.*

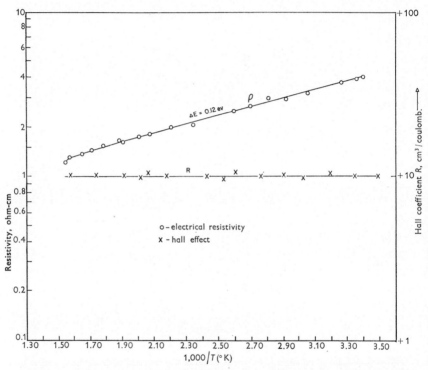

Fig. 24.6. Hall coefficient and electrical resistivity of heat-treated poly-copper
phthalocyanine as a function of inverse absolute temperature [$1{,}000/T(°K)$].

* Although the above expression can be used to represent the experimental
data, an interpretation of the relationship is not so simple. Evidence presented
in the text points to a great dependence of the electrical resistivity on both
the molecule and the intermolecular barriers, hence ΔE may be a composite
of both effects. The number of electrons available for conduction in the ring
compound may actually not be as temperature dependent (or temperature
sensitive) as the transport phenomena leading to conduction. Such a picture

If we assume intrinsic conditions and a hole mobility of $\mu_h \gg \mu_e$, we find, providing we can use the simple expression for the Hall effect, that $n \approx 1/Re \approx 10^{18}$ cm^{-3} and $\mu_h \approx 2.5$ cm^2 volt-sec^{-1} at room temperature, increasing to a value of ~ 10 cm^2 volt-sec^{-1} at 350°C. It is noteworthy that the activation energy reported for the resistivity versus temperature curve may be associated more closely with a mobility variation than with a change in the number density of carriers. The new characteristics are believed associated with a new structure resulting from a breaking of the C—N bonds and a rearrangement within the molecules with an over-all loss of nitrogen.

n- and p-type Conductivity

The indication of *n*-type conductivity in the low-temperature material at room temperature appears to be related to gaseous impurities or vapors associated with the atmosphere and can be altered by either outgassing, high-temperature cycling *in vacuo*, or use of oxygen. In Fig. 24.7 the Hall coefficient is plotted at a temperature of 25°C as a function of time (time being measured from the instant the system is pumped down to 10^{-2} mm Hg). It will be noted that the magnitude of the Hall coefficient decreases continually until a value of -20 cm^3 coulomb^{-1} is attained, a factor of 10 decrease. The resistivity on the other hand remains unchanged with time. We may convert the type from n to p by the following two methods: (1) use of oxygen at room temperature and (2) temperature cycling. In Table 24.1 the Hall coefficient is shown as a function of oxygen pressure.

The sign of the Hall coefficient is observed to change with an oxygen pressure greater than 490 mm Hg. Evidence for the effect of temperature cycling affecting the Hall coefficient can be seen

---

is quite different from that found in elementary structures of the inorganic type, such as germanium or silicon, where the dependence on neighboring atoms and lattice interactions may account for the availability of electrons and holes and a greater dependence of carrier density on temperature than is found for the mobility.

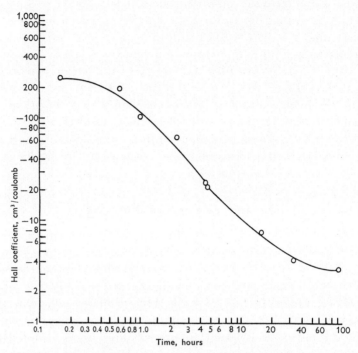

Fig. 24.7. Variation of Hall coefficient of poly-copper phthalocyanine, sample 30, with time at a temperature of 25 °C.

in Fig. 24.3 where, on heating to $\sim$250°C *in vacuo* of 10^{-2} mm or better, we can convert from n type to p type at $T = 25$°C.

Table 24.1. Effect of Hall Coefficient on Oxygen Pressure

P oxygen, mm Hg	Hall coefficient, cm³ coulomb⁻¹
0*	−252
209	−103
414	−39
490	0
775	105

* The sample was initially evacuated to a pressure 10^{-5} mm Hg for a period of 42 hr, with $T - 23$°C maintained at the constant temperature.

Qualitative adsorption studies made on the material at room temperature reveal the possibility of water-vapor adsorption. It is therefore not improbable that the low-temperature Hall reversal observed in Fig. 24.3 may be related to a physical (adsorption) desorption process.

Table 24.2. Effect of Doping on the Conductivity Type of the Polymer of Copper Phthalocyanine

	Additive agent, treatment or preparation	Conductivity type	Thermoelectric power, μv deg^{-1}
Low-temperature form of stoichiometric polymer of copper phtalo-cyanine		p	12–18
	Water vapor	n	59
	Hydrogen sulfide	n	30
	Bromine	p	1
	Ozone	p	5
	Polymer of copper phthalocyanine prepared with copper deficiency	n	8
	Polymer of copper phthalocyanine prepared with copper excess	p	4
Poly-copper phthalocyanine	Heat-treated	p	33–37

Other supplementary additives or dopants, when purposely introduced either in the preparation of the compound or after the compound has been formed, can alter or modify the conductivity type of the low-temperature form of the stoichiometric polymer of copper phthalocyanine. The results of doping either by physical or chemical means are presented in tabular form in Table 24.2 together with the thermoelectric power. Also included are the values for the low-temperature form of the stoichiometric polymer and the results obtained on the heat-treated polymer. All data presented are for measurements made at a temperature of 23°C.

Thermoelectric Power

As seen from Table 24.2, the thermoelectric power of the untreated polymer of copper phthalocyanine is $\sim$15 μv deg^{-1} at 23°C, whereas heat-treating the polymer (irreversibly) increases the value to $\sim$35 μv deg^{-1}.

While the addition of water vapor or hydrogen sulfide to the polymer appears to increase the thermoelectric power considerably, it is not believed that these additives are necessarily chemically combined or highly stable over a wide range of temperatures.

The values given for the thermoelectric power are only to be taken as examples of "doping" and are not necessarily indicative of any trend. No attempt has been made to relate these values to the electrical resistivity or Hall effect.

Discussion

The measurement of p-type conductivity observed at higher temperatures, both in the untreated and heat-treated polymer, fits in well with the observations of Kleitman of p-type conductivity in phthalocyanine,[2] the predictions of Winslow et al.,[4] the results of Chynoweth et al. on anthracene,[5] and the observations on polymer carbons.[4]

Polymer SI

The results of our measurements on this low-temperature polymer of copper phthalocyanine reveals that "intrinsically" the material is the p type and has an "activation energy" of 0.26 ev. R/ρ roughly corresponds to $\sim$10 cm^2 volt-sec^{-1} with a number density of carriers of $\sim$10^{16} cm^3 at $T = 25$°C. The carrier density is temperature dependent. In a very general way this characterizes the low-temperature polymer that we call "SI".

Transition

Above approximately 250°C a transition occurs, characterized by a minimum in the Hall coefficient and a changing slope in the resistivity. Provided the material is not heated above 350°C, the apparent change in structure is small. Above 350°C, quite pronounced changes occur. If we can assume that the Hall curve above 350°C represents equilibrium conditions characterizing the change in structure, then the slope of the Hall curve may provide information on the energy characterizing the change. The activation energy of the Hall curve is 2.5 ev. Energy required to break a C—N bond is ~3 ev, or within range of the experimental activation energy. It is possible that the heat treatment leads to a breaking of bonds, giving rise to a new chemical composition. Such an effect has been detected chemically by heating the polymer at 410°C. The chemical analysis of the "heat-treated" polymer showed a marked decrease in the percentage of nitrogen when compared to the analysis of the starting polymer, thus providing some chemical evidence for such a change.

A 0.65-g sample of the polymer was heated for 18 hr at 410°C/ 0.25 mm. During this treatment the weight loss of the sample was 10.8 per cent. No material collected at room temperature on the walls of the sublimation apparatus. The material had the following analysis: C, 52.65, 52.78; H, 1.42, 1.22; N, 24.30, 24.18.

Heat-Treated Polymer SII

The heat-treated material in contrast to the unpyrolyzed polymer showed a large increase in the carrier density to ~10^{18} cm^{-3}, a decrease in the mobility, and a very small activation energy of 0.12 ev, which, with a constant Hall coefficient, could be associated with the mobility. The conductivity still remains p type.

P-Type Conduction

The increase in carrier density noted on going from the original polymer SI to the heat-treated polymer SII could be associated with an increase in unsaturation and of unpaired electrons. Such an action could then lead, as Winslow et al.[4] have postulated, to p-type conduction by a mechanism of the type $Me^{n+} + Me^{(n+1)+} \rightarrow Me^{(n+1)+} + Me^{n+}$. Where Me^{n+} and $Me^{(n+1)+}$ represents an atom (or molecule) in two stages of ionization. These radical sites are able to drift through the conjugated network in successive steps resembling holes.

Mobility

The increase in mobility with increase of temperature in heat-treated polymer SII points to the possibility of intermolecular barriers or to a strong dependence of the transport coefficient on the number of unsaturated bonds. For a mobility of the order of 10 cm² volt-sec^{-1}, assuming a thermal energy of $kT \sim 0.025$ ev, we find an upper limit for the mean free path of ~ 1 A.

Molecular Weight versus Energy Gap

Eley et al.[6] and Inokuchi[7] have discussed the effect of energy gap on molecular weight, remarking that for increasing molecular weight the energy gap decreases. Eley has proposed an explanation for the observed activation energies in ring molecules making use of a band theory that could arise from consideration of the wave functions of the overlapping π electrons. From the Eley theory, for the case of this polymer of copper phthalocyanine SI with 140 π electrons,* we should calculate an activation energy of ~ 0.20 ev. This is in fair agreement with the observed activation energy of 0.26 ev, especially considering the simplicity of the model used. Perhaps a more refined picture is the one suggested by Fox[8] in which he uses a modification of Lyons[9] and accounts for the observed p-type conduction and the low R/ρ ratio by the introduction of a second conduction band (narrow in width) to simulate a jump process as suggested above. This may lead to closer agreement and perhaps a somewhat better interpretation of the electrical conduction process.

---

* This value was calculated on the basis of five phthalocyanine units

Thermal Properties

Thermal Measurements. The thermal conductivity of the low-temperature state of the polymer of copper phthalocyanine SI was measured in the range of temperatures from $T = 25°C$ to 170°C, using a comparison method [10] with Armco iron as a

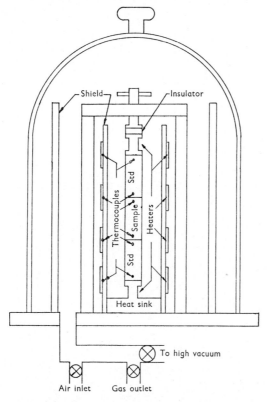

Fig. 24.8. Experimental arrangement for measurement of thermal conductivity.

standard.[11] The sample was pressed into a disk 1.27 cm in diameter by 0.43 cm in height, using a pressure of 70,000 lb in^{-2}. No attempt was made to orient or order the samples of polycopper phthalocyanine. Losses by convection and radiation were reduced by carrying out the measurements under forepump pressure

(10^{-3} mm Hg) and using suitable accessory heaters and shields. The experimental arrangement is shown in Fig. 24.8.

The thermal conductivity of the low-temperature form of the polymer is plotted against the absolute temperature in Fig. 24.9.

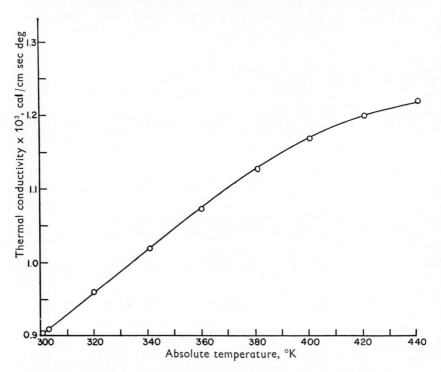

Fig. 24.9. Thermal conductivity of low-temperature state of poly-copper phthalocyanine as a function of absolute temperature.

Discussion

The thermal conductivity is observed to increase from a value of 9×10^{-4} cal cm^{-1} sec^{-1} °K^{-1} at 300°K to a value of $\sim 1.22 \times 10^{-3}$ cal cm^{-1} sec^{-1} °K^{-1} at 440°K. The increase with temperature above 380°K shows a deviation from a linear relationship. The material was found to have an electrical resistivity at 25°C of 137 ohm-cm and a carrier density of $\sim 10^{16}$ cm^{-3}. The electronic contribution to the thermal conductivity, assuming use of the

Wiedemann-Franz relationship is $\sim 10^{-8}$ cal cm^{-1} sec^{-1} °K^{-1}, a value well below that observed, indicating that the phonon contribution is the main contribution to the thermal conductivity.

Since the polymer is generally thought to be composed of loosely bound molecules, each molecule being composed of a group of strongly bound atoms, we might suggest that a short-range mechanism might be dominant, especially when there is a lack of crystallinity present. It would appear that the results for poly-copper phthalocyanine might fall into the general category of amorphous glasses where local order predominates. Some qualitative agreement is noted, especially with glassy selenium, crown glass, and flint glass, while poorer agreement is found in comparison with quartz, as seen in Table 24.3.

Table 24.3. Comparison of Thermal Conductivities of Some Glasses and Poly-Copper Phthalocyanine at 300°K

Material	Thermal conductivity at 300°K, cal cm^{-1} sec^{-1} deg^{-1}
Fused quartz [12]	3.4×10^{-3}
Crown glass [12]	1.63×10^{-3}
Flint glass [12]	1.43×10^{-3}
Poly-copper phthalocyanine	0.9×10^{-3}
Glassy selenium [13]	0.5×10^{-3}

If we attempt to estimate the phonon mean free path for this polymer of copper phthalocyanine qualitatively, using the Debye relationship and assuming a specific heat ~ 0.2 cal g^{-1} deg * and a velocity of sound $\sim 10^5$ cm sec^{-1}, then at 300°K the mean free path turns out to be ~ 13 A, which is approximately the value given for one dimension of the unit cell in monomeric copper phthalocyanine.[14]

If, following the case for glasses,[12] we assume the mean free path at these temperatures to be constant, then the increase in thermal conductivity with temperature, as shown in Fig. 24.9, might be ascribed to the heat capacity, which is known to increase with increasing temperature.

* From unpublished results.

356 ARNOLD EPSTEIN AND BERNARD WILDI

Conclusions

We have been able to determine on a polymer of copper phthalocyanine by Hall-effect measurements the existence of p-type conduction and a carrier mobility in the polymer of ~ 10 cm^2 volt-sec^{-1}. Two states of this polymer have been studied: one (SI) has an activation energy of 0.26 ev and a carrier density of $\sim 10^{16}$/cm^3 (the density varying with temperature); a second state (SII) is also found to give p-type conduction, but the carrier density is $\sim 10^{18}$ cm^{-3}, and constant and the mobility increases with increasing temperature. n-type conductivity observed in SI is believed to be a consequence of impurities.

The thermoelectric power of the low-temperature state of the polymer SI is found to be ~ 15 μv deg^{-1}, while the heat-treated form of the polymer has a value of ~ 35 μv deg^{-1} at room temperature.

The thermal conductivity of the low-temperature state of the polymer of copper phthalocyanine SI has a value of 9×10^{-4} cal cm-sec^{-1} deg at a temperature of 25°C, increasing to 1.2×10^{-3} cal cm-sec^{-1} deg at 170°C. The contribution is believed entirely due to phonons as expected. The behavior of the thermal conductivity suggests some similarity with amorphous glasses.

Acknowledgment. Acknowledgment is made to the *Journal of Chemical Physics* for permission to use some of the material previously published in that journal by the authors.[15]

References

1. K. Venkataraman, "The Chemistry of Synthetic Dyes," pp. 1118–1142, Academic Press, Inc., New York (1952).
2. D. Kleitman, "Electrical Properties of Phthalocyanine," PB 111419 (August, 1953).
3. A. D. Vartanyan, *J. Phys. Chem. (U.S.S.R.)* **22**, 769 (1949); *Acta Physicochim. (U.S.S.R.)* **22**, 201 (1947).
4. F. H. Winslow, W. O. Baker, and Y. A. Yager, *J. Am. Chem. Soc.* **77**, 4751 (1951).
5. A. G. Chynoweth and W. G. Schneider, *J. Chem. Phys.* **22**, 1021 (1954).
6. D. D. Eley, *Nature* **162**, 819 (1948); D. D. Eley, G. D. Parfitt, M. J. Perry, and D. H. Taysum, *Trans. Faraday Soc.* **49**, 79 (1953); D. D. Eley, *Trans. Faraday Soc.* **51**, 152 (1955).

7. H. Inokuchi, *Bull. Chem. Soc. Japan* **24**, 222 (1951); **25**, 281 (1952); **27**, 22 (1954); *J. Chem. Phys.* **18**, 8101 (1950).
8. D. Fox, *J. Phys. Chem. Solids* **8**, 439 (1959).
9. L. E. Lyons, *J. Chem. Soc.* **1957**, 5001.
10. J. Francl and W. D. Kingery, *J. Am. Ceram. Soc.* **37**, 80–84 (1954); M. S. van Duesen and S. M. Shelton, *J. Research Nat. Bur. Standards* **12**(4), 429–440 (1934).
11. L. D. Armstrong and T. M. Dauphinee, *Can. J. Research* **25**, 357 (1947).
12. C. Kittel, *Phys. Rev.* **75**, 972 (1949).
13. G. K. White et al., *Phys. Rev.* **112**, 111 (1958).
14. M. Robinson and G. Klein, *J. Am. Chem. Soc.* **74**, 6294 (1952); J. M. Robertson, *J. Chem. Soc.* **1935**, 615; **1936**, 1736.
15. A. Epstein and B. S. Wildi, *J. Chem. Phys.* **32**, 324 (1960).

25

Long Scintillation-Decay Times in Anthracene

P. E. Gibbons and D. C. Northrop

Introduction

The fluorescence of anthracene when irradiated with ultra-violet light is a simple process involving decay to the ground state from the lowest singlet excited state of the anthracene molecule. It is known that this excited state is a mobile-exciton state and that the energy associated with it can move in a random manner by jumping from one molecule to a nearest neighbor. For this reason impurity centers that trap excitons can have a dominant effect on the fluorescence. However, apart from this short-range cooperative effect between molecules, the existence of a crystal lattice has comparatively little importance, and the behavior can be understood in terms of the properties of a single molecule.

When a high-energy particle is used instead of ultraviolet light to excite the crystal, the largest part of the resulting light emission has the same decay time and spectral distribution as the fluorescence process, indicating that the same excited state has been produced. Closer examination of a single scintillation shows that some important differences exist, however, and in particular that light continues to be emitted for several microseconds after the main scintillation pulse, which is only about 30 nanosec in duration. It can also be shown that the ratio of the energy in this tail emission to that in the main pulse depends on the kind of particle used to excite the crystal. The practical importance of this fact as a means of discrimination between fast neutrons and gamma rays is already well established; the aim of the present work is to find out what physical process is involved in the tail emission.

Unfortunately, the results of particle bombardment are not as simple as those of ultraviolet irradiation, for in addition to exciton states the particle also produces some permanent damage to the lattice and a large amount of ionization. It is possible that the damaged centers interact with the excitons, that charge-carrier recombination is a radiotive process, or that the triplet-excited states produced by carrier recombination may play some part in the light emission. In this chapter an explanation is put forward that takes no account of these possible complications but that is based only on the properties of excitons. A number of experiments are described below that give further information about the tail emission, and these are discussed in terms of such a model. Much of the information found in this way could be used to support the assumptions that ionization and triplet-excited states are unimportant here.

Experimental

Oscillograph traces showing typical tail emission from anthracene under γ-ray and α-particle bombardment are shown in Fig. 25.1.

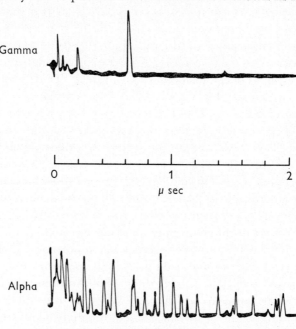

Fig. 25.1. Scintillation afterpulses in anthracene.

The main scintillation pulses, which do not appear in this illustration, are approximately the same size in the two cases and contain all but a few per cent of the total energy in the scintillation. Manual analysis of traces like the ones shown reveals that each individual pulse is due to a single photon falling on the cathode of the photomultiplier, the spread in pulse sizes being due to the statistical nature of the multiplication processes. To relate the oscilloscope signals to the light emission from the scintillator, it is necessary merely to count these pulses, taking no account of their size. All the experimental data are derived in this way.

First, by placing optical filters between the scintillator and the photomultiplier and comparing their effect on the tail and main pulse, it is possible to show that their spectral distributions are the same within the limits of experimental error. There is certainly not sufficient difference to suggest that two different excited states are involved. Nevertheless, by dividing each trace into a number of time channels and integrating the results of a large number of experiments, it can be shown that the decay scheme, given in Fig. 25.2, is very different from that expected for straightforward decay of the first singlet-excited state. It is the same for α-particle or γ-ray irradiation. Figure 25.3 shows that the decay scheme is not dependent on temperature over the range 90 to 300°K, so that the decay scheme is not a thermally activated one; it appears to refer to a true electronic-excited state. It may be noted that the form of the decay scheme is complicated and cannot be accurately represented either by a power law or by a single exponential. It could be analysed into two exponential components, but at this stage there is no physical reason for doing so.

The most revealing experimental evidence concerns the behavior of impure anthracene, where the impurity is of a kind that can trap excitons. The main scintillation pulse is modified in exactly the same way as the fluorescence emission. It was expected that the tail emission might be modified identically, too, if it is due to the same exciton-decay process, but in fact something much more spectacular happens. The part of the tail emitted from anthracene molecules reduces vary rapidly with impurity concentration, as is shown in Fig. 25.4, falling by a factor of 10,

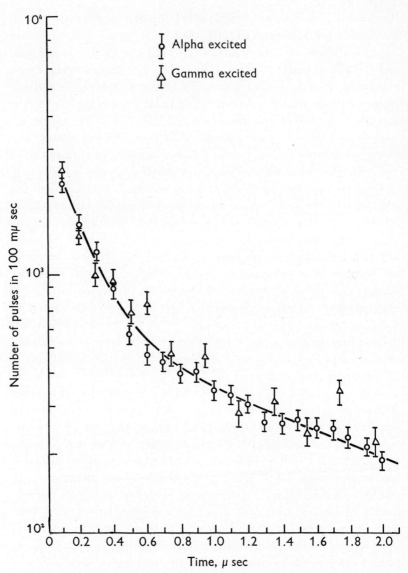

Fig. 25.2. Anthracene tail emission.

while that in the main pulse is only reducing by a factor of 2. If we make the assumption that the impurities have no other effect than to trap excitons, this experiment indicates that the tail emission is a cooperative effect between excitons.

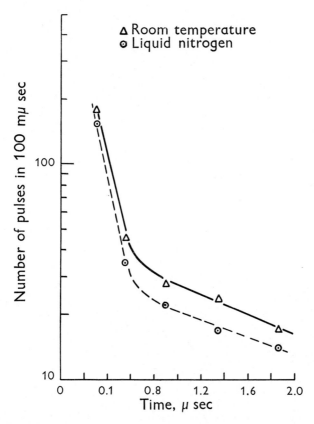

Fig. 25.3. Effect of temperature on the emission in anthracene (gamma excited).

Suppose that we are dealing with an electronic-excited state of a system consisting of two adjacent molecules, each similarly excited and designated A^*A^*. This system might well have a existence of its own, and if we suppose that it decays with its own characteristic lifetime to give back a free exciton, we can explain the observed behavior as follows. If there are N excitons in a volume containing

M molecules, the rate of creation of excited pairs A^*A^* is

$$\gamma N^2/M$$

where γ is the exciton jump frequency. And the total number created is

$$(\gamma N_0{}^2/M) \int_0^\infty \exp(-2t/\tau)\, dt = \gamma N_0{}^2\tau/2M$$

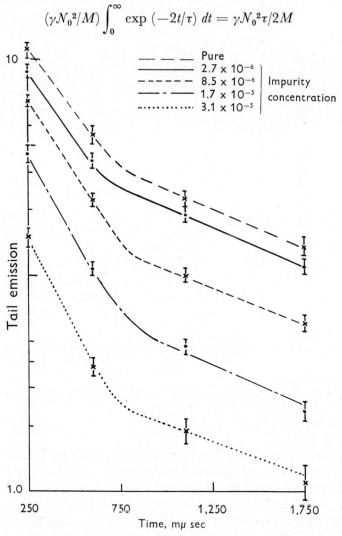

Fig. 25.4. Pentacene impurity effect on tail emission.

where τ is the free-exciton lifetime, and M is the assumed constant.

In fact, M increases as the excitons move to fill a larger volume around the particle track, but the greatest chance of collision occurs soon after the passage of the particle, when the excitons still occupy approximately the volume in which they were created. This being so the approximation of constant M is a reasonable one.

After the lifetime of the complex state this number of excitons will be released and will have a further chance of being captured at an impurity, so that the ultimate intensity of the tail emission from anthracene molecules is

$$(\gamma N_0^2 \tau / 2M)[\alpha/(\alpha + \gamma cq)]$$

where α is the probability per unit time of radiative decay, c is the fraction of the lattice sites filled by impurity molecules, and q is an exciton-capture cross section. Since

$$\tau = 1/\alpha + \partial cq$$

this gives

$$(\partial \alpha N_0^2 / 2M) \tau^2$$

for the anthracene tail intensity. τ can be found for a given impurity concentration from the ratio of the main pulse energy in pure and impure anthracene, and in Fig. 25.5 the measured tail intensity due to anthracene is plotted against τ. It has the form $\propto \tau^n$, where $\tau = 2.14$.

This agreement is as good as could be expected in view of the assumption made about M and must be regarded as strong confirmation of the model.

Developing these ideas one stage further we may look at the tail emission from the impurity molecules, which decay radiatively after exciton capture. This should consist of two components, the first of which has the same time dependence as the anthracene emission and is due to exciton capture after the decay of the $A*A*$ complexes. The second will have a somewhat different shape and will be due to the decay of $A*I*$ complexes, where one molecule is an impurity. They can be separated experimentally, for the first component should be given by the tail emission from anthracene, reduced by the ratio of the main pulses in impure and pure anthracene. The second component can then be obtained by subtraction. In Fig. 25.6 this measurement is shown, and the analysis is performed giving a single exponential

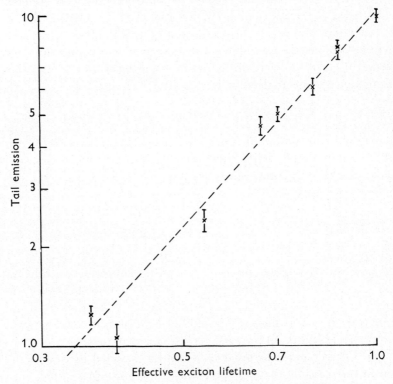

Fig. 25.5 Pentacene impurity effect on tail emission.

for the deduced decay scheme of the A^*I^* complex. Excitons released on the decay of this state have a high chance of capture at the impurity and will have a small effect on the anthracene emission.

Discussion

The model proposed is capable of explaining the observed effect and withstands some experimental cross examination. In addition it is possible to suggest a number of refinements to explain more detailed experimental findings. At least three different kinds of A^*A^* complex exist, with different relative configurations of the

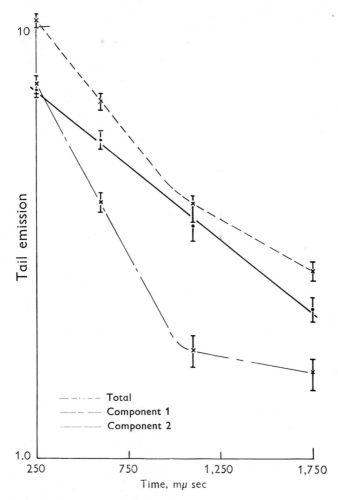

Fig. 25.6. Analysis of naphthalene impurity on tail emission.

two molecules, and these would presumably have different decay times. We may therefore be justified in analyzing the curve of

Fig. 25.2 as two exponentials. There are signs of a possible third component as well, but its intensity is very near noise.

Two points would bear considerable further investigation. First, there is the theoretical question of whether such complex excited states could exist and what their properties would be. At the moment, they are pure conjecture. Second, according to this model it should be possible to excite the long-lived states with ultraviolet light if the exciton density became high enough, i.e., equal to that near an α-particle track. This is not an easy experiment, as we have necessarily to use a surface layer of the crystal as thick as the extinction depth for the light. A system is under construction at the Services Electronics Research Laboratory that we hope will achieve the necessary light intensity for the long decay components to be observed.

Biological Aspects*

J. GERGELY

This brief survey deals with some biological phenomena to which the ideas and facts presented in this book are applicable. It is by no means an exhaustive one, and the reader wanting more complete information is referred to several recent books and monographs covering this topic in a much more thorough fashion.[1-4]

The application of concepts of solid-state physics to phenomena of energy and electron transport in biological systems has been of great interest for the last twenty years or so, and Szent-Györgyi's Korinyi lecture can be considered a landmark.[5,6]

At times the migration of electrons or positive holes has been at the center of attention, while at others processes involving not movement of charge carriers but energy transfer by means of excitons have been considered more important.[7]

We should like to start with the discussion of some processes where the movement of electrons through an organized macromolecular matrix is not lightly to be dismissed, namely, the flow of electrons through the cytochrome system — a sequence of Fe containing proteins — to O_2. This belongs to the area known to biochemists as "electron transport," although for them this term has a much broader connotation than it would have for physicists. For a meaningful discussion of this problem some of the biochemical facts of life have to be considered.

Most of the energy-yielding biological processes in the last analysis involve a flow of electrons from a foodstuff, such as a carbohydrate or fat, to O_2. This is accomplished in a series of steps, the net result of which is the breakdown of the original substance into smaller bits, often to CO_2 and H_2O, with the

* This research was supported by a grant from the National Heart Institute, United States Public Health Service (grant H-1166 (C-7-8)).

[369]

trapping of the free energy of oxidation in so-called "high-energy phosphate" compounds, a prototype of which is adenosine triphosphate, or ATP, for short. The splitting off of its terminal phosphate furnishes a free energy of around 10,000 cal mole^{-1}, the exact value *in vivo* depending on the concentration of ATP, ADP, and phosphate *in situ.**

Not all the steps in the flow of electrons mentioned above make a prima facie case for bringing in the solid-state-physics concepts discussed in this book. Clearly, whenever there is a possibility of an interaction between freely diffusible molecules, the classical concepts of oxidation reduction will do. Needless to say, even in this case a flow of electrons through a small molecule might occur, as the recent work of Taube and his associates on the reduction of organic Co^{+++} complexes by Cr^{++} strongly indicates.[10]

Taking carbohydrates as an example, we should like to show briefly those processes in which flow of electrons through macromolecular biological systems could be adduced as a working hypothesis — and we must emphasize that all this has to be considered as a working hypothesis rather than something definitive — and those processes where this is not necessary at all.

The breakdown of a glucose residue, possibly derived from its polymerized storage form, glycogen, undergoes a sequence of complicated enzymatically catalyzed reactions leading to the formation of pyruvic acid in what is known as the glycolytic cycle (Fig. 26.1). These reactions have been studied by biochemists for almost 50 years, and what made them rather easy to get at is the fact that the enzymes catalyzing these reactions are, as it were, freely dissolved inside the cell and can be extracted with great ease. This is in contrast to the enzymes localized in the insoluble cell structure to be discussed below.

In connection with Fig. 26.1 the following points must be made. The over-all reaction, glucose → pyruvate, involves a removal of electrons, in the so-called phosphoglyceradlehyde (PGA) dehydrogenase step, involving a coenzyme, diphosphopyridine nucleotide, or DPN, for short.

* For general information see Refs. 8 and 9.

Coenzymes are small molecules that combine with the protein moiety of the enzyme and are necessary for its activity. Coenzymes are not necessarily involved in every enzyme system. When they

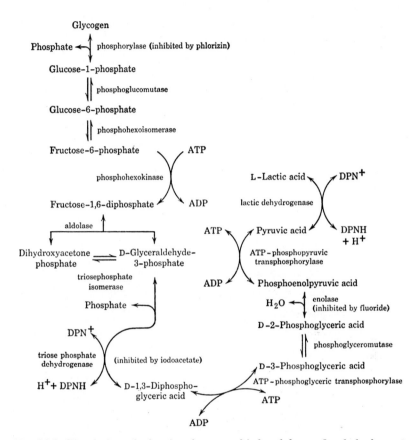

Fig. 26.1. Glycolytic cycle showing the anaerobic breakdown of carbohydrates.[8]

are, the coenzyme first reacts with the substance undergoing a change — in our discussion, oxidation or reduction — and is then able to react in another enzyme system. Thus DPNH, the reduced form of DPN[+], formed in the PGA dehydrogenase step has two possibilities: if there is no O_2 present or if O_2 is present in insufficient amounts, it will react with pyruvic acid on the surface of the lactic dehydrogenase protein; thus, in this so-called "anaerobic" case, the end product would be lactic acid, with the DPNH restored to DPN$^+$, the latter then being able to react again with a molecule of PGA. These reactions do not require the consideration of any unusual — unusual for the biochemist — mechanisms, such as those discussed in this book, for the DPN molecule can act as a shuttle between the various reaction sites

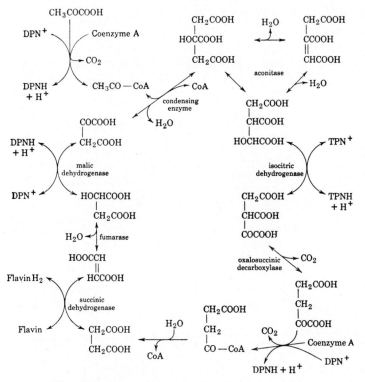

Fig. 26.2. The reactions of the citric acid cycle.[8]

In the presence of O_2 the DPNH formed in the PGA dehydrogenase reaction will be oxidized in a sequence that very strongly suggests the participation of electron transport in the sense used for solids. The enzymes responsible for these subsequent steps are located, in a spatially restricted position, in highly organized

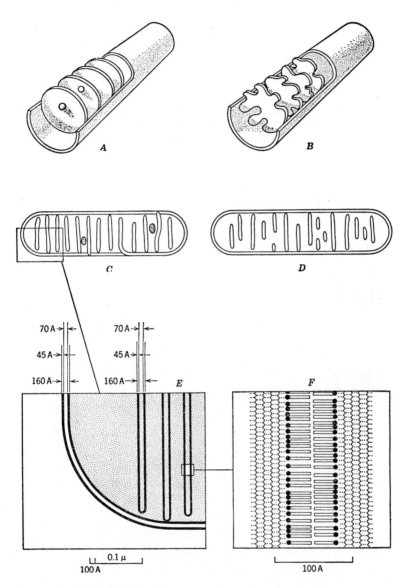

Fig. 26.3. Detailed structure of mitochondria showing surrounding double membranes, which in turn give rise to septa known as "cristae." Insert F shows a suggested arrangement of lipids (center) with proteins adjacent to the hydrophilic end (black dots) of the lipid component.[13]

structures of the cell, the mitochondria.[11,12] The enzymes responsible for the further breakdown of pyruvic acid — formed at the
end of the chain of events discussed above — are also located in
the mitochondria. The cycle of enzymatic reactions that leads to
the complete breakdown to H_2O and CO_2 of a pyruvate molecule,
the latter having first combined with a coenzyme known as CoA,
is usually referred to as the Krebs cycle or the citric-acid or
tricarboxylic-acid cycle (Fig. 26.2.) The mitochondria in which
all this enzymatic apparatus is located reveal under the election
microscope, a highly organized pattern. The current view is
that the various enzymes are part of the double membranes shown
in Fig. 26.3, and the layers facing each other consist of lipid
material with protein located on the outer side.[13]

   The reactions of the Krebs cycle (Fig. 26.2) also involve DPN
and TPN, the latter being DPN with another phosphate residue
attached to it. As shown in the figure, there is no reaction within
the cycle itself to restore the reduced form of these coenzymes
or of the flavin involved in the oxidation of succinate, the oxidized
state. This is accomplished, for the DPNH formed in the glycolytic cycle, by the so-called "cytochrome" system, the reaction
being

$$DPNH \rightarrow \overset{+}{DPN} + H^+ + 2\varepsilon$$

The electrons are used to reduce the Fe^{+++} of the first cytochrome (Fig. 26.4), a heme protein, the heme being very similar
in structure to the copper phthallocyanine discussed earlier in
this book, containing, of course, Fe instead of Cu. Even if we assume that the coenzyme could directly react with the heme
of the first cytochrome, the problem arises, "How does the first
cytochrome react with the second, the second with the third?"
Moreover, there is evidence that suggests that the heme is buried
inside the protein structure and not directly located on the surface.[14]
Thus the interaction of the hemes in the adjacent cytochromes
presents a challenging problem to the physicist or the biophysicist,
one that could be suitably thought of in terms of the mobility
of electrons within the protein fabric.

As proposed about ten years ago[15] the extended H-bonded system of $-C\!\!=\!\!O \ldots H-N-$groups in proteins could furnish the basis of an electron conduction band. Dr. Eley has discussed some of the experimental evidence relating to the semiconductivity

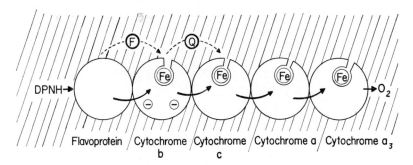

Flavoprotein / Cytochrome / Cytochrome / Cytochrome a / Cytochrome a₃
                        b   c

Fig. 26.4. Simplified scheme of electron flow from reduced DPN to O_2 through cytochrome sequence. Solid arrows indicate electron movement through protein structure; dotted arrows indicate possible shuttles. $F =$ flavin; $Q =$ a recently suggested quinone-type coenzyme.[12] Fe indicates heme, buried in a protein "crevice." [14]

in proteins[16] and found a reasonable agreement between the experimental and theoretical value of the energy gap between the highest filled and the lowest empty electronic levels. The value of this gap is about 3 ev * and, as Kasha pointed out,[7] would prove, strictly speaking, that proteins could be photo-conductors but are not semiconductors in the usual sense. Whether charge carriers other than electrons might be involved in these conductivity measurements is perhaps still somewhat of an open question.[18] The recent work of Kopple and Svatosia on the reduction by Cr^{++} of polypeptide-Co^{+++} complexes lends considerable further support to the view that electron conduction takes place in protein structures.

* The original calculations were based on a model of H-bonded, stretched, parallel polypeptide chains, and the application to an α helix[17] — with the H-bonded groups within the same polypeptide chain — may require some changes in the parameters.

Let us now turn to processes that primarily involve the transfer of energy rather than that of electrons. Here, the various exciton-migration concepts come in useful. The source of the original energy input could, broadly speaking, be either radiation or a

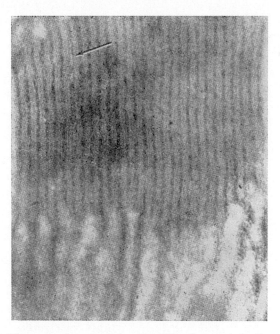

Fig. 26.5. Electron micrograph ($\times$ 220,000) of granum in Zea chloroplast. The arrow shows that the dark lines are resolvable into two denser layers.[22]

chemical process. Among the interactions with radiation, photosynthesis is one of the phenomena that have been studied in considerable detail.* The plant's basic problem is to utilize the energy of photons and convert it into chemical energy. Some of the steps in this process are of a perfectly ordinary chemical-biochemical nature and can be understood in classical terms; others are such that the ideas discussed in this book become pertinent. All this takes place in a structure known as the chloroplast, where electron microscopy shows a beautiful order [22]

* For recent reviews, see Refs. 20 and 21.

(Fig. 26.5). This, as in the case of mitochondria, suggests that various interacting structures are lined up in a well-defined spatial relation with each other. A possible arrangement of the various components in the chloroplast suggested by Calvin is shown in Fig. 26.6.

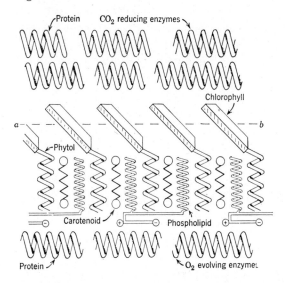

Fig. 26.6. Suggested arrangement of various components in single layer of chloroplast membrane shown in Fig. 26.5.[20]

It has been assumed for a long time that the energy of the photons absorbed by the chlorophyll could travel by means of an exciton mechanism.* Whether charge separation could at some point take place has also been the subject of speculation.[21] Calvin [23] has recently suggested that at suitable spatially separated points reduction of a quinone could take place, with a positive hole traveling to a cytochrome where oxidation would occur. Electron-spin-resonance results suggest the presence of free electrons during photosynthesis.[24, 25] The further processes following primary reduction and oxidation steps can be described in terms of biochemical reactions similar to those found in other systems.

* For a discussion of carriers see Ref. 7.

Calvin and his colleagues have worked out a great many details of the metabolic pathways.[20]

Without going through the whole gamut of phenomena involving the interaction of biological matter and radiation — including radiation-induced changes in the genetic material — a few words should be said about another important area, namely, vision. Considerable insight into this problem has been obtained through the work of Wald and his colleagues[26] and a good deal is known about the biochemistry of the process. In the rods of the retina a substance related to vitamin A, retinene, combined to a protein, opsin, responds to the absorption of light and changes its configuration [27] (Fig. 26.7). Again, electron micrographs show a layered structure in the retinal rods,[13, 28] and we may speculate how the photoinduced isomerization of retinene affects the complementary protein, how this is related to the ultrastructure, and how all this eventually results in an electrical signal traveling to the brain and may involve various mechanisms

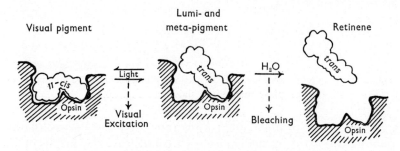

Fig. 26.7. Scheme of vision showing photoisomerization of retinene and dissociation from protein, opsin. Possible configurational changes in the protein are not shown.[27]

of energy or charge transport. In addition, there is, as in the examples discussed above, some classical biochemistry, e.g., the restoration of transretinene formed by the action of light to the 11-*cis* form, which then combines again with opsin, depends on some complex, but in principle straightforward, biochemical processes.[26]

Let us now turn to bioluminescence, which occurs in a variety of organisms. These chemical reactions are accompanied by the release of photons. The reason for including these phenomena in the present discussion is that they provide a pattern by which electronic excitation, whose energy is of the order required for the excitation of protein electron into the conduction band, can take place. The details of bioluminescence vary from organism to organism. It seems that oxygen is always required, but the substrate of oxidation may be rather different. There is also a considerable variation in the requirement for other factors such as ATP and Mg^{++}.[29] If similar processes were closely coupled to a system in which electronic excitation can take place, one would have a mechanism for the transformation of chemical energy into mobile electronic energy in a radiationless process.

Let us now turn to the consideration of resonance-energy transfer in macromolecular systems of biological significance. These processes have recently received considerable attention as possible links in biological energy transfer.

A classic example that can be interpreted in terms of this mechanism is the photodissociation of carbon monoxide-myoglobin by light of a wavelength that cannot be absorbed by the heme to which the CO is attached (280 mμ) but is absorbed only by the aromatic amino acid residues of the protein.[30] Since the publications of Bucher and Kaspers' work, a considerable body of evidence has accumulated that shows the operation of this mechanism. Studies made on systems that contain artificially coupled chromophores [31] or on protein naturally containing such groups[32] clearly demonstrate that light energy absorbed by the protein leads to the excitation of the chromophore and emission of fluorescence. Quantitative theoretical studies support the view that resonance-energy transfer is highly efficient[33] over distances up to about 50 A, and the experimental correlation between transfer efficiency and the average distance between the groups participating in the transfer is in good agreement with the theoretical results.[34-36] It has also been shown that resonance-energy transfer takes place between the two rings in reduced DPN, manifested by fluorescence characteristics of the pyridine ring when light is absorbed by the adenine ring.[37]

The participation of triplet states and charge-transfer complexes in bioenergetics has been emphasized by Szent-Györgyi and his coworkers.[1,38] The impressive spectral changes observed when tryptophan and riboflavin-phosphate interact[39] suggest a profound rearrangement of the electronic structure, and this kind of interaction between tryptophan in a protein and a flavinlike coenzyme may play an important part in energy transfer to the protein moiety.

Isenberg and Szent-Györgyi[40] have recently found an electron-spin-resonance signal in ATP. Although this signal is rather weak, corresponding to only a small fraction, perhaps of the order of 10^{-4}, of the ATP molecules present, it may be suggestive of an intramolecular charge-transfer complex between the adenine ring and the terminal phosphate, with an electron donated by the adenine to the phosphate.

The existence of such intramolecular charge-transfer complexes opens up interesting speculation about their role in various biological processes, including such knotty problems as the energy utilization in muscle contraction. The possibility of another kind of intramolecular charge-transfer complex is suggested by the theoretical calculations of Pullman and Pullman on the energy levels in the base-pairs of DNA.* They have shown — subject to the assumptions involved in such calculation — by means of the LCAO method that the guanine-cytosine pairs are both better electron donors and electron acceptors than the adenine-thymine pairs. If charge-transfer complexes between adjacent guanine-cytosine pairs play a part in the stabilization of the DNA molecule, there would be an interesting correlation with the experimentally found stabilization by a higher guanine-cytosine content.[43]

We should like to conclude our discussion with a constituent of all biological systems in which considerable interest has recently been shown, namely, water. Over the last few years attention has been called to the possibility of there being so-called "icelike" domains in biological systems.[1,44,45] The existence of various H-

---

* For a general review of the structure of DNA, see Ref. 4.

bonded water structures and hydrates has been widely discussed.[46] Eigen and de Maeyer[47] have recently drawn attention to the remarkable mobility of protons in ice, almost approaching that of electrons in a metal. This would make the existence of such "icebergs," as they have been called, of great significance in biological systems. A few years ago Jacobson and his colleagues[48] claimed that in dilute nucleic acid solutions a considerable part of the water protons did not contribute to the NMR signal, and they inferred that the "missing" protons were present in an ordered, icelike lattice. Recent studies[49] suggest that this is not quite the case, that in solutions of biologically important macro-molecules signal areas always show the value corresponding to pure water. A definite increase is observable, however, in the width of the resonance line, and the relaxation times are short-ened.[49] These recent NMR results support the view that part of the water exists in a state that is different from normal water and that could be perhaps considered as being localized in a thin shell around the macromolecules. This icelike layer around protein or nucleic acid molecules may then play an important part in lining up other molecules that enter into the energetic and electronic interactions discussed above, and — in view of the situation in ice — the increased proton mobility may become of importance in biological charge-transfer processes.

To sum up, the problems discussed in this chapter are examples of biological situations in which an approach based on concepts borrowed, as it were, from solid-state physics and quantum chemistry appears fruitful. On the one hand the list is by one means complete; on the other hand, we must not be too rigid about these suggestions. With the accumulation of new data, what seems today to be understandable only in terms of these nonclassical notions may be resolved into ordinary chemistry by new dis-coveries, and apparently clear and simple cases may require much more sophisticated explanations.

References

1. A. Szent-Györgyi *in* L. G. Augenstine (ed.), "Bioenergetics," Academic Press, Inc., New York (1957).

2. C. Reid, "Excited States in Chemistry and Biology," Academic Press, Inc., New York (1957).
3. *Discussions Faraday Soc.* **1959**, 27.
4. L. G. Augenstine (ed.), "Bioenergetics," Academic Press, Inc , New York (1960).
5. A. Szent-Györgyi, *Science* **93**, 609 (1941).
6. A. Szent-Györgyi, *Nature* **148**, 157 (1941).
7. M. Kasha, *Rev. Mod. Phys.* **31**, 162 (1949).
8. J. S. Fruton and S. Simmonds, "General Biochemistry," 2d ed., John Wiley & Sons, Inc., New York (1957).
9. E. Baldwin, "Dynamic Aspects of Biochemistry," 3d ed., Cambridge University Press, London (1957).
10. H. Taube, *Advances in Inorg. and Radiochem.* **1**, 25 (1959).
11. A. L. Lehninger, *Rev. Mod. Phys.* **31**, 136 (1959).
12. D. E. Green, *Discussions Faraday Soc.* **27**, 206 (1959).
13. F. S. Sjostrand, *Rev. Mod. Phys.* **31**, 301 (1959).
14. A. Ehrenberg and H. Theorell, *Acta Chem. Scand.* **9**, 1193 (1955).
15. M. G. Evans and J. Gergely, *Biochim. et Biophys. Acta* **3**, 188 (1949).
16. For further references, see M. H. Cardew and D. D. Eley, *Discussions Faraday Soc.* **27**, 115 (1959).
17. L. Pauling, R. B. Corey, and H. R. Branson, *Proc. Nat. Acad. Sci. U.S.* **37**, 205 (1951).
18. P. Taylor, *Discussions Faraday Soc.* **27**, 237 (1959).
19. K. Kopple and G. F. Svatos, *J. Amer. Chem. Soc.* (in press).
20. M. Calvin, *Rev. Mod. Phys.* **31**, 147 (1959).
21. E. Rabinowitch, *Discussions Faraday Soc.* **27**, 161 (1959).
22. A. J. Hodge, *Rev. Mod. Phys.* **31**, 331 (1959).
23. M. Calvin, Light and Life Conference, The Johns Hopkins University (1960).
24. B. Commoner, J. J. Heise, B. B. Lippincott, R. E. Norberg, J. V. Passonneau, and T. Towsend, *Science* **120**, 57 (1959).
25. M. Calvin, *Rev. Mod. Phys.* **31**, 157 (1959).
26. G. Wald, *Exptl. Cell Research*, suppl. 5, 398 (1958).
27. R. Hubbard and A. Knopf, *Ann. N.Y. Acad. Sci.* **81**, 388 (1959).
28. H. Fernandez-Moran, *Rev. Mod. Phys.* **31**, 319 (1959).
29. F. H. Johnson, H. Eyring, and J. J. Chang, *Discussions Faraday Soc.* **27**, 191 (1959).
30. T. Bucher and J. Kaspers, *Naturwissenschaften* **33**, 93 (1946).
31. V. G. Shore and A. B. Pardee, *Arch Biochem. Biophys.* **62**, 355 (1956).
32. T. T. Bannister, *Arch. Biochem. Biophys.* **49**, 222 (1954).
33. G. Karreman and R. H. Steele, *Biochim et Biophys. Acta* **25**, 280 (1957).
34. S. F. Velick, *J. Biol. Chem.* **233**, 1455 (1958).
35. L. Stryer, *Biochim. et Biophys. Acta* **35**, 242 (1959).
36. G. Weber and F. J. W. Teale, *Discussions Faraday Soc.* **27**, 134 (1959).

37. G. Weber, *Nature* **180**, 1409 (1957).
38. I. Isenberg and A. Szent-Györgyi, *Proc. Nat. Acad. Sci. U.S.* **44**, 519 (1958).
39. R. H. Steele and A. Szent-Györgyi, *Proc. Nat. Acad. Sci. U.S.* **43**, 477 (1957).
40. I. Isenberg and A. Szent-Györgyi, *Proc. Nat. Acad. Sci. U.S.* **45**, 1232 (1959).
41. B. Pullman and A. Pullman, *Biochem. et Biophys. Acta* **36**, 343 (1959).
42. A. Rich. *Rev. Mod. Phys.* **31**, 191 (1959).
43. J. Marmor and P. Doty, *Nature* **183**, 1427 (1959).
44. B. Jacobson, *Svenska Kem. Tidskr.* **67**, 1 (1955).
45. I. M. Klotz, *Science* **128**, 815 (1958).
46. L. Pauling, in D. Hadzi (ed.), "Hydrogen Bonding," Pergamon Press, Ltd., London (1959).
47. M. Eigen and L. de Maeyer, *Z. Elektrochemi.* **60**, 1037 (1956); **61**, 856 (1957).
48. B. Jacobson, W. A. Anderson, and J. T. Arnold, *Nature* **173**, 772 (1954).
49. J. Gergely, J. S. Waugh, and E. A. Balazs, Abstr. 5th Ann. Meeting Biophys. Soc., SB 3 (1960); E. A. Balazs, A. A. Bothner-By, and J. Gergely, *J. Mol. Biol.* **1**, 147 (1959).

27

Energy Transfer by Aqueous Solutions of Human Serum-Albumin (SAH): Photosensitized Reactions

P. Douzou, J. C. Francq, R. Goldstein, and J. M. Thuillier

1. Introduction and Theorical

In peptidic chains, it does not seem that energy absorbed at the level.of aromatic nuclei is transferred[1,2] or converted[3] along the chain, since these aromatic nuclei are insulated from one another by bonds that do not lead to electronic conduction.[4,5]

However, some proteins, especially SAH, behave as photo-conductors and show thermoelectric power when illuminated with light of 3,650 to 4,100 A that is only very weakly absorbed by molecule in solution. It seems that the corresponding energy gap of about 3 ev is characteristic of peptidic bonds, which would thus be responsible for the conductivity phenomenon observed in protein in the solid state.[6-9]

The creation of hole-electron pairs should result in the appearance at the ends of the chain of "free valencies" or at least sites of high polarizability. A quantum-energy-level diagram would look as indicated in Fig. 27.1.

Ionic semiconductors react through their quasi-free electrons or their positive holes, with molecules to which they give a charge or a polarization.

$$n \text{ (semiconductor)} + O_2 \rightarrow O_2^- \text{ (adsorbed)}$$

$$O_2^- \text{ (adsorbed)} + HOH + h\nu \rightarrow \text{(photodesorbed)} \ HO_2 + OH^-$$
$$\rightarrow \cdots \rightarrow H_2O_2$$

A series of reactions leading to synthesis or destruction of H_2O_2 can thus be observed, the proton donor being, in many cases, hydroquinone (QH2) rather than HOH. These reactions, which proceed slowly if at all in the dark, are catalyzed by radiation absorbed in the fundamental band of the semiconductor.

Although the exact mechanism of these reations is still a matter of controversy,[11–12] and the energy of photons responsible of the catalysis in the case of ionic semiconductors is much higher than that of any energy available *in vivo*, it has been thought worthwhile to investigate more fully similar reactions in the case of SAH. The more so as protein dispersion (solvatation) should permit, in successful investigations, allotment of observed phenomenon to the macromolecules themselves and not to their aggregated state only.

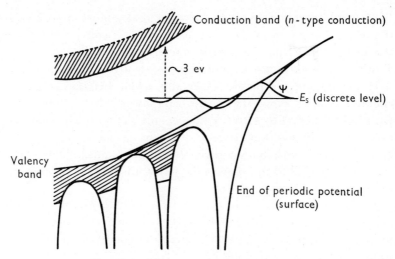

Fig. 27.1. Quantum-energy-level diagram.

The particular photocatalytic test reaction studied has been hydrogen peroxide formation-destruction in the presence of photons selectively absorbed by the protein. As a first step, we established pH values that inhibited or started these reactions and studied the influence of other seric proteins, contaminants of the batch of SAH used. After this, effects due to the modification of the steric arrangement of the molecule, by abstracting or adding metallic ions (which behave as electronic impurities) were measured.

2. Experimental

The human serum-albumin used was provided to us by Army CNTS and lyophilized, after dialysis at pH 5.5. As immuno-electrophoretic analysis shows, the batches used contained about 2 per cent proteic impurities: alpha and beta-1 globulins, including ceruleoplasmin, control experiments have been performed with other SAH (Squibb) immunoelectrophoretically pure horse serum-albumin, pure human gamma globulin, and so on. Moreover, participation of impurities (and especially ceruleoplasmin) to oxidative processes was discarded by zone electrophoresis.

Photocatalysis Method. Aqueous solutions (bidistillated water) of SAH were tested at 37°C by illumination in a thermostated bath with very high-pressure mercury vapor lamps (Osram HBO 200), with light between 3,500 and 5,500 A. Short ultraviolet and infrared were quite well eliminated (with an interferential filter), as was proved by dark and proof experiments.

Analytic Experiments.

a. The Warburg manometric method, as recommended by Schwabb[11] and Pascher,[14] allowed accurate measurement of O_2 absorbed by the solutions under experiment. The solutions were of concentrations 0.5, 1, and 2 per cent, of serum-albumin. The volume experimented on was 4 ml.

b. Hydrogen peroxide (at 3,500 A with the iodomolybdic method) and hydroquinone were titrated in a Jobin and Yvon spectrophotometer.[10]

c. Hydroquinone oxidation has also been performed by illumination, at pH 7.2, of SHA samples inside the agar film of zone electrophoresis.

3. Results

Under the conditions of the above experiment, SAH absorbed O_2, while no such reaction was observed in the dark.

a. In the pH range 5.5 to 7.5, O_2 absorption depends on protein concentration (Fig. 27.2) and on pH (Fig. 27.3). It is reproducible

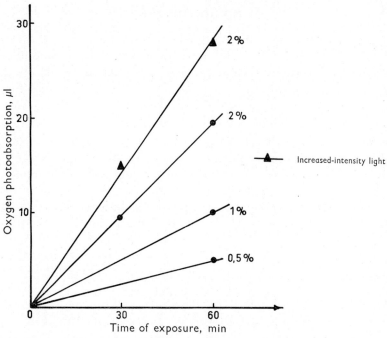

Fig. 27.2. Photoabsorption of oxygen with various concentrations of serum-albumin (pH 6.9).

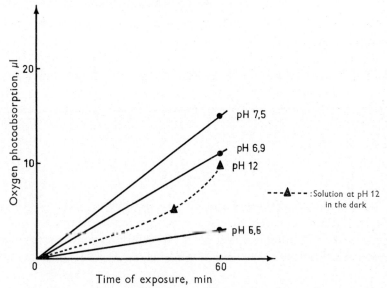

Fig. 27.3. Photoabsorption of oxygen at different pH. (Solutions of 1 per cent; irradiated 60 min).

and obeys a linear kinetic law (Fig. 27.4). As many as 15 O_2 molecules per molecule of SAH can be absorbed without denaturing this protein.

Above pH 8, SAH absorbs in the dark as much as five times the O_2 (for pH 12) as in the preceding experiment, and light does

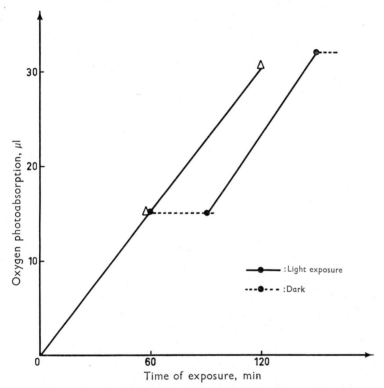

Fig. 27.4. Oxygen absorption as a function of time $\varDelta$ and during repeated exposures. (SAH: 1 per cent solution; ph: 6.)

not exert any appreciable effect. In this pH range, protein denaturation proceeds quickly.

b. Titrimetric analysis shows that between pH 5,5 and pH 7.5, the amounts of H_2O_2 evolved correspond to 1 0/00 to 2 0/00 of the absorbed O_2. It is impossible to research for possible organic peroxides, because SAH reacts with the appropriate reagents.

Aqueous solutions of SAH decompose H_2O_2 even in the dark, and this reaction is further catalyzed by light (Figs. 27.5 and 27.6). It appears that below pH 7, at least 80 per cent of the H_2O_2 is decomposed without liberation of O_2. If we assume that this decomposition proceeds according to $H_2O_2 \rightarrow OH+OH$, it thus appears that SAH does combine with these radicals, thus stopping secondary reactions (and liberation of O_2) that they could enter into. It is to be noted that after such combinations,

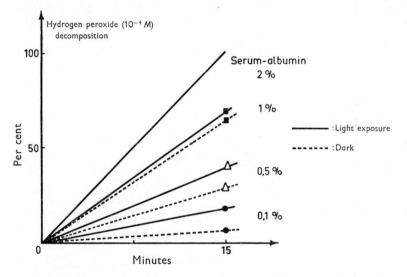

Fig. 27.5. Hydrogen peroxide decomposition by various concentrations of serum-albumin.

up to as much as 100 per molecule of SAH, no modification of the absorption spectrum is observed.

c. It seems that heavy metal ions such as Cu^{++} are responsible for the dark decomposition of H_2O_2. It is indeed possible do reduce this dark reactivity by dialysis against EDTA. When this activity is reduced to 20 per cent of its original value, the amount of O_2 absorbed also goes up 20 to 25 per cent, to pH 6 to 6.5. On the other hand, adding Cu^{++} ions (2 to 4 per molecule of SAH) results in a reduction of the amount of O_2 absorbed.

d. As already described, the hydroquinone oxidation, often used for testing the chemical behavior of semiconductors,

$$O_2^- \text{ (adsorption} + QH_2 \rightarrow QH^- \rightarrow \cdots \rightarrow \text{quinone}$$

has been studied to eliminate any effect of proteic impurities in

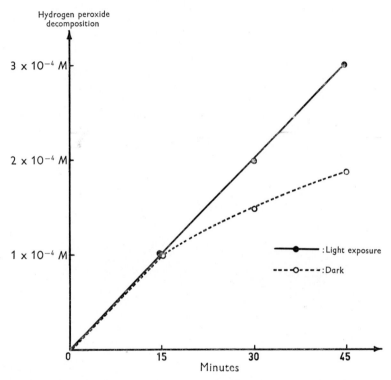

Fig. 27.6. Decomposition of hydrogen peroxide by aqueous solution of serum-albumin (2 per cent). (pH: 6.5.)

the observed oxidizing activity. Figure 27.7 shows a picture of an agar-film electrophoresis: the pink color of hydroquinone appears only on the SAH "spot" in correlation to the quantity under migration.

e. Among proof experiments, we may quote successful use of SAH (Squibb) and pure horse serum-albumin, which do not contain any detectable proteic impurities, and pure human γ

globulin, which shows clearly that catalytic reactivity is not a measure of some specific property of the serum-albumin structure, (SAH jelly also reacts to light absorption).

On the other hand, negative results have always been encountered with SAH-precipitated samples, glutathion (tripeptid), or with the equivalent aromatic heterocyclic amino acids or SH groups (cystein-cystin) of serum-albumin.

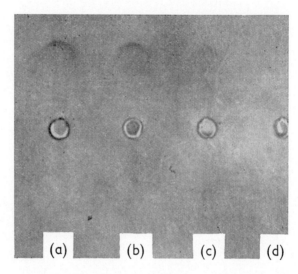

Fig. 27.7. Transformation of hydroquinous inside agar-zone electrophoresie support. (a) Solution of 20 per cent in serum-albumin; (b) 10 per cent; (c) 5 per cent; (d) 2 per cent.

4. Discussion

In a narrow range of pH (5 to 7.5) an activation energy of 3 ev, corresponding to absorption by peptidic chains, is enough for SAH to react with O_2. As no such reaction occurs in the dark, it can be assumed that, if this reaction corresponds to a surface sensitization by free charges, SAH behaves as a p-type semiconductor.[14] This explains why O_2 can only be chemisorbed under illumination.

It seems further that O_2^- chemisorbed is not released, which shows that there is as a barrier against holes at the surface. This model is summarized in Fig. 27.8, where the barrier is attributed to the surface groups of higher activation energy than the bulk of the protein.

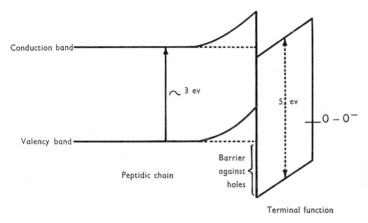

Fig. 27.8. Oxygen chemisorption.

The experiment in which hydroquinone is used as proton donor shows that O_2 is indeed chemisorbed as O_2^-, since it transforms into hydroperoxide O_2H. The reducing power of our solutions should result in the liberation of OH radicals. The fact that these disappear without producing the usual secondary reactions shows they react with the protein, which they can indeed do without any activation energy, since, unlike the original O_2, they are already charged and do not require the presence of a "free valency."

Above pH 7.5, self-oxidation of SAH corresponds to a reduction in the activation energy previously required. This phenomenon can be attributed to ionization of electron-donor sites (OH groups of tyrosin, which are very reactive above pH 8; groups that become accessible after denaturation, etc.).[15-17] The theory would be, in this case, that of Lewis bases.[18]

Photocatalytic reactions evidenced in this work are not specific to SAH. It is expected that excitation transfer occurs over very short distances; the small electron mobility in the dry state and the small extinction coefficient prove this clearly. Finally, there is a link between the physical properties and chemical reactivity of SAH, but the remaining problem seems to be the interpretation of such properties for the biological role displayed by the serum-albumin *in situ*.

Unfortunately, there are obstacles to the development of this study, both in the theoretical and experimental field; we adopt without caution principles of solid-state chemistry and physics because specific principles for proteins are lacking, and our chemical methods are unsuitable for following the small changes in protein structures.

Acknowledgements. We are indebted to Mr. Aigrain, to Drs. Perez and Stork, and to Mr. Deprade for valuable help and devices, and to the S.T.R.E.S.S.A (Médecin-Générale Jaulmes) for the support that made this work possible.

References

1. T. T. Bannister, *Arch. Biochem. Biophys.* **49**, 222 (1954).
2. V. G. Shore and A. B. Pardee, *Arch. Biochem. Biophys.* **62**, 355 (1956).
3. Bucher and Kaspers, *Biochim. et Biophys. Acta* **1**, 21 (1947).
4. Arnold and Oppenheimer, *J. Gen. Physiol.* **33**, 423 (1950).
5. A. Szent-Györgyi, "Bioenergetics," Academic Press, Inc., New York (1957).
6. D. D. Eley, G. D. Parfitt, M. J. Perry, and D. H. Taysum, *Trans. Faraday Soc.* **49**, 79 (1953).
7. P. Douzou and J. M. Thuillier, *J. chim. phys.* (in press).
8. M. H. Cardew and D. D. Eley, *Discussions Faraday Soc.* **27**, 115 (1959).
9. For general references, see *Discussions Faraday Soc.* **1959**.
10. Hochnadel, *J. Phys. Chem.* **56**, 587 (1952).
11. Schwabb, "Advances in Catalysis," Academic Press, Inc., New York (1957).
12. J. M. Thuillier, Thesis, University of Paris (1958).
13. Schuttler, Janton, and P. Douzou, *Compt. rend. Acad. Sci. Paris* **250**, 506 (1960).
14. Pascher, Ph.D. thesis, University of Munich (1956).
15. Macheboeuf and Robert, *Bull. Soc. Chim. Biol.* **35**, 399 (1953).
16. Robert, Barbu, and Macheboeuf, *Bull. Soc. Chim. Biol.* **36**, 217 (1954)
17. Robert, *Bull. Soc. Chim. Biol.* **36**, 587 (1954).
18. Schwabb and Hartman, *Z. physik. Chem. (N.F.)* **6**, 56 (1956).

28

The Influence of Electrode Material on the Photoconductivity in Anthracene*

H. Boroffka

The dependence of the photocurrent of an anthracene single crystal on the applied voltage, light intensity and electrode separation is measured in a sandwich-type arrangement. Al, Au, Fe, Ag, Cu and CuI were used as electrode materials. It has been observed that the range of behavior of these electrode materials falls between that observed for the Al electrodes on the one hand and the CuI electrodes on the other. For this reason only the Al and CuI electrodes will be discussed in detail here. Results are also given for insulating electrodes.

Table 28.1

	CuI	Al
photocurrent	$i \sim \sqrt{(B)}\ (V^2/d^3)$	$i \sim B\ (V/d)$

The results of the measurements with CuI and Al electrodes are summarized in Table 28.1, where i is the photocurrent, B the rate of absorbed quanta, V the voltage, and d the electrode separation.

In order to explain these results four assumptions will be proposed.

1. Carriers are being created only at the interface crystal electrode

2. The quantum efficiency of carrier production is proportional to the electric field strength

---

* This paper was presented fifth on the program, but the manuscript was received too late for inclusion in its proper place.

3. All carriers move from the point of creation to the electrode of opposite sign

4. Holes, when leaving the crystal at the negative electrode, can be replenished from the positive CuI electrode a replenishment of electrons is not possible. Neither holes nor electrons can be replenished from Al electrodes.

From these assumptions a dependence of the photocurrent on voltage, electrode separation and light intensity can be derived, which is in agreement with the experiments. This may be shown first in the case of a crystal with CuI electrodes with the illuminated electrode being positive.

A simple equation for the photocurrent is the following expression:

$$i = \eta Be\,[(w_+ + w_-)/d] \qquad (28.1)$$

where η means the quantum efficiency, e the elementary charge and w_+, w_- the mean ranges of the positive and negative carriers respectively. When the illuminated electrode is positive w_- can be neglected, because the carriers are being created at the positive electrode and therefore the main contribution to the photocurrent is positive carriers. For w_+ one can introduce the product $u_+ \cdot \tau_+$ where u_+ is the velocity and τ_+ is the lifetime of the positive carriers.

Then one has

$$i = \eta Be\,(u_+\tau_+/d) \qquad (28.2)$$

In accord with the second assumption the quantum efficiency is given by

$$\eta = c_1(V/d)$$

with c_1 being a constant.

The velocity is given as

$$u_+ = \mu_+(V/d)$$

where μ_+ is the mobility.

If the lifetime τ_+ is limited by a bimolecular recombination process, then the lifetime is proportional to the reciprocal square root of the rate of absorbed light quanta

$$\tau_+ = (c_2/\sqrt{B})$$

with c_2 being another constant.

Inserting these three equations in formula (28.2) gives

$$i = c_1 c_2 e \mu_+ (\sqrt{B})(V^2/d^3)$$

in agreement with the experimental result.

In the case of a crystal with Al electrodes and the illuminated electrode again being positive the mean range of the negative carriers w_- can be neglected as in the case quoted above. The quantum efficiency is again given by

$$\eta = c_1' V/d$$

as before but the mean range of the positive carriers w_+ is not proportional to the electric field strength as in the case of CuI electrodes. From the third and the fourth assumption it follows that:

$$w_+ = d$$

This gives the following expression for the photocurrent:

$$i = c_1' e B(V/d)$$

which again is in agreement with experiment.

So far only the case of the illuminated positive electrode has been considered. When the illuminated electrode is negative the discussion is a little more complicated but in principle leads to the same results.

The above model indicates that the difference between the photoconductive behavior of a crystal with CuI or Al electrodes is established by the existence or nonexistence of a replenishment of positive carriers.

Now some further facts should be stated, which will confirm the proposed model.

The magnitude of the photocurrent of a crystal with Al electrodes on the one hand and with insulating electrodes on the other has been compared under equal experimental conditions. The result is that the photocurrent is ten to fifteen times smaller in the case of insulating electrodes than in the case of Al electrodes. This proves the first assumption to be correct, that the creation of carriers occurs only at the interface crystal electrode, since if carriers are being created also in deeper layers of the crystal then one would expect an initial value of the photocurrent of the same magnitude in both cases.

Taking into account now that it is possible to maintain a constant photocurrent over a long time by using conducting electrodes, one can conclude that the mean range of the carriers must be at least equal to the spacing of the electrodes. If this would not be the case, strong space charge would be built up decreasing the photocurrent in the course of time in disagreement with the experiment. Hence the third assumption also appears to be correct.

A confirmation of the fourth assumption is provided by dark-current observations. The dark conductivity of a crystal with CuI electrodes is at least four orders of magnitude higher than that of a crystal with Al electrodes. A combination of a CuI and an Al electrode gives a strong rectifying effect, with a high current flow when the CuI electrode is positive. From this fact it is concluded that hole injection is the origin of the high dark conductivity, which appears in a crystal with CuI electrodes. Therefore only a replenishment of holes is assumed in the fourth assumption.

Until now there is no confirmation of the second assumption, but with the other assumptions valid, it is the only way to describe the measured dependence of the photocurrent on the applied voltage.